The Frontal Lobes Revisited

The Frontal Lobes Revisited

Edited by

Ellen Perecman

Department of Neurology
New York University School of Medicine
New York, New York

The IRBN Press
New York, New York

THE IRBN Press
360 East 72nd Street
New York, New York 10021

Library of Congress Cataloging in Publication Data

The Frontal lobes revisited.

Based on a conference sponsored by the Institute for Research in Behavioral Neuroscience in 1985.
Includes bibliographies and index.
1. Frontal lobes—Congresses. 2. Neuropsychology—Congresses. I. Perecman, Ellen. II. Institute for Research in Behavioral Neuroscience (U.S.)
[DNLM: 1. Frontal Lobe—physiology—congresses.
WL 307 F935 1985]
QP382.F7F76 1987 152 86-80192
ISBN 0-936925-00-0

Printed in the United States of America
9 8 7 6 5 4 3 2 1

This volume is dedicated to the memory of my grandparents
Mendel and Leyah Wexler
Avrom and Chaya Gubersky

Contents

7 The Midline Frontolimbic Cortex and the Evolution of Crying and Laughter

Paul D. MacLean

8 The Frontal Lobes and Control of Cognition and Memory

Donald T. Stuss and D. Frank Benson

9 The Frontal Lobes and Hierarchical Organization of Cognitive Control

Elkhonon Goldberg and Robert M. Bilder, Jr.

10 Concept Formation and Frontal Lobe Function: The Search for a Clinical Frontal Lobe Test

Paul L. Wang

Contributors

Numbers in parentheses indicate the pages on which the authors' contributions begin.

Clifford L. Barnes (41), Edith Nourse Rogers Memorial Veterans Hospital, Bedford, Massachusetts 01730

D. Frank Benson (141), Department of Neurology, UCLA School of Medicine, Los Angeles, California 90024

Robert M. Bilder, Jr. (159), Department of Psychiatry, Columbia University College of Physicians and Surgeons, New York, New York, and Special Treatment Unit, Creedmoor Psychiatric Center, Queens Village, New York 11427

Jason W. Brown (251) Department of Neurology, New York University School of Medicine, New York, New York 10016

Joaquin M. Fuster (109), Department of Psychiatry and Brain Research Institute, School of Medicine, University of California at Los Angeles, Los Angeles, California 90024

Elkhonon Goldberg (159), Department of Psychiatry, Montefiore Medical Center, Bronx, New York 10467, and Department of Psychiatry, Albert Einstein College of Medicine, Bronx, New York 10467

Gary Goldberg (273), Clinical Neurophysiology Service, Moss Rehabilitation Hospital, Philadelphia, Pennsylvania 19141, and Department of Rehabilitation Medicine and Physiology, Temple University School of Medicine, Philadelphia, Pennsylvania 19122

Saran Jonas (241), Department of Neurology, New York University School of Medicine, New York, New York 10016

B. L. J. Kaczmarek (225), Uniwersytet Marie Curie-Sklodowskiej Wydzial Pedagogiki i Psychologii, Instytut Psychologii, Plac Litewski 5, Lublin, Poland

Paul D. MacLean (121), National Institute of Mental Health, Poolesville, Maryland 20837

Paul Malloy (207), Butler Hospital, Providence, Rhode Island 02906, and Division of Biology and Medicine, Brown University, Providence, Rhode Island 02912

Deepak N. Pandya (41), Edith Nourse Rogers Memorial Veterans Hospital, Bedford, Massachusetts 01730, and Departments of Anatomy and Neurology, Boston University School of Medicine, Boston, Massachusetts 02215

Ellen Perecman (1), Department of Neurology, New York University School of Medicine, New York, New York 10016

Michael Petrides (91), Department of Psychology, McGill University, and Montreal Neurological Institute, McGill University, Montreal, Quebec, Canada H3A 2B4

Karl H. Pribram (11), Neuropsychology Laboratories, Stanford University, Stanford, California 94305

John S. Stamm (73), Department of Psychology, State University of New York at Stony Brook, Stony Brook, New York 11794–2500

Donald T. Stuss (141), Ottawa General Hospital, Ottawa, Ontario, Canada K1H 8L6, and Departments of Neurology and Psychology, University of Ottawa School of Medicine, Ottawa, Ontario, Canada

Paul L. Wang (189), Department of Neuropsychology, Mount Sinai Hospital, Toronto, Ontario, Canada M5G 1X5, and Department of Rehabilitation Medicine, University of Toronto, Toronto, Ontario, Canada

Preface

The frontal lobes of the brain continue to fascinate brain scientists and neuropsychologists in spite of the fact that, or perhaps because, their functions remain elusive. In *The Frontal Lobes Revisited,* authors examine data available to date on neuroanatomical as well as neurobehavioral aspects of frontal lobe function in animals and man. What emerges is a picture in which the frontal lobes appear to be responsible for shaping our attitudes and organizing our repertoire of behaviors.

The scope of this volume is such that it addresses the concerns of neuroscientists, cognitive psychologists, and neuropsychologists, as well as mind-brain philosophers and students of rehabilitation medicine.

The Frontal Lobes Revisited largely documents the fruits of a provocative conference sponsored by the Institute for Research in Behavioral Neuroscience in the fall of 1985. It also has the distinction of being the first publication of The IRBN Press, the recently founded publishing arm of the Institute for Research in Behavioral Neuroscience.

The tireless efforts of Harriet Damon Shields and John Sollami have made this volume possible; to them I owe a debt of gratitude. I would also like to thank all of the contributors for making my task an easy one.

1

Consciousness and the Meta-Functions of the Frontal Lobes: Setting the Stage

Ellen Perecman

INTRODUCTION

The frontal lobes of the brain are presumed to be involved in the highest level of goal-directed acts including complex sequencing, the creation of long- and short-term plans, and the internal manipulation of representational systems. They have, furthermore, come to be associated with behaviors that are bound up with consciousness and its manifestations: self-awareness, self-regulation, intentionality, etc. Indeed, Luria (1973) argued that the frontal lobes play a fundamental role in constructing and maintaining human conscious activity.

Consistent with this notion of the frontal lobes as the "seat of consciousness" is the fact that they are most recent in the phylogenetic development of the brain; they are hardly visible in lower animals, are considerably larger in primates, and occupy up to one-fourth of the total mass of the cerebral hemispheres in man. Moreover, on the ontogenetic time scale, the frontal lobes do not mature until a child is between 4 and 7 years old (Luria, 1973, p. 183).

Clinical as well as experimental studies of focal brain damage have indicated that a lesion in the prefrontal cortex of humans (Milner, 1964, 1971), as well as monkeys (Fuster, 1980) and rats (Kesner, 1985), results in a number of intellectual and behavioral deficits. Thus, changes in social behavior, affect, and behavioral initiative and spontaneity are associated with damage to the orbitofrontal region, while disorders of cognitive function, such as memory for the temporal sequence of events, spatial orientation, and poor control of movement, are typically seen with dorsolateral lesions.

Note that each of the functions in question refers not to a particular behavior per se, but to the regulation of that behavior, to the integration of that specific behavior into some larger scheme of behavior. This is not surprising in view of the extensive connections of the frontal cortex with subcortical and cortical sensory, motor, and limbic systems.

ISBN 0-936925-00-0

In the present volume, Deepak Pandya and Clifford Barnes (Chapter 3) focus on the connectional relation of the frontal lobes with other areas of the brain. They set out to elucidate the afferent and efferent connections of the monkey frontal lobe with other cortical and subcortical regions, as an "indispensable prerequisite to any consideration of frontal lobe function," explaining how, in addition to limbic, thalamic, and hypothalamic input to the frontal lobe, successive parasensory association areas for all three major modalities of sensation send projections progressively to premotor, prefrontal, orbital, and medial cortices of the frontal lobe. They also identify an anatomical convergence of different sensory afferents in the frontal lobe that may be the basis for intermodal and cross-modal exchange of information. It is in fact such delineation of the connectional anatomy which has led to the conclusion that the frontal cortex "constitutes an essential anatomic substrate for functional unification of the higher mental processes" (Thatcher & John, 1977, p. 24).

AN OVERVIEW

Spatial Processing and the Frontal Lobes

In Chapter 4, John Stamm offers a historical review of research on frontal lobe function in monkeys, cats, and dogs, using delayed-response (DR) and delayed-alternation (DA) tasks. He discusses experimental work that supports the view that kinesthetic cues are important in guiding delayed-alternation responses and in identifying two distinct forms of behavioral impairment: (1) spatial response differentiation in the absence of exteroceptive cues and (2) inhibition of interfering response tendencies. Stamm concludes that principalis cortex plays a role in the formation of self-regulating kinesthetic processes that guide its subsequent choice responses, and that the solution to the riddle of the monkey's delayed-response deficit lies in the principalis cortex.

Karl Pribram (Chapter 2) questions the kinesthetic hypothesis as the basis for the spatial aspect of the frontal deficit, suggesting instead that kinesthetic cues relate more to the temporal than to the spatial deficit that follows anterior frontal lesions and that the difficulty with "spatial" problems is due to an increase in sensitivity to distraction under certain specifiable conditions.

Pribram distinguishes between lesions that interfere with classic delay tasks and lesions that interfere with object alternation. He identifies a gradient of relationships of delay problem performance in sensory mode reaching from a periarcuate auditory and visual to a more anterior kinesthetic location and argues that "these relationships fit with the general hypothesis that the function of the anterior frontal cortex is to relate the processes served by the limbic forebrain to those of the somatosensory motor systems."

It is precisely the role of sensory modality in delineating zones within the periarcuate region which is the focus of Chapter 5 by Michael Petrides. Petrides reviews work on the effects on conditional learning in spatial tasks of selective lesions of the periarcuate region in humans and nonhuman primates that shows the degree to which this region may be divided into anatomically distinct zones mediating conditional responses as a function of the sensory modality through which stimuli are presented and the type of responses that must be produced. Petrides reviews experiments on conditional learning and presents an explanation for why monkeys with periarcuate lesions will often perform normally on many of the tasks used in these studies.

Temporal Integration and the Frontal Lobes

Joaquin Fuster (Chapter 6) focuses on the role of the prefrontal cortex in temporal processing. He argues that the three cognitive functions assigned to various parts of the prefrontal cortex, namely, short-term memory, anticipatory preparation for action, and inhibition or control of interference, all subserve a superordinate function essential for the organization of goal-directed behavior in the temporal domain: the "mediation of cross-temporal contingencies," or "the structuring of behavioral actions on the basis of temporally separate but mutually contingent items of information."

This chapter reviews evidence from single-unit studies that substantial numbers of cells in prefrontal cortex are attuned to two or more events in a task, and that cells with widely different properties may be seen in close proximity to each other. Fuster points out that short-term memory is temporally retrospective while preparatory set is prospective, and that delay tasks involve a need to bridge the time between interdependent events. He concludes that neurons of the prefrontal cortex participate in that supraordinate function.

In experimental studies, one often loses sight of the fact that the data collected are only as interpretable as the parameters of the task administered. In other words, if task parameters are ambiguous, results are at best uninterpretable and at worst misleading. In the present volume, this issue is addressed explicitly by Pribram (Chapter 2) and implicitly by Paul Wang (Chapter 10).

Pribram reviews the experimental literature on the frontal lobes with particular attention to overcoming the lack of uniformity in terminology used to refer to particular lesions, and to an analysis of the tasks used to isolate frontal lobe function. He then goes on to reinterpret research findings in light of his reanalysis of the tasks themselves. He proposes, for example, that one can resolve the apparent inconsistency in the finding that limbic resections impair recognition memory, though it is the parietal convexity that has always been associated with agnosia, if one reinterprets the delay task to test for novelty/familiarity, not object identification.

In Chapter 10, Wang presents a critical review of tests created for the purpose of evaluating concept formation. After analyzing the Halstead Category

Test, the Wisconsin Card Sorting Test and the Modified Vygotsky Concept Formation Test, he isolates four factors common to all of these. Each tests (1) the ability to apply varied and pertinent solutions based on confined but implicit information, (2) the ability to create hypotheses in accordance with feedback, (3) the ability to maintain a set and avoid erratic responses, and (4) the ability to recognize changes of condition and flexibility in thinking in order to shift response approach. On the basis of this analysis, Wang proceeds to outline his notion of the optimal test for frontal lobe dysfunction.

The evolutionary school of behavioral neurology is rather well represented in this volume. Pandya and Barnes (Chapter 3) point out that classic cytoarchitectonics does not provide any theoretical framework for understanding the pattern or organization of the frontal lobes, and suggest that a productive theoretical framework is found in the evolutionary model of cerebral morphology proposed by Sanides (1971, 1972).

According to Sanides's theory, the six-layered isocortex ultimately has a dual origin in the hippocampal formation, for the spatial analysis of information, and in the olfactory cortex, concerned with the emotional tone of sensory information. Pandya and Barnes describe the patterns of connections which suggest that a given cortical region within each of these two trends projects both to an architectonically less well-differentiated area and to a region with more developed cortical laminar organization.

Pandya and Barnes speculate that each further differentiation in cytoarchitecture and each new set of connections "might reasonably be expected to subserve a new and more advanced behavior." These authors share with Jason Brown, Gary Goldberg, and Elkhonon Goldberg and Robert Bilder a concept of the process of a behavioral act in which each stage in the generation of the behavior contributes to the definition of that behavior and, in this particular case, that "by virtue of the interconnectivity among these units, each would contribute a part that would ultimately affect the motor cortex and result in the properly planned behavior."

Brown has explored this concept extensively in the domain of language (Brown, 1977, 1982; see also Brown and Perecman, 1986) and visual perception (Brown, 1983). In Chapter 14 of this volume, he applies the concept to action.

Action and the Frontal Lobes

In a chapter on the contribution of the frontal lobes to the microtemporal processing—the microgenesis—of action, Brown proposes that the action system develops out of a rhythmic configuration that is bilaterally represented at early stages and becomes gradually biased to left hemisphere representation. Brown takes as his premise the idea that perception and action systems are interrelated ("exteriorize together"), arguing that just as "early stages in object formation [perception] provide the contextual background out of which objects develop and persist abstractly as levels of conceptual or symbolic content within the object itself . . . early stages in action elaborate the instinctual and affective bases that drive the action forward to its goal." For him, conscious awareness develops with the action (or perception) itself and is not superimposed upon the action development.

He characterizes the motor envelope of an action as an early processing stage that elaborates an archaic stage in speech and motility, centered on the space about the body axis and linked to respiratory, locomotor, and other rhythmic automatisms close to motivational and drive-like states.

Brown develops the argument that in the case of action development the evolutionary progression from limbic to motor cortices retraces the sequence of processing stages in the microtemporal elaboration of an action and that disruption at successive points gives rise to symptoms which reflect this progression.

The notion that pathological symptoms identify different levels of representation within a neurocognitive hierarchy is central to the chapter by E. Goldberg and Bilder on motor perserveration. These authors argue that prefrontal pathology may lead to the disintegration of hierarchic relations among representational levels, and that different types of perseveration mark the different levels of representation. They suggest, however, that focal prefrontal damage is not necessary to produce "executive syndrome" and that this syndrome may be relatively common with global cerebral deterioration, in view of the fact that any diffuse brain dysfunction affecting much of the brain to an equal extent from structural and/or from biochemical points of view will disrupt executive functions before it will disrupt other functions.

They point out that while various focal nonfrontal syndromes may lead to perseverative behavior, perseveration in these cases is usually limited to a specific sensory modality or type of behavior. In cases of massive prefrontal pathology, "perseveration is more ubiquitous, permeating virtually every cognitive domain and manifest at every level of the neurocognitive hierarchy." The levels they isolate are (1) a level of selection of a general cognitive mode, (2) a level of retrieval from semantic store, (3) a level of execution of individual task items, and (4) a level of elementary or motor operations.

The role of frontal lobe systems in the organization of action is treated from yet another perspective in Chapter 15, where Gary Goldberg addresses the issue of the relation between intention and expressed action. Goldberg proposes the "dual premotor systems hypothesis": that there are at least two frontal premotor systems, a lateral and a medial system, and that each corresponds to a distinct evolutionary trend in frontal lobe differentiation over phylogeny. The lateral system controls action which is triggered in direct response to external information, and the medial system is used for the prospective control of behavior.

Goldberg presents data on the "alien hand sign" to illustrate his point that a range of clinical and basic physiological observations may be understood in the context of the dual premotor systems hypothesis. He suggests that, in patients with medial frontal infarcts whose symptoms are in the hand opposite the lesion, purposeful action is occurring independent of conscious volition. Patients report unambiguous identification of one hand as alien and the other as the force used to control the alien hand.

Goldberg believes that volitional control is limited to proximal limb musculature. He interprets these "wayward" behaviors as resulting from unconstrained action of the lateral premotor system of the damaged hemisphere, though limited volitional control occurs through activation of the medial system of an intact ipsilateral hemisphere.

The Frontal Lobes and Memory

Donald Stuss and D. Frank Benson (Chapter 8) point out that one of the earliest theories attempting to explain behavioral deficits in animals with frontal lobe lesions attributed the deficit to loss of recent memory, and that in fact the role of frontal lobes in memory remains a controversial issue. Kesner (1985) suggests that the role of the prefrontal cortex in memory is to process information on the basis of expectancy, that is, to process "abstract" time. This is in contrast to the role of the hippocampus, which, he suggests, codes "real" time, or information based on data input (p. 130).

Stuss and Benson propose that frontal lobe disturbances are characterized not by memory loss per se, but rather by "forgetting to remember" and a "loss of the controlling factor of knowledge." While failing to remember is a problem of memory, forgetting to remember is rather a problem of conscious awareness of a memory, irrespective of the quality of that memory or the ability to access it; it is one step removed from the actual memory, and in that sense is a problem in representing a memory at a more abstract level.

Speech and the Frontal Lobes

In Chapter 7, Paul MacLean presents his theory of the evolution of the forebrain, with particular reference to forms of behavior that characterize the distinction between reptiles and mammals. Among these behaviors is audiovocal communication. MacLean argues that these behaviors are represented in the thalamocingulate division of the limbic system of mammals and that this region had not yet evolved in the reptilian brain. MacLean has shown that the limbic system originates with early mammals and that the forebrain of advanced mammals has evolved as a triune structure comprising three neural assemblies that, anatomically and chemically, reflect an ancestral relationship to reptiles, and to early and late mammals.

MacLean reports evidence that, while in humans vocalization is associated with the supplementary motor area just above the anterior cingulate cortex, in the squirrel monkey aspiration of corresponding cortex results in transitory elimination of the separation call, with full recovery after nine weeks. Rather, for the squirrel monkey, the structure and/or presence of the separation cry was a function of damage to the core of the brainstem at the thalamo-midbrain junction, and the anterior cingulate cortex is the main cortical area for eliciting vocalization.

MacLean concludes from his own and other research that the medial frontal limbic area, supplementary area, and striopallidal structures that converge on ventral anterior and ventral lateral nuclei of the thalamus are implicated in the initiation of various forms of vocalization, including crying and laughing.

In Chapter 13, Saran Jonas reviews the clinical and experimental literature on disturbances of speech in humans associated with lesions of the frontal parasagittal supplementary motor region. He interprets the literature to support the idea that the voluntary initiation of motor speech involves the transmission of instructions from the supplementary motor region (SMR) to the primary motor area, and that SMR plays an inhibitory, gating role with respect to motor cortex, preventing entry into the primary motor area of influences which would disrupt ongoing primary motor area programs.

Jonas speculates that when the elements in a sequence of actions are different SMR must emit instructions as steadily as primary motor cortex, but that when the elements in a sequence are identical to one another primary motor cortex can control the activity without the participation of SMR.

The contribution of prefrontal cortex to human language at the level of discourse is addressed by Bozydar Kaczmarek in Chapter 12. After a review of work on the role of language in the regulation of behavior, Kaczmarek investigates the hypothesis that impairment in regulatory function is related to a disturbance in language production in a predictable way and that the regulatory function of the prefrontal region is bound up to a great extent with language.

Kaczmarek presents results of a study of narrative structure in three groups of patients with prefrontal pathology. He analyzed narrative production with respect to semantic and syntactic structure and found that, although all patients with prefrontal lesions "have difficulty processing verbal messages," the structure of narratives differed as a function of whether patients had dorsolateral prefrontal, left orbitofrontal, or right frontal lesions.

The Relation between Motor and Sensory Systems

Contrasting views of the relation between motor and sensory processing systems are presented in Chapters 6 and 14 by Fuster and Brown, respectively. Fuster takes the more or less traditional stance that motor and sensory processing hierarchies are mirror images of each other, with the motor system processing from the abstract to the concrete, and the sensory system taking as input the concrete and yielding abstract entities. Fuster refers to the profuse reciprocal connections between the precentral sulcus and postcentral sulcus, which are the substrate for the cybernetic "perception-action cycle."

Brown, on the other hand, conceives of the relation between motor and sensory processing as parallel, that is, that both motor and sensory systems process stimuli in the same direction. Indeed, he sees both perception and action as "exterioriz[ing]" together, both "build up, partition and arborize external space." For Brown, "A world of real objects and the effects of actions in that world are part of the same microgenetic end point . . . the increasing passivity and final detachment of an object representation mirrors the activity of an action and the realization of an intentional attitude to movements directed toward those object representations."

Psychiatric Implications of Frontal Lobe Dysfunction

Paul Malloy (Chapter 11) explores the hypothesis that there is a functional disconnection in obsessive-compulsive disorder (OCD). He observes that patients with dorsolateral lesions display deficits in self-monitoring, often overlooking important details in their environments. They demonstrate a failure to maintain set, and fail to respond to long-term consequences. In contrast, patients with OCD behave as though their dorsolateral frontal zones are hyperactive. They demonstrate constant self-monitoring, inflexible mental set, and excessive concern with long-term consequences.

Applying an evoked potential mapping technique to patients with OCD, Malloy found that a subset of particularly disturbed OCD patients reveals significantly lower amplitude than non-OCD individuals in orbital frontal areas. Malloy suggests that because orbital/inferior medial areas connect directly with limbic structures, they may provide a crucial route between dorsolateral frontal cortex and the limbic system, and he speculates that lesions interrupting reciprocal connections may prevent the frontal cortex from fulfilling its role in modulating limbic drives.

Creativity and the Frontal Lobes

The role of the frontal lobes in the manipulation of representational systems suggests that the frontal lobes are involved in the creative process and creative thinking. Stuss and Benson (Chapter 8) administered to frontal lobe patients the visual-verbal test, a test of concept formation, but one that also taps into creative thinking. On this test, patients are asked to find first one and then another dimension of similarity among three or four figures on a card. These authors discovered that frontal lobe patients had no difficulty making the first abstraction, but could not make the second. On the assumption that creativity is at least in part defined as the ability to see a single stimulus from multiple points of view, the visual-verbal test is sensitive to creative thinking and these patients are impaired in precisely that function.

CONCLUDING REMARKS

Throughout this volume, authors refer to "higher mental processes." Consider for a moment what we mean when we use the term "higher mental processes." We mean by it those mental functions that are basically meta-functions: complex sequencing, creation of plans, manipulation of representational systems. They are meta-functions in the sense that they represent a higher level of organization than the functions they subserve. And, insofar as they are meta-functions, they appear to be bound up with consciousness and conscious experience, which, as defined by Vygotsky (1962), "denote awareness of the activity of the mind—the consciousness of being conscious" (p. 91).

This notion is very Jacksonian in that Hughlings Jackson saw the "centres for consciousness . . . as centres which 'play upon' lower centres . . . [and] represent in greater complexity, speciality, and multiplicity of associations, the very same impressions and movements which the lower, and through them the lowest, centres represent" (Taylor 1958, Vol. I, p. 172). Hughlings Jackson speculated that "if the centres for consciousness could be sliced away without disturbing the rest of the organism, the physical operations of the body would be positively uninterfered with, although negatively there would be no 'volitional impulses' sent down to put the body in this or that movement" (1958, Vol. I, p. 159).

For Spencer "[t]he seat of consciousness is that nervous centre to which, mediately or immediately, the most heterogeneous impressions are brought" (Vol. I, p. 105). But consciousness is not a *state* of mind. It is "a process in which information about multiple individual modalities of sensation and perception is combined into a unified multidimensional representation of the state of the system and its environment" (Thatcher & John, 1977, p. 294). The content of consciousness is the ever-changing constellation of these different types of information.

If one were to adopt these definitions, it would appear that the chapters which follow may be construed to support the case that consciousness is mediated by the frontal lobes, and that the frontal lobes are "the seat of consciousness."

In 1973 Luria wrote:

> It will be unnecessary to remind the reader that the functional organization of the human frontal lobes is one of the most complex problems in modern science, and so far only the first step has been taken in the analysis of the various syndromes which can arise in lesions of the corresponding parts of the brain. Nothing is more certain, therefore, than that the next decade will see a substantial increase in our knowledge of this complex region. (p. 225)

Indeed, our understanding of the frontal lobes increased considerably between 1973 and 1986, and the present volume attests to that. As Karl Pribram concludes from his "revisitation" of the frontal lobes in Chapter 2 of this volume: "The profusion of data collected by hard labor over the past 50 years can . . . [now] be fitted into a tentative scheme. No longer are we stuck with vague concepts of frontal lobe function." Yet, in the tradition of scientific progress, Pribram interprets this achievement as a new challenge reminds us that "we have as yet only begun to explore *how* the various portions of the frontal cortex do their work" and proposes that it is the *how* to which we now turn.

REFERENCES

Brown, J. W. (1977). *Mind, brain, consciousness.* New York: Academic Press.

Brown, J. W. (1982). Hierarchy and evolution in neurolinguistics. In M. Arbib, et al. (Eds.), *Neural models of language processes* (pp. 447–467). New York: Academic Press.

Brown, J. W. (1983). The microstructure of perception: Physiology and patterns of breakdown. *Cognition and Brain Theory, 6,* 145–184.

Brown, J. W., & Perecman, E. (1986). Neurological basis of language processing. In R. Chapey (Ed.), *Language intervention strategies in aphasia* (pp. 12–27). Baltimore: Williams & Wilkins.

Fuster, J. (Ed.) (1980). *The prefrontal cortex: Anatomy, physiology, and neuropsychology of the frontal lobe.* New York: Raven Press.

Kesner, R. P. (1985). Correspondence between humans and animals in coding of temporal attributes: Role of hippocampus and prefrontal cortex. In D. S. Olton, et al. (Eds.), Memory dysfunctions: An integration of animal and human research from preclinical and clinical perspectives. *Annals of the New York Academy of Sciences, 444,* 122–136.

Luria, A. R. (1973). *The working brain.* New York: Basic Books.

Milner, B. (1964). Some effects of frontal lobectomy in man. In J. M. Warren & K. Akert (Eds.), *The frontal granular cortex and behavior* (pp. 313–334). New York: McGraw-Hill.

Milner, B. (1971). Interhemispheric differences in the localization of psychological processes in man. *British Medical Bulletin, 27,* 272–277.

Sanides, F. (1971). Functional architecture of motor and sensory cortices in primates in the light of a new concept of neocortex development. In C. R. Noback & W. Montana (Eds.), *Advances in primatology* (Vol. I, pp. 137–208). New York: Appleton-Century-Crofts.

Sanides, F. (1972). Representations in the cerebral cortex and its areal laimination patterns. In G. F. Bourne (Ed.), *Structure and function of nervous tissue* (Vol. 5, pp. 329–453). New York: Academic Press.

Spencer, H. (1977). *The principles of psychology* (Vol. I). New York: Longman. (Original work published 1881)

Taylor, J. (1958). *Selected writings of John Hughlings Jackson* (Vol. I). London: Staples Press.

Thatcher, R. W., & John, E. R. (1977). *Foundations of cognitive processes.* Hillsdale, NJ: Erlbaum.

Vygotsky, L. (1962). *Thought and language.* In E. Hanfman & G. Vakar (Eds. and Trans.), Cambridge, MA: MIT Press.

2

The Subdivisions of the Frontal Cortex Revisited

Karl H. Pribram

INTRODUCTION

Gallia est omnia divisa in partes tres. With these words Caesar set out to conquer Gaul and to unify it. My purpose in this chapter is no less ambitious: to describe the various subdivisions of the frontal lobe in order to find some unitary principle that unites them. Fortunately, there are available the endeavors of massive troops, endeavors that make the enterprise possible. The hoped-for conquest will proceed as follows: The initial section describes anatomical data, and serves as an orientation; the second section is concerned with reviewing and interpreting the mass of neurobehavioral data that deal with the functional parcellation of the anterior frontal systems; and finally a summary and synthesis section will attempt to portray an understanding of primate frontal lobe function in terms of the currently available data.

SOME ANATOMICAL CONSIDERATIONS

Thalamocortical Definition of Subdivisions

As with Caesar's Gaul, the frontal cortex of primates can be divided into three major parts, each of which is made up of subprincipalities. The three major divisions are the precentral (including the pre- and supplementary motor), the anterior (also called prefrontal, orbitofrontal, and far frontal), and the cingulate (also called limbic). These major divisions can be defined on the basis of their thalamic projections: The precentral derives its thalamic input from the ventrolateral group of nuclei, the anterior frontal from the nucleus (n.) medialis dorsalis, and the cingulate from the anterior group (for reviews, see Pribram 1958a, 1958b).

ISBN 0-936925-00-0

The subdivisions of these major divisions can also be defined in terms of their thalamic input: The immediate precentral cortex receives an input from the n. ventralis lateralis, pars caudalis, and the n. ventralis posterior, pars oralis, which in turn are the major terminals of cerebellar projections. The premotor portions of this division receive an input from the n. ventralis lateralis, pars oralis, which in turn is the major termination of input through the globus pallidus of the lateral nigrostriatal system. A further subdivision can be made between the lateral premotor and the supplementary motor systems in that the more laterally placed systems deal more with orofacial, and the supplementary motor systems with other axial muscular projections (Goldberg, 1985).

The subdivisions of the cingulate cortex follow the subdivisions of the anterior thalamic nuclei: N. anterior medialis projects to the anterior cingulate cortex, n. anterior lateralis to the posterior cingulate cortex (Pribram & Fulton, 1954). The n. lateralis dorsalis (which ought to be classified as part of the anterior group) projects to the retrosplenial portion of the cingulate gyrus.

Finally, the primate anterior, far frontal cortex can be subdivided according to the subdivisions of the n. medialis dorsalis: The microcellular portion projects to the dorsolateral frontal cortex, the perilammilar magnocellular portion to the periarcuate cortex, and the midline magnocellular portion to the orbitofrontal cortex (Pribram, Chow, & Semmes, 1953).

A Frontolimbic versus Cortical Convexity Distinction

There are additional, hitherto ignored, interesting and important (for understanding the functional relationship to psychological processing) findings regarding the thalamocortical projections. The thalamus is a three-dimensional structure, whereas the cortex is (from the standpoint of thalamic projections) essentially a two-dimensional sheet of cells. Thus, the projections from thalamus to cortex must "lose" one dimension. When one plots the precisely arranged "fan" of projections from each thalamic nucleus one can readily determine which dimension is eliminated.

With regard to the projections from the anterior nuclear group and the n. medialis dorsalis, the anterior-posterior dimension is eliminated. An anterior-posterior file of cells in the thalamus projects to a single locus of cortex. Thus, for example, one finds degeneration of such an extended row of thalamic cells ranging from the most anterior to the most posterior portion of the n. medialis dorsalis after a resection limited to the frontal pole (Pribram et al., 1953).

With regard to the ventrolateral group of nuclei, the situation is entirely different. Here the anterior-posterior dimension is clearly maintained: The front part of the nucleus projects to the forward parts of the cerebral convexity; as one proceeds back in the thalamus the projections reach the more posterior portions of the cortex, curving around into the temporal lobe when the projections of the pulvinar are reached. On the other hand, a file of cells extending, more or less, dorsoventrally (but angled somewhat laterally from its medial edge) projects to a single locus on the cortex (Chow & Pribram, 1956).

This distinction between the anterior and medial nuclei, on the one hand, and the ventrolateral group of nuclei, on the other, is supported by the fact that the internal medullary lamina separates the two classes of nuclei. Clearly, therefore, we should seek commonality among the functions of the anterior, far frontal parts of the cortex and the limbic formations, as well as among the functions of the precentral and postcentral portions of the cerebral mantle (Pribram, 1958a, 1958b).

The close anatomical relationship of the far frontal cortex and the limbic medial forebrain is also emphasized when comparative anatomical data are reviewed. In cats and other nonprimates, gyrus proreus is the homologue of the far frontal cortex of primates. This gyrus receives its projection from the midline magnocellular portion of the n. medialis dorsalis. This projection covers a good share of the anterior portion of the medial frontal cortex; gyrus proreus on the lateral surface is limited to a narrow sliver. It is as if there has been a rotation of the medial frontal cortex laterally (just as there seems to have occurred a rotation medially of the occipital cortex—especially between monkey and man) during the evolution of primates.

Apraxia: A Rolandic versus Extra-Rolandic Distinction

A further lesson can be learned from an analysis of the precise arrangement of thalamocortical projections and from comparing nonprimate with primate cortical anatomy. In tracing the thalamic projections to the precentral cortex, a surprising finding came to light. The dorsoventral arrangement of terminations, both pre- and postcentrally, is diametrically opposite to the arrangement of the projections farther forward and farther back. The dorsoventral terminations of the Rolandic projections reflect a lateral-medial origin from the thalamus; the dorsoventral terminations both forward and back of the peri-Rolandic cortex reflect a medial to lateral origin (Chow & Pribram, 1956).

Again, comparison of nonprimate with primate cortical anatomy clarifies this surprising finding. In nonprimate species such as the carnivores, the suprasylvian and ectosylvian gyri extend the full length of the lateral surface of the cerebral convexity. The cruciate sulcus, the homologue of the Rolandic fissure, is mainly found on the medial surface of the hemisphere, with only a minimal extension onto the lateral surface. It is as if in the evolution of primates this sulcus has migrated laterally to become the prominent central fissure, which is so intimately related to the cerebellar system.

Such a migration seems to have split the supra- and ectosylvian gyri into anterior and posterior segments. That such a split has occurred is supported by the fact that terminations of thalamocortical projections to the anterior and posterior segments originate in adjacent parts of the ventrolateral nuclei. Should this conjecture regarding a split be correct, it would go a long way in accounting for the difficulty in making a differential diagnosis between apraxias that are due to frontal damage and those that are due to parietal damage.

Brown (1985), in a review of frontal lobe syndromes, defines apraxia as "a substitution or defective selection of partial movements with lesions of the left premotor cortex [which] is due to an alteration of motor timing or a change in the kinetic pattern for a particular motor sequence" (p. 37).

To test whether, in fact, damage to both parietal and frontal (premotor) systems can produce apraxia and to pin down in a quantitative fashion just what changes in timing, in the kinetic pattern of movement, occur in apraxia, the following (K. H. Pribram, unpublished) experiment was performed: Monkeys were trained (using peanuts as reinforcements) to move a lever in a T-shaped slot beginning at the juncture of the arms of the T with its stem. The movements were then to be directed to the right, to the left, and finally down and up, in that order. Records were kept of the monkeys' abilities to perform the movements in the correct order and the number and duration of contacts with the sides of the slots that formed the T. (This was done by having the sides and the lever lined with copper and wiring them so that contact could be recorded.)

Resections were made of precentral cortex, of the cortex of the inferior parietal lobule, of the premotor cortex, and of the latter two lesions combined. Precentral resections led to many more and briefer contacts along the path of the lever within the T slot, a loss of fine motor skill. No change in overall sequencing occurred. Both the parietal and the premotor resections produced a breakdown in the sequencing of the movements but only insofar as the same movement was carried out repetitiously, which was interpreted as evidence of apraxia. There was no observed difference between the effects of the anterior resection and those of the posterior resection, and the overall order of the act was not disturbed. When the parietal and premotor resections were combined, this deficit was enhanced; still, there was no change in overall ordering of the action. I will say more about this distinction between the systems that deal with skill and with apraxia in the summary and synthesis section.

SUBDIVISIONS OF THE ANTERIOR FRONTAL CORTEX

The main body of this review concerns the parcellation of the anterior frontal cortex, in part because so much work has been done on the topic and this work has not been adequately reviewed elsewhere, and in part because such a review leads directly to the current aim—which is to find some unifying principle for frontal lobe functioning.

When lesions occur in the Rolandic and premotor portions of the frontal lobe, neurological signs and symptoms occur that are relatively easy to spot. By contrast, the lesions of the anterior frontal cortex are essentially "silent" unless specific and sophisticated inquiries are addressed to the organism. Such inquiry has been greatly aided by the use of nonhuman primate models of deficits in behavior produced by anterior frontal lesions.

Description of Tasks

The tasks that have been found most useful in delineating the deficit following anterior frontal damage are all characterized by a delay between stimulus presentation and the opportunity for a response to occur. During this delay distractors are introduced and the cue to the correct response disappears. The tasks fall into two main categories: delayed response and delayed alternation. Further, variations in the tasks have produced several subcategories of each category, variations that have been found to be extremely useful both as tools for subdividing the anterior frontal cortex and for understanding the nature of the deficit.

The delayed-response task, in its direct form, involves hiding, within sight of the subject, a reward in one of two identical-looking boxes set side by side, bringing down a distracting opaque screen for at least 5 seconds, and then raising the screen to provide the subject with just one opportunity to locate the reward. The boxes are immediately withdrawn beyond the subject's reach and the next trial begun. Should the subject fail to find the reward, the trial is repeated (correction technique); that is, the reward is again hidden within sight of the subject in the same box as in the previous trial. Should the subject succeed in finding the reward, another location (i.e., the box) for the hiding of the reward is chosen according to a (pseudo)random order number table.

The indirect form of the delayed-response task is more often called a delayed matching from sample. In this task a cue is presented instead of the reward during stimulus presentation; at the time of choice this cue and some other are available and the subject must choose the same cue as that initially presented in order to obtain the reward. A further variant of this task is the delayed nonmatch in which the subject must choose the cue that was not present at the time of stimulus presentation. This version combines the attributes of the delayed-response task with those of the delayed-alternation procedure.

In the delayed-alternation task the subject is not shown where the reward is located; he is simply given the opportunity to choose between two boxes. On the first trial both contain a reward. After the choice has been made, a distracting opaque screen is interposed between the boxes and the subject for at least 5 seconds and the next opportunity for choice is given. On this second trial the subject will find the reward in the box other than the one he chose initially and, if he continues to choose successfully, he will do so by adopting a win-shift strategy. Should the subject choose the empty box, the trial is repeated (correction technique). Unless this correction procedure is used, monkeys, when they are the subjects, fail to learn the alternation task (at least in 5,000 trials: K. H. Pribram, unpublished data).

Three variants of delayed alternation that have proved especially useful are a go/no-go version, the object-alternation procedure, and discrimination reversals. In the go/no-go task the subject must alternately go to fetch the reward on one trial and withhold his response on the subsequent trial. Failure to go or failure to withhold results in the repetition of the trial (correction procedure). In the object-alternation procedure the reward is alternated between two different objects rather than between two different locations. In this variant the spatial aspect of the task is reduced, a reduction that is enhanced when the objects are placed among 6, 8, or 12 locations according to a random number table (Pribram, Gardner, Pressman, & Bagshaw, 1963, 1969a). Discrimination reversals are, in fact, alternations that vary the numbers of trials that occur between the shift of reinforcement that signals the alternation. There is a gradual transition between alternation, double alternation, triple alternation, etc., and the ordinary non-reversal discrimination task. The inflection point occurs at three nonalternation trials in normal subjects, but is raised to four or five such trials after frontal lobe damage (Pribram, 1961a).

Description of Lesion Sites

Earlier, an anatomical rationale for subdividing the anterior frontal cortex was given in terms of the thalamic projections that terminate in different portions of this cortex. Unfortunately, all of the investigators involved in pursuing the parcellation experiments did not adhere to this particular mode of subdividing: Many experimenters simply divided the anterior portion of the frontal lobe into a dorsal portion centered on the sulcus principalis and a ventral portion that included both the lip of the lobe and the entire orbital surface. Furthermore, surgical result does not always match surgical intent. The fibers in the depth of the sulci (medial, orbital, and principal) in the anterior portion of the frontal lobe are separated by only millimeters and can be differentially spared only by exercising the greatest care and skill.

Despite this, meaningful conclusions can be teased out of the results of such experiments provided the various lesions are kept clearly differentiated by appropriate labels. It is therefore necessary to adopt a uniform terminology for the resections that often differs from that used in the original reports because different investigators used the same term to describe different lesions or different terms to describe the same lesion.

The greatest problem arises from the use of the term *orbital*. Here the convention will be followed that the term orbital refers to the general expanse of the ventral portion of the lobe and that, when specific portions of this cortex are referred to, orbital will be conjoined to a modifier. Thus, posterior orbital refers to the agranular cortex located in the most posterior part of the orbital cortex (Area 13 of Walker, the projection of the midline magnocellular portion of n.

medialis dorsalis of the thalamus). This cortex is intimately related through the uncinate fasciculus to the anterior insula, temporal pole, and amygdala.

The term *medial orbital* will be used to refer to the dysgranular cortex of the medial orbital gyrus that is continuous with the cortex on the medial surface of the lobe and receives a projection from the anterior thalamic nucleus (Pribram & Fulton, 1954). In keeping with the agranular and dysgranular cytoarchitecture of the posterior and medial orbital cortex, it was found to be electrically excitable; that is, head and eye movements and a host of visceral responses (respiratory, heart rate, blood pressure) are obtained when this cortex (as well as that of the anterior cingulate gyrus with which it is continuous) is electrically stimulated (Kaada, Pribram, & Epstein, 1949). This finding gave rise to the concept of a mediobasal motor cortex, and to the existence of a limbic system motor cortex, in addition to the more classical Rolandic and precentral systems (Pribram, 1961b).

The eugranular cortex on the lateral orbital gyrus is continuous with that forming the ventral lip and adjacent ventral gyrus of the frontal lobe. This cortex is part of the projection of the microcellular portion of the n. medialis dorsalis. When a lesion of this cortex is reported in conjunction with a lesion of posterior and medial orbital cortex, the lesion is here labeled as *orbitoventral*. When a lesion of this cortex is made in isolation, the lesion is referred to as *ventral*. When the resection extends laterally up to the gyrus adjacent to the sulcus principalis, the lesion is called *ventrolateral*.

Finally, a *dorsolateral* resection is identified as including the eugranular cortex surrounding the sulcus principalis. Such lesions usually extend to and include the marginal gyrus. The dorsolateral cortex is the termination of the remaining projection of the microcellular portion of the n. medialis dorsalis.

When smaller lesions are reported (e.g., periarcuate, around the arcuate sulcus; periprincipalis, around the sulcus principalis), the nomenclature is reasonably clear. When larger lesions are made they are simply referred to as *lateral frontal* when they exclude the posterior and medial orbital gyri. The resections are referred to as *medial frontal* when they are restricted to these gyri and to the medial surface of the lobe. When the entire anterior frontal cortex is removed, the lesion is referred to as *anterior frontal*.

The Orbital Contribution: The Feeling of Familiarity

A good place to begin is the orbital contribution to psychological processing because it is so closely linked to that of the limbic forebrain. Damage limited to either the medial orbital (Pribram, Mishkin, Rosvold, & Kaplan, 1952) or the posterior orbital (Pribram & Bagshaw, 1953) does not produce any impairments in performance of the direct form on the delayed-response task. Damage to both the medial and posterior orbital cortex does, however, produce a deficit in delayed-alternation performance (Pribram, Lim, Poppen, & Bagshaw, 1966; Pribram et al., 1952; Pribram, Wilson, & Connors, 1962). This deficit is due to the accumulation of many repetitive errors of both commission and omission, which become especially apparent in the go/no-go version of the task. In fact, these lesions produce a greater deficit in this variant of the task than on the right/left version (Pribram, 1973), a result which is opposite that obtained when lateral frontal resections are made (Mishkin & Pribram, 1955).

Other effects observed after resections of the medial and/or posterior orbital damage are a decrease in aggression (Butter, Mishkin, & Mirsky, 1968; Butter, Snyder, & McDonald, 1970) and an increased tendency to put food items in mouths (Butter, McDonald, & Snyder, 1969). Both of these effects had previously been observed when posterior orbital lesions are combined with those of the anterior insula, temporal pole, and amygdala (Pribram & Bagshaw, 1953). It is such results that link the effects of orbital lesions on behavior to those of the limbic forebrain.

The following question arises: To what are such changes in behavior due? Brutkowsi has argued that the orbital lesions in monkeys and dogs produce disinhibition of ordinarily present drive inhibition rather than the more obvious perseverative interference (see the extensive reviews of the conditioning literature by Brutkowsi, 1964, 1965, and Konorski, 1972). The finding that monkeys with orbital resections continue to work harder than normals for nonfood items despite a normal preference for food items (Butter et al., 1969), a result similar to that obtained with amygdalectomized monkeys (Weiskrantz & Wilson, 1958), would seem to support Brutkowski's hypothesis, which was based mainly on work with dogs.

However, data showing that the response rates following orbital or lateral frontal resections are the same as those of normal monkeys during conditioning of an intermittently reinforced bar-press response (Butter, Mishkin, & Rosvold, 1963) plus the additional data that monkeys with orbitoventral lesions stop responding for longer periods than do monkeys with dorsolateral frontal resections when novel stimuli are introduced during a similar bar-pressing task (Butter, 1964) cast considerable doubt on a disinhibition hypothesis based solely on an increased drive for food.

The fact that failure in delayed alternation is characterized by proportionately as many errors of omission as of commission also mitigates against the drive disinhibition hypothesis (Pribram et al., 1966). Similarly damaging to a drive disinhibition hypothesis were the results of an experiment testing the object reversals using the go/no-go technique with monkeys who had sustained resections of orbital cortex (McEnaney & Butter, 1969). Once again the animals not only made more errors of commission than normals, but also more errors of omission. They perseverated their refusal to respond to the previously negative stimulus.

Further evidence along these lines comes from the fact that monkeys with large orbitoventral lesions show a greater resistance to extinction of a bar-press response even in the absence of food reinforcement (Butter et al., 1963). These results confirmed and extended those obtained earlier with total anterior frontal and limbic (posterior orbital, insula, temporal pole, and amygdala) resections (Pribram, 1961b; Pribram & Weiskrantz, 1957) and are consistent with the finding that frontal and limbic lesions enhance the extinction of a conditioned avoidance response (Pribram & Weiskrantz, 1957).

These last results would readily fit a response disinhibition hypothesis (one that plagued limbic system research for many years) were it not for the finding of errors of omission in the delayed-alternation task. Also, monkeys with large orbitoventral resections take longer to habituate to novel stimuli (Butter, 1964) than do monkeys with total anterior frontal resections (Pribram, 1961b; and those with amygdalectomy, Schwartzbaum & Pribram, 1960). These results and those from a long series of conditioning experiments led Mishkin to propose that anterior frontal resections produce perseveration of "central sets" of whatever origin. Subsequent experimental results (Butter, 1969) showed, however, that monkeys with orbital resections do not perseverate in place- or object-reversal tasks. Furthermore, the meaning of central set, when it is extended to include a failure to habituate to novelty, tends to lose whatever precision it might previously have had.

The enhanced distractibility and sensitivity to proactive and retroactive interference, which accounts for the failure to habituate (see Malmo, 1942; Pribram, 1961a), may well be dependent on the organization of drive states, provided we understand by this that such states are composed of endocrine and other neurochemical systems (Estes, 1959). The limbic forebrain has been found to be a selective host to a variety of neuroendocrine and neurochemical secretions that can form the basis of a neural representation of the internal state of the organism by way of which neural control over peripheral endocrine and exocrine secretions is exerted (Martinez, 1983; McGaugh et al., 1979; Pribram, 1969b, 1977).

The import of this research for this review is that such neuroendocrine and neurochemical factors influence the organization of attention and intention: Habituation to novelty (registration and consolidation in the face of distraction), and therefore the organization of what is responded to as familiar, is disturbed by the lesions. Experimental psychologists test for familiarity with "recognition" tasks, and recently Mishkin (1982) has used the delayed nonmatching from sample as an instance of such a recognition procedure. Not surprisingly, he has found deficits with limbic (amygdala and hippocampus) resections and drawn the conclusion that these structures are involved with recognition memory. For those working in the neurological tradition where, since the time of Freud and Henry Head, agnosias, have been related to lesions of the parietal convexity, this conclusion is confusing. The confusion is resolved when it is realized that the delay tasks test for the dimension novelty/familiarity and not the identification of objects, which is the neurologist's definition of recognition. In short, the orbital contribution to psychological processing is to provide a critical facility to the feeling of familiarity based on processing both interoceptive and exteroceptive inputs.

Parcellation of the Lateral Frontal Cortex: Alternation Tasks

The performances of animals with partial resections of the lateral surface of the anterior frontal cortex show that a small midlateral periprincipalis lesion is sufficient to produce severe deficits in both delayed response (Blum, 1952; Goldman, Rosvold, Vest, & Galkin, 1971; Gross & Weiskrantz, 1962; Pinsker & French, 1967) and delayed alternation (Goldman & Rosvold, 1970; Mishkin, 1957). These results have been confirmed and refined by experiments in which electrical stimulation across the sulcus principalis has impaired performance (Stamm, 1967). In fact, these experiments as well as lesion data (Butters & Pandya, 1969) have demonstrated that the middle third of the sulcus serves as the focus for the deficit.

Although these forms of the tasks failed to help with further parcellation, their variants have proved most useful. In an early experiment attempting to analyze the variables important in producing the frontal deficit in solving delay problems, Mishkin and Pribram (1955) found that changing the delayed-alternation procedure from a left/right spatial alternation to an up/down spatial alternation did not improve the performance of the frontal animals. On the other hand, changing the task to a nonspatial go/no-go alternation did improve their performance. The logical conclusion from these results was that it was the spatial nature of the delayed-alternation and delayed-response cues that was significant. To test that conclusion, they followed that experiment with experiments using object-alternation tasks. These were difficult experiments as no one up to that time had been able to train monkeys successfully on object alternation. Pribram and Mishkin (1956) succeeded in training highly sophisticated monkeys on the task using the traditional two-box tray described earlier. Later Pribram (1961a) designed a six-box tray to eliminate the interference of position preferences. Both experiments found that monkeys with lateral frontal lesions were significantly impaired. In fact, the monkeys with lateral frontal lesions did almost as poorly on object alternation as on spatial alternation.

However, when monkeys were given dorsolateral lesions that did not include the ventrolateral cortex, their performances on object alternation were significantly better than those of monkeys given orbitoventral lesions (Mishkin, Vest, Waxler, & Rosvold, 1969). Moreover, examination of the data from the previous study testing monkeys with total lateral lesions (Pribram, 1961a) reveals that the orbitoventral lesion produced as much of a deficit as had the total lateral lesion. Taken together, these results suggest that the focus for producing the deficit lies in the ventrolateral cortex.

Thus, dorsolateral lesions interfere more with classical delay tasks, and ventrolateral lesions interfere more with object alternation. Further, as noted in the previous section, classical right/left alternation is more impaired by lateral frontal lesions than is go/no-go alternation, whereas limbic lesions produce the reverse. These data suggest that the variations of the delayed-response and delayed-alternation tasks tap somewhat different functions. Pribram and his collaborators, therefore, performed a series of experiments (Anderson, Hunt, Vander Stoep, & Pribram, 1976; Pribram, Plotkin, Anderson, & Leong, 1977) using monkeys with total lateral frontal lesions that aimed at discerning the difference between the two tasks. The deficit in delayed-response performance was shown to depend on the elimination or production of distraction. Further, spatial distractors had been found to be especially potent (Grueninger & Pribram, 1969) and proved to be critical even in a test of "object constancy," where a piece of food was simply hidden as in the ordinary delayed-response task. Finally, when the location of the hiding place was shifted within sight of the monkeys, a profound deficit was produced in the operated group despite the fact that the task proved to be a rather easy one for the control subjects.

A replication of the experiment in which "parsing" with temporal tags overcame the deficit on delayed alternation was used to analyze the factors critical to the performance of that task (Pribram et al., 1977; Pribram & Tubbs, 1967; Tubbs, 1969). As expected, in this situation, spatial variables were found to be subservient to temporal. However, location of prior response proved more potent than whether that response had been rewarded in both the operated and control groups, a result that had previously also been obtained by Wilson (1962).

Thus, a mix of spatial and temporal factors is critical to the performance of both delayed response and delayed alternation. But the mix is not equal. The spatial factor is more important in delayed response than in delayed alternation where it can be dispensed with entirely in variants such as the go/no-go and object alternation. As was noted earlier, the delayed-response deficit is maximal when lesions are made in the dorsolateral cortex, whereas lesions of ventrolateral cortex produce the greater deficit on object alternation. These results suggest that there is a focus for spatial tasks in the dorsolateral and one for the visual (and perhaps other exteroceptive tasks) in the ventrolateral frontal cortex.

These modalities are, however, superimposed on a temporal factor that is common to all delay tasks and is disrupted most severely not by lesions of the lateral frontal cortex but by limbic lesions (the go/no-go alternation evidence). If sensory modality is a factor in parcellation of the lateral frontal cortex, variations of the indirect variant of delayed response using matching from sample should prove even more useful than variants of the alternation tasks. In addition, discrimination reversal problems can be used to the same end. The next section examines such evidence.

Parcellation and Discrimination Problems

Mishkin (1964) initiated the attempts to parcel the total lateral frontal lesions, using the matching problems. He began by contrasting the effects of dorsolateral lesions with those produced by resecting a combination of ventrolateral, medial, and posterior orbital cortex. He reported that these orbitoventral lesions produced an even greater deficit than dorsolateral lesions on all of the nonspatial tasks he and his colleagues (Brush, Mishkin, & Rosvold, 1961; Mishkin, Prockop, & Rosvold, 1962) had previously found difficult for monkeys with total lateral lesions. He suggested at the time that the hypothesis of perseverative interference to account for the animals' difficulties might be most appropriate to those with orbitoventral damage.

Since that report, the impairment in object discrimination reversal learning after orbitoventral lesions has been replicated (Butter, 1969; Butters, Butter, Rosen, & Stein, 1973; Goldman, Rosvold, & Mishkin, 1970). The impairment in nonreversal shifts between different types of discrimination problems (object and position) reported by Settlage and his colleagues (Settlage, Butler, & Odoi, 1956; Settlage, Zable, & Harlow, 1948) was replicated in animals with orbitoventral lesions, and also with lesions limited to the ventrolateral surface (Passingham, 1972a). Animals with dorsolateral lesions excluding the ventrolateral surface did not show a deficit either on object discrimination reversal learning (Butter, 1969; Goldman et al., 1970) or on reversal shifts between color, position, and size in visual discrimination problems (Passingham, 1972b). Further, although monkeys with dorsolateral lesions were at a higher performance level than monkeys with ventrolateral lesions on a successive visual-spatial discrimination problem, when a delay was added to change the problem into an indirect delayed-response task the performance of the dorsolateral group became much worse than that of the ventrolateral group (Oscar-Berman, 1975).

Place reversal is another spatial task in which significant impairments were found after total lateral surface anterior frontal lesions (Butter, 1969; Mishkin, 1964) or dorsolateral lesions (Pohl, 1973). Again, monkeys with total anterior frontal lesions performed more poorly than those with principalis lesions, whereas monkeys with damage to small nonprincipalis areas either dorsal to the principalis region or in the arcuate sulcus showed normal performance on this task (Goldman et al., 1971). By contrast, the ventrolateral lesions produced a severe deficit equal to that produced by the total lateral lesion (Butter, 1969). This finding is in accord with that on object-reversal learning as noted above. Neither monkeys with dorsolateral lesions (Pohl, 1973) nor monkeys with total lateral lesions (Butter, 1969; Pribram, 1961a) show any performance impairments, but monkeys with the ventrolateral lesion show severe initial impairments (Butter, 1969; Iversen & Mishkin, 1970).

There has also been some attempt to use discrimination problems to pin down a specifically auditory role for a subdivision of lateral frontal cortex. Gross and Weiskrantz (1962) found that animals with nonprincipalis lesions were significantly worse on an auditory go/no-go differentiation than principalis animals, in contrast to their superior performance on delayed response. However, stimulation of the arcuate and the principalis regions failed to confirm the speculation (Weiskrantz & Mishkin, 1958) that the arcuate sulcus was a focus for the anomalous auditory deficits; stimulation of either region did not produce a drop in auditory differentiation performance (Weiskrantz, Mihailovic, & Gross, 1962). Furthermore, Gross (1963a) was unable to repeat his earlier finding of significant differences in auditory differentiation performance after nonprincipalis lesions when he redid the study using younger animals.

By contrast, more recently Petrides (this volume, Chapter 5) was able to demonstrate an auditory deficit on resection of the tissue dorsal to the arcuate sulcus. This result places the focus for auditory function proximal to the superior limb of the arcuate sulcus beyond the part of the frontal cortex ordinarily resected when lateral frontal lesions are made. Furthermore, arcuate lesions have been shown to affect performance differentially on the auditory conditional position task (Goldman & Rosvold, 1970; Stamm, 1973). Such lesions have no detrimental effects on performance of simultaneous visual discrimination tasks (Chow, 1952; Pribram et al., 1952; Pribram, 1954), successive visual discrimination (Pribram & Mishkin, 1955; Stamm, 1973), or place reversal (Goldman et al., 1971).

The auditory conditional position task was intended to test the animal's ability to make spatial associations when immediate memory is not taxed. As might be expected from what Petrides has shown, animals with dorsolateral lesions excluding principalis and the ventrolateral surface performed better than the arcuate animals (Goldman & Rosvold, 1970), as did animals with ventrolateral lesions excluding arcuate (Stamm, 1973), suggesting a possible arcuate focus.

It is not clear from these results alone whether the auditory or the spatial aspect of the task is most relevant, a consideration that also plagues the finding that monkeys with ventrolateral lesions are as poor as dorsolateral monkeys on an auditory delayed-response task, though they perform better than they do on a visual delayed-response task (Oscar-Berman, 1975). However, Stepien and Stamm (1970) tested a nonauditory spatial opposition task in which the monkey was required to go to a side of the maze opposite from the visual signal. They found that animals with total lateral lesions or lateral lesions excluding principalis were impaired, but animals with damage limited to any of the smaller segments of the dorsolateral surface, including the anterior banks of the limbs of the arcuate sulcus, were unimpaired. This finding suggests that it is the spatial rather than the auditory aspect or the confound between them that is responsible for the deficits following lesions of the anterior frontal cortex forward of the arcuate sulcus.

The evidence from discrimination testing of monkeys with partial lateral frontal lesions is thus not as clear-cut as one would like. Nonetheless, a focus for visual functions may tentatively be discerned in the anterior ventrolateral cortex and one for auditory functions in the dorsal periarcuate cortex (see also Milner, & Petrides, 1984, and Petrides, this volume, Chapter 5). Place reversal that taxes both a temporal and a spatial factor fails to distinguish between portions of the lateral frontal cortex—a finding consonant with that obtained with the classical right/left alternation which, as noted in the previous section, also tests both factors. What remains to be reviewed are the experiments that aim to determine the biological nature of the spatial and temporal factors and their relationship to sensory input.

The Spatial Deficit Is Not Kinesthetic

On the basis of his work with cats and dogs, Konorski (1967) elaborated the hypothesis that the lateral frontal deficit was specifically important for kinesthetic memory and suggested that the cue in the delayed-response task is encoded into memory as the differential movements that are to be made at the end of the delay. Pribram (1961a) had earlier considered this hypothesis on the basis of results in which two types of operant schedules (fixed ratio and fixed intervals) were alternated without benefit of the visual signals used in training. When the signals were removed, the monkeys with lateral frontal lesions, in contrast to their controls, responded indiscriminately. But Pribram was forced to abandon the hypothesis after demonstrating that monkeys with total lateral lesions also had deficits on nonspatial alternation tasks that did not involve kinesthetic feedback.

However, as the data previously discussed accumulated, indicating that the nonspatial alternation deficit had a more central focus, Stamm began to reexamine the kinesthetic hypothesis by adding kinesthetic cues to the delayed alternation. He first trained monkeys on the delayed-alternation task in apparatuses that required different degrees of movement and hence allowed different amounts of kinesthetic feedback (Stamm, 1970). In support of Konorski, Stamm did find that the animals with dorsolateral frontal lesions performed best in the primate chair and worst in the maze, although preoperatively the opposite trend had been significant. Konorski's hypothesis could also account for the data indicating that stimulation across the principalis region at the beginning of the delay has no effect if the task is a delayed match-to-sample task (Kovner & Stamm, 1972) but produces a striking drop in performance if the task is a delayed successive visual discrimination task (Cohen, 1972). Two different visual cues must be differentiated on the basis of pattern, not position, for both of these tasks, but only in the second task does the visual cue signal a spatially distinct response. In an earlier study Mishkin and Pribram (1956) also found that monkeys with total lateral lesions failed the task when it was presented in a manner similar to Cohen's technique.

In another ablation study Stamm and Weber-Levine (1971) found that adding either conditional color or kinesthetic cues to the alley leading to the response doors greatly improved the performances of monkeys with total lateral or principalis lesions on delayed alternation tested in a maze. Stamm and Weber-Levine further found that the improvement produced by the addition of these conditional cues lasted through the subsequent testing of delayed alternation without additional cues for the monkeys with principalis, but not total lateral lesions. Similarly, Gentile and Stamm (1972) found that adding different weights to the manipulanda to provide additional cues improved the performance of monkeys with principalis but not total lateral lesions during delayed alternation tested in the Wisconsin General Testing Apparatus (WGTA). The introduction of supplementary articular-somesthetic cues, on the other hand, improved delayed-alternation performance of both the monkeys with principalis lesions and those with total lateral lesions. Such improvement is in contrast to the lack of improvement for monkeys with total lateral lesions after the addition of supplementary visual (Gentile & Stamm, 1972; Tubbs, 1969) or auditory cues (Tubbs, 1969), or for monkeys with principalis lesions after the addition of supplementary visual cues (Gentile & Stamm, 1972; Stamm & Weber-Levine, 1971).

On the basis of these data, Stamm and Gentile concluded that they had evidence for the hypothesis that kinesthetic memory is relevant to the role of the frontal deficit in ordering spatial responses and that their data indicated that the use of kinesthetic memory was specific to the principalis area. Gentile (1972) then elaborated the kinesthetic concept, bringing it more in line with a suggestion by Pribram (1960) that the frontal cortex acts to partition sets of afferent activity. She suggested that, in the standard delayed-alternation tasks, movement-produced feedback from left and right responses cannot be distinguished and therefore cannot be coded with respect to recency. Unlike additional visual or auditory cues, the additional force or articular-somesthetic differences helped to partition the feedback cues. By this reasoning, temporal parsing (Pribram & Tubbs, 1967) would aid in differentiating the movement-produced cues because the trace of the kinesthetic cues would be different after responses to the one side followed by the longer delay.

However, there is an objection to localizing this kinesthetic deficit to the cortex surrounding the sulcus principalis. Pribram and Tubbs (1967) and Pribram et al. (1977) have argued that temporal parsing provides monkeys with anterior frontal lesions with a stimulus organization they could not provide for themselves since they lack their frontal cortex. Gentile and Stamm would similarly like to argue that, since providing kinesthetic cues improves the performances of monkeys with principalis lesions, the principalis must normally utilize kinesthetic cues. However, monkeys with total lateral lesions were unable to utilize the additional kinesthetic cues, so it is likely that it was the nonprincipalis frontal cortex that enabled the monkeys to learn to use these cues. Even the fact that additional articulosomesthetic cues allow monkeys with total lateral lesions to improve their performance means only that other cortical areas are able to utilize these particular cues, much as in humans verbal cues are used to overcome the deficit (Luria, Pribram, & Homskaya, 1964). In fact, Gentile's (1972) data showing that preoperative training that emphasizes kinesthetic cues makes it difficult for the animals to utilize additional articulosomesthetic cues after surgery suggest that some kind of adaptive cortical reorganization is going on.

More devastating to localizing the kinesthetic deficit in the region of the sulcus principalis, however, is a deficit on object-reversal performances when the reversals happened after only 30 trials. Gross (1963b) used animals with lesions confined to the principalis to obtain these effects. Monkeys with nonprincipalis lesions showed normal performance. Thus, even when the cues are not spatial or kinesthetic, the principalis region itself is essential for encoding them into short-term memory (see also Stamm, Chapter 4, and Petrides, Chapter 5, this volume).

In summary, the kinesthetic hypothesis as the basis for the spatial aspect of the frontal deficit, though it has found substantial support, fails to account for all of the data. Certain discrepancies plague the evidence, which makes the kinesthetic-spatial connection difficult to accept uncritically. The spatial deficit is conceived to be primary in causing difficulty in delayed-response performance. Principalis lesions are the focus for this difficulty, but, as I have argued above, not for the kinesthetic deficit. Further, kinesthesis is essentially a response-produced stimulus and the early experiments of Mishkin and Pribram (1955, 1956) reviewed above had shown that cue differentiation rather than response distinction was the critical variable in determining the delayed-response deficit. Interestingly, Stamm, who has provided the most persuasive evidence in favor of the kinesthetic (which is essentially a response distinction) hypothesis, argues most strongly against another response-based hypothesis, namely, the suggestion that failures in response inhibition are responsible for the frontal deficit. It is likely, therefore, that the kinesthetic hypothesis relates more to the temporal than to the spatial deficit that follows anterior frontal lesions. We thus turn next to a review of the evidence that has been gathered with this hypothesis in mind.

The Temporal Deficit and Kinesthetic Stimulus Differentiation

The initial argument that failure in response inhibition accounts for the frontal deficit came from the observation of an impairment on visual and auditory go/no-go discrimination tasks that follow orbitoventral lesions (Brutkowsy, Mishkin, & Rosvold, 1963; Lawicka, Mishkin, & Rosvold, 1966). In these tasks the errors of the operated monkeys, unlike those of the normals, seemed to occur mainly on no-go trials (Iversen & Mishkin, 1970). Then, in order to further characterize the nature of the deficit due to ventrolateral damage, Iversen and Mishkin (1970) tested monkeys with specific medial and posterior orbital lesions and with ventrolateral lesions on auditory and visual go/no-go differentiation as well as on an object-reversal series. The medial and posterior orbital group made more go/no-go errors than the normals on the successive visual discrimination task and demonstrated a significant nonspecific difficulty on the object reversals that lasted throughout the series. The ventrolateral group, on the other hand, showed perseverative no-go errors on both the auditory and visual tasks, an extremely poor original performance on the auditory task, and a large number of perseverative errors confined to the first reversal of the object-reversal series. Thus, the ventrolateral animals showed perseverative interference that was transient in nature.

This transience of the perseverative effect had also been noted after total lateral lesions in nonreversal shifts (Settlage et al., 1956), go/no-go differentiation (Battig, Rosvold, & Mishkin, 1962), and delayed alternation and successive visual discriminations (Stamm, 1970; Stamm & Weber-Levine, 1971). The transience of the effect might also explain why sophisticated monkeys with lateral lesions did not perseverate their initial preferences (Oscar & Wilson, 1966) when trained in the same learning set paradigm in which more naive monkeys with lateral lesions did perseverate their initial preferences (Brush et al., 1961).

Iversen and Mishkin (1970) concluded that there was a separable transient perseveratory factor that could be attributed to the ventrolateral region. However, Stamm (1973) later found that animals with lesions confined to the ventrolateral surface excluding the arcuate sulcus were impaired on successive pattern discrimination tasks but not on the auditory conditional position task or on the spatial opposition task (Stepien & Stamm, 1970). Stamm argued that since both tasks involve spatial differentiation between instrumental responses, a perseverative interference theory ought to have predicted a deficit on both tasks, which did not occur. In agreement with Stamm, the previously discussed data make it appear more likely that any perseverative interference factor has more to do with spatial differentiation between responses. But it is not the spatial factor that is involved by the ventrolateral lesion. More likely, as noted above, the ventral lip of the frontal lobe is the focus of the temporal aspect of the frontal deficit, but relatively extensive damage surrounding the lip is required to produce the full-blown behavioral effect.

Passingham and Ettlinger (1972) presented evidence that the tactile deficit previously seen in monkeys with lateral lesions (Ettlinger, Morton, & Moffet, 1966; Ettlinger & Wegner, 1958) was specific to the orbitoventral region and that the impairment could be alleviated by adding weights to the manipulanda to make the responses more effortful. Under these conditions the orbitoventral monkeys made as many stimulus comparisons as did the controls and considerably more than they had made during the no-effort condition, suggesting that their difficulty had indeed been due to a lack of response inhibition.

However, Passingham (1972a) was not able to demonstrate that animals with orbitoventral lesions responded incorrectly more than the control animals to a panel that had been deliberately given a higher probability of containing the correct visual stimulus. Passingham had reasoned that the animals would have developed a response set to the higher probability panel and would have to inhibit that set to respond to the other panel correctly. But, despite the fact that orbitoventral animals had previously demonstrated a significant impairment on a simultaneous visual object discrimination, they distributed their errors in the differential probability problem in the same manner as did the normals. The results of this study confirm those of two experiments (Grueninger & Pribram, 1969; Wilson, 1962) performed in Pribram's laboratory on monkeys with total lateral frontal lesions.

But Stamm is correct in questioning the response inhibition hypothesis as adequate in accounting for the temporal aspect of the anterior frontal deficit. Recall that, in discussing the drive inhibition hypothesis forwarded by Brutkowski (1964) to explain the posterior and medial orbital deficit, we noted that errors of omission were proportionately as frequent as errors of commission in the go/no-go alternation task (Butter, 1964; Pribram et al., 1966). Errors of omission—especially failures to respond on the go trials—provide a strong argument against a response inhibition hypothesis. In addition, it should be pointed out that occasional monkeys with either posterior and medial orbital lesions or lateral frontal lesions are reluctant to be tested after surgery despite prior experience. Thus, their overall experience, which has trained them primarily to "go," appears to be negated by a tendency to "no-go." Sometimes these monkeys appear so confused and so reluctant that extensive gradual reshaping must be undertaken before they can be tested. Of course, such shaping trials do not appear in the quantitative descriptions of test performance, which can therefore be misleading when hypotheses as to basic process are being derived.

Stamm's evidence suggests that, rather than response inhibition, the temporal factor in the lateral frontal deficit is related to kinesthetic stimulus differentiation, perhaps on the basis of a central representation of kinesthetic events. Such kinesthetic stimuli are produced by a convergence of muscle afferents with others, such as those from the skin, to produce a motor representation (Malis, Pribram, & Kruger, 1953; Pribram, 1971; Pribram, Sherafat, & Beekman, 1984). The anatomical adjacency of the entire anterior frontal cortex to the classic precentral and to the limbic mediobasal motor cortices makes the hypothesis a reasonable one (see also Petrides, this volume, Chapter 5).

As noted above, the hypothesis received attention in earlier experiments. For instance, Pribram et al. (1952), in an unpublished portion of their study, attempted to show that the delayed-response performance of normal monkeys is dependent on self-generated kinesthetic cues. It was found that movements specific to the correct solution of the delay problem did occur initially but that, as the monkeys became proficient, these peripheral indicators became less and less frequent. The assumption was made that the proficient monkeys used a central representation to solve the problem—that brain events replaced the peripheral kinesthetic stimuli. It was anticipated that, perhaps after anterior frontal surgery, the monkeys might revert to a peripheral response mode (as was shown for the chimpanzee by R. A. Blum, J. Semmes, and K. H. Pribram, presented at the annual meeting of the APA in 1947), but this did not occur—thus, the data were left unpublished. Further, as noted above, other experimental results (e.g., the deficit in object alternation) mitigated against the kinesthetic hypothesis until Stamm noted that these results could be ascribed to a ventral focus in the lateral frontal cortex. This left the possibility that some other focus could be found responsible for the kinesthetic deficit. Stamm has suggested that this focus is the cortex surrounding the sulcus principalis but, as reviewed above, this localization does not hold up. Instead, Petrides's (this volume, Chapter 5) evidence leads to a more ventral and posterior periarcuate focus, which, of necessity, must be separable from the visual focus (more anteriorly situated around the anterior lip of the arcuate sulcus extending to the lip of the lobe) that produces the object alternation deficit if the kinesthetic hypothesis is to be supported.

To summarize this section, the results of attempts to subdivide the lateral frontal cortex lead to the following conclusions:

1. There is a focus centering on the sulcus principalis that influences performance on both the spatial delayed-response and the spatial delayed-alternation tasks but *not* on the go/no-go or object versions of alternation, suggesting that a spatial factor important to task performance has been interfered with by the lesion of this cortex. Further, the presumed kinesthetic basis for the spatial deficit common to the impaired performances proves to be related to the temporal and not the spatial aspects of these and other tasks. This leaves the spatial deficit unexplained. An explanation of the spatial deficit in terms of the effects of spatial distractors was suggested and will be enlarged on in the next section.

2. The remainder of the lateral frontal cortex influences all types of alternation performance and can be further subdivided according to modality by tests involving variants of alternation (e.g., object alternation, discrimination reversal). Dorsal periarcuate auditory, perhaps anterior periarcuate visual, and posterior periarcuate kinesthetic subdivisions can be identified. The deficit produced by lesions in these subdivisions is sensitive to the *sensory load* imposed as a requirement for performing adequately. This suggests that some sort of sensory servocontrol (negative feedback) mechanism is involved. Goldman-Rakic (1978; Goldman-Rakic & Schwartz, 1982) has elegantly worked out the connections between frontal and parietal cortex and these with the corpus striatum, connections that can serve such a sensory servosystem.

SUMMARY AND SYNTHESIS

When I began research on the functions of the anterior frontal cortex I found that neurobehavioral considerations related this part of the brain to the functions of the limbic portions of the forebrain, not to the motor functions of the precentral cortex. The peri-Rolandic cortex, on the basis of neurobehavioral analysis, belonged with the remainder of the cerebral convexity. Thus, a major distinction was made between the functions in behavior of the frontolimbic formations and those of the posterior cerebral convexity (see reviews by Pribram, 1954, 1958a, 1958b, and the initial part of this chapter).

Nonetheless, the proximity of the anterior frontal cortex to those portions of the cortex that were electrically excitable in terms of motor functions (including those on the medial and basal surfaces of the hemisphere) continued to be of considerable concern. Only recently have I hit upon an idea around which this concern can be precisely formulated. It is this formulation that forms the core of the final portion of this review.

The idea is simple. There is an important attribute by which the systems in the central portion of the cerebral mantle differ from others: They are concerned with somatosensorimotor processes. Somatic processing differs from all other processing in that whatever is experienced, whether through the epicritic systems of the posterior convexity or the protocritic (interoceptive plus pain and temperature—see Chin, Pribram, Drake, & Green, 1976, Pribram, 1977, for data and definition) systems of the frontolimbic formations, no precise communication with other organisms or the physical or cultural environment is possible without the participation of somatosensorimotor mechanisms.

For the anterior frontal cortex, this means that we should be able to discern in its functions a mechanism that relates protocritic processing to somatosensorimotor functions. As with any such endeavor based on an arbitrary dichotomous classification, problems immediately arise: The exteroceptors are part of the body, and those processes that are concerned not so much with regulating their specific function but with controlling their overall "somatic" expressive relationship to the world need, on the basis of the evidence, also to be included in the somatosensorimotor mechanism.

A good place to begin the attempt to tie all this together is Brown's (1985) review of frontal lobe syndromes, which is organized within the frame of three major groups of disorders: "Damage to frontal limbic formations leads to impaired activation (response bias, motor neglect, and lack of initiation); damage to 'integration' cortex on the convexity leads to derailment of the action after adequate initiation (distractibility, confabulation); and damage to premotor and precentral cortices leads to a defect of final implementation (misarticulation, dyspraxia)" (p. 37).

Pribram and McGuinness (1975) have further delineated the evidence for "stop" and "go" systems within the frontolimbic forebrain. The "stop" mechanism deals with emotion (to be "hung up," out of motion) and involves those portions of the frontal and temporal lobes connected to the amygdala by way of the uncinate fasciculus. The other mechanism deals with motivation and is constituted of the "go" dopaminergic nigrostriatal-frontal system (see also Goldman-Rakic & Schwartz, 1982).

With regard to Brown's second category, the data reviewed in the section on the subdivision of the anterior frontal ("integration") cortex show that distractibility is responsible for the "spatial" deficit obtained when the dorsolateral frontal cortex is damaged. Confabulation, on the other hand, may well be the human counterpart of the "temporal" deficit that follows periarcuate and ventrolateral frontal damage, a deficit sensitive to sensory input.

Brown's third category, centering on the premotor and precentral cortex, holds the key to bringing together the various aspects of frontal lobe function. The key is provided by the proposals made by Goldberg (1985; also this volume, Chapter 15) regarding the functions of the premotor systems, which, in turn, are based on the concepts of Sanides (1966, which are also reviewed and extended by Pandya and Barnes, this volume, Chapter 3). These proposals divide the premotor cortex into a medial, supplementary premotor region and a lateral, periarcuate premotor region. On the basis of evidence from comparative anatomical studies, the medial region is shown to be derived from archicortical origins, and the lateral region from paleocortical primordia. The two regions are suggested to function differently: The medial is concerned in developing models that program behavior in a feedforward fashion; by contrast, the lateral region programs behavior via a variety of sensory feedback mechanisms.

This analysis can be readily extended to the remainder of the motor cortex: The evidence regarding the difference in orientation of the projection fan of thalamocortical connections, presented in the first part of this chapter, indicates that the primary somatosensorimotor cortex also derives from the medial surface of the hemisphere, perhaps from the cortex of the cingulate gyrus. Accordingly, it would seem that the supplementary motor cortex participates in sketching the outlines of the model while the precentral cortex implements its finer aspects. Such a scheme is supported by the fact that the supplementary motor cortex receives an input from basal ganglia (known to determine postural and sensory sets) while the precentral motor cortex, in its involvement with the cerebellum, provides the details necessary to carry out a feedforward regulated action. I have elsewhere (Pribram et al., 1984) provided a review of the evidence and a mathematical description based on a model developed by Houk & Rymer (1981), by which such a feedforward process operates.

The lateral premotor region is intimately interconnected with the inferior-posterior parietal cortex as indicated by Schwartz and Goldman-Rakic (1984), by Goldberg (1985), and by the thalamocortical and comparative anatomical data reviewed at the beginning of this chapter. As indicated there, it is damage to this system that produces apraxias, which, according to Goldberg's thesis, should devolve on faulty feedback processing. It is not too farfetched to wonder whether the repetitions which the lesioned monkeys made in the task reported in the first part of this chapter might not have been due to the necessity for gaining additional sensory feedback before proceeding.

There is one further speculation regarding apraxia that is worth considering. Elsewhere (Pribram & Carlton, 1987) I have described the neural mechanism involved in the construction of objects from images. Essentially this mechanism operates to extract invariances (constancies) from sets of images by a process of convolution and correlation. An object is experienced when the resultant correlation remains constant across further transformation of the set of images.

When objects are constructed in the somatosensorimotor domain they are of two kinds. One sort of object is the familiar external "objective" object. Damage to the peri-Rolandic cortex (including the superior parietal gyrus) results in object agnosia. When, however, the lateral premotor and inferior parietal cortex is damaged, apraxias and neglect syndromes develop. Could the apraxias be thought of as a mild form of neglect in the sense that the "object" that is constructed by this premotor-parietal system is the "self"? If this hypothesis is correct, apraxias result from a failure in the appreciation (based on feedback?) of self: an awkwardness more pervasive than the impairment of skills. Thus, one can envision a gradual increased impairment ranging from apraxia through Parkinsonian tremors at rest, etc., to neglect. This syndrome can be clearly distinguished from the one produced by cerebellar-Rolandic damage, which is characterized by loss of skill, intention tremor, and paresis.

A word of caution: The statements made above could be interpreted as a denial of distinctions between such syndromes as Parkinson's, neglect, and apraxia. This is definitely *not* what is meant. Even apraxias of frontal origin can be expected to differ subtly from those of parietal origin and it may well be as Brown (1975) suggests—that the lesions which produce apraxia must invade the limbic forebrain. As evident in the work of Terrence W. Deacon (personal communication), parietal and frontal cortex, though reciprocally connected, show an upstream/downstream relationship to one another. According to Deacon, a downstream corticocortical connection terminates most heavily in Layers iiic–iv; an upstream connection terminates in Layer i and sometimes in bands in vb. Thus, there is a clear hierarchical connectivity from anterior cingulate to anterior frontal to periarcuate to premotor and motor cortices. At the same time, parietal cortex is upstream from posterior cingulate, as well as from all of frontal cortex.

What I *am* trying to convey is that a *class* of disorders due to damage to systems of paleocerebral origin can be discerned. Within that class a variety of syndromes traceable to differences in neuroanatomical and neurochemical substrates can be made out.

How does this approach to the problem help connect the functions of the anterior frontal cortex to those of the somatosensorimotor regions? As noted in this chapter, delay problem performance is related to sensory mode: a periarcuate locus for auditory and visual, a more anterior location for kinesthetic. These relationships fit with the general hypothesis that the function of the anterior frontal cortex is to relate the processes served by the limbic forebrain to those of the sensorimotor systems, broadly defined as above. The results also support the suggestion that these relationships are of a feedback nature, namely, Stamm's experiments in which kinesthetic feedback was manipulated.

Furthermore, there are the strong connections through the uncinate fasciculus to the structures of the temporal lobe derived from paleocerebral systems (amygdala, pyriform cortex, and adjacent temporal polar juxtallocortex), which indicate that these portions of the anterior frontal cortex are to be considered relatives of the lateral premotor system rather than relatives of the precentral motor system.

On the other hand, there are heavy connections between the cortex surrounding the sulcus principalis and the hippocampus (Nauta, 1964). It is this part of the anterior frontal cortex that has resisted fractionation with respect to sensory mode, but which is especially sensitive to the "spatial" aspects of the delay task. This is exactly the situation with regard to hippopcampal function. In fact, the deficits produced by resections of the primate hippocampus and those produced by resections of the cortex surrounding the sulcus principalis mimic (with the critical exception that spatial delayed response remains intact after hippocampectomy) each other to such an extent that it is hard to distinguish between them.

I have extensively reviewed above and elsewhere (Pribram, 1986) the evidence for considering the difficulty with "spatial" problems as being due to an increase in sensitivity to distraction under certain specifiable conditions. Briefly, the essential evidence is that, when such interference is minimized, as when the delay interval is darkened, monkeys with frontal resections can perform the delay task (Anderson et al., 1976; Malmo, 1942). Further, spatial cues have been found to be more distracting than visual and auditory cues for normal monkeys, and especially so for monkeys with resections of the anterior frontal cortex and, to a somewhat lesser extent (thus the sparing of delayed response?) of the hippocampal cortex (Douglas & Pribram, 1969; Grueninger & Pribram, 1969). Whatever the interpretation of the "spatial" deficit, the data are consonant with the conclusion that the cortex surrounding the sulcus principalis is derived from an archicerebral primordium.

The profusion of data collected by hard labor over the past 50 years can thus be fitted into a tentative scheme. No longer are we stuck with vague concepts of frontal lobe function. The role of the anterior frontal cortex in emotion and motivation is seen as relating protocritic (interoceptive plus pain and temperature) to epicritic processes in the feedback mode. Evaluation (what Arnold [1970] calls appraisal) of one's feelings with regard to what one wishes to do is the function of the periarcuate and ventrolateral portions of this cortex (Konow & Pribram, 1970). Evaluation is a sort of internal rehearsal, a feedback by way of which the feeling becomes refined, that is, more in keeping with current sensory input and with the consequences of actions.

The role of the anterior frontal cortex in attention and intention (planning) relates protocritic to epicritic processing in the feedforward mode. This is the function of the dorsolateral frontal cortex. In the feedforward mode, current and consequent inputs form the context within which "models" are constructed in "fast time," models which in turn are used to modify subsequent behavior. Thus the role of the frontal cortex in one form of "short-term memory" is clarified: The close connection between the dorsolateral frontal cortex and the hippocampus; the similarity of the cytoarchitecture of the hippocampus and that of the cerebellum; the close connection of the peri-Rolandic cortex (which is most likely derived, as noted, from the archicerebrum, as is the hippocampus) and the cerebellum; and the known function of the cerebellum as a feedforward mechanism (see, e.g., Pribram, 1971, 1981; Ruch, 1951) all attest to the likelihood that the dorsolateral frontal cortex is indeed involved in such "projective" processes.

One final word: Brown (this volume, Chapter 14) has suggested that the mechanism for feedback and feedforward depends on the operation of sets of tuned relaxation oscillators that constitute the brainstem and spinal cord systems, which are influenced by the various frontal lobe processes under consideration. The evidence for the existence of such tuned oscillators has been repeatedly presented from the time of Graham-Brown (1914) through von Holst (1937, 1948) and Bernstein (1967) and his group (Gelfand, Gurfinkel, Tsetlin, & Shik, 1971). This evidence has been thoroughly reviewed by Gallistel (1980). The mechanism whereby a cortical influence can be imposed on such systems of oscillators has also been worked out within the concept of an "image of achievement." Such a motor image must operate within the spectral frequency domain (Pribram, 1971), and Pribram et al. (1984) have presented evidence that neurons in the motor cortex are tuned to different frequencies of movement (independent of velocity and acceleration). These authors also detail the mechanism whereby such tuned cortical cells can program the subcortical motor systems.

Is the task then completed? Heavens, no! We have as yet only begun to explore *how* the various portions of the frontal cortex do their work. This is especially true of the anterior frontal cortex, the part of the lobe that was so cavalierly severed from the rest of the brain during the heyday of the leukotomy (lobotomy) procedure. Nonetheless, as this review and the contents of the other chapters of this volume indicate, a half-century of investigation has not been in vain, and the promise of the future is that we will, in due time, also get to know the *how*.

ACKNOWLEDGMENTS

I am deeply indebted to Betty Ann Brody, whose review chapter in her thesis formed the basis for the part of this essay concerned with the subdivisions of the anterior frontal cortex. The work reported in this essay was supported in part by an NIH Career Award to the author.

REFERENCES

Anderson, R. M., Hunt, S. C., Vander Stoep, A., & Pribram, K. H. (1976). Object permanency and delayed response as spatial context in monkeys with frontal lesions. *Neuropsychologia, 14,* 481–490.

Arnold, M. B. (Ed.). (1970). *Feelings and emotions.* New York: Academic Press.

Battig, K., Rosvold, H. E., & Mishkin, M. (1962). Comparison of the effects of frontal and caudate lesions on discrimination learning in monkeys. *Journal of Comparative and Physiological Psychology, 55,* 458–463.

Bernstein, N. (1967). *The coordination and regulation of movement.* Oxford: Pergamon.

Blum, R. A. (1952). Effects of subtotal lesions of frontal granular cortex on delayed reaction in monkeys. *AMA Archives of Neurology and Psychiatry, 67,* 375–386.

Brown, J. W. (1985). Frontal lobe syndromes. *Handbook of Clinical Neurology, 1,* 23–41.

Brush, E. S., Mishkin, M., & Rosvold, H. E. (1961). Effects of object preferences and aversions on discrimination learning in monkeys with frontal lesions. *Journal of Comparative and Physiological Psychology, 54,* 319–325.

Brutkowski, S. (1964). Prefrontal cortex and drive inhibition. In J. M. Warren & K. Akert (Eds.), *Frontal granular cortex and behavior* (pp. 219–241). New York: McGraw-Hill.

Brutkowski, S. (1965). Functions of prefrontal cortex in animals. *Physiological Reviews, 45,* 721–746.

Brutkowski, S., Mishkin, M., & Rosvold, H. E. (1963). Positive and inhibitory motor reflexes in monkeys after ablation of orbital or dorsolateral surface of the frontal cortex. In E. Gutman & P. Hnik (Eds.), *Central and peripheral mechanisms of motor functions* (pp. 133–141). Prague: Czechoslovak Academy of Sciences.

Butter, C. M. (1964). Habituation of responses to novel stimuli in monkeys with selective frontal lesions. *Science, 194,* 313–315.

Butter, C. M. (1969). Impairments in selective attention to visual stimuli in monkeys with inferotemporal and lateral striate lesions. *Brain Research, 12,* 374–383.

Butter, C. M., McDonald, J. A., & Snyder, D. R. (1969). Orality, preference behavior and reinforcement value of nonfood object in monkeys orbital frontal lesions. *Science, 164,* 1306–1307.

Butter, C. M., Mishkin, M., & Mirsky, A. F. (1968). Emotional responses toward humans in monkeys with selective frontal lesions. *Physiology and Behavior, 3,* 213–215.

Butter, C. M., Mishkin, M., & Rosvold, E. H. (1963). Conditioning and extinction of a food rewarded response after selective ablations of the frontal cortex in rhesus monkeys. *Experimental Neurology, 7* (1), 65–75.

Butter, C. M., Snyder, D. R., & McDonald, J. A. (1970). Effects of orbital frontal lesions on aversive and aggressive behaviors in rhesus monkeys. *Journal of Comparative and Physiological Psychology, 72,* 132–144.

Butters, N., & Pandya, D. N. (1969). Retention of delayed-alternation: Effect of selective lesions of sulcus principalis. *Science, 165,* 1271–1273.

Butters, N., Butter, C. M., Rosen, J., & Stein, D. (1973). Behavioral effects of sequential and one-stage ablations of orbital prefrontal cortex. *Experimental Neurology, 39,* 204–214.

Chin, J. H., Pribram, K. H., Drake, K., & Greene, L. O., Jr. (1976). Disruption of temperature discrimination during limbic forebrain stimulation in monkeys. *Neuropsychologia, 14,* 293–310.

Chow, K. L. (1952). Further studies on selective ablation of associative cortex in relation to visually mediated behavior. *Journal of Comparative and Physiological Psychology, 45,* 109–118.

Chow, K. L., & Pribram, K. H. (1956). Cortical projection of the thalamic ventrolateral nuclear group in monkeys. *Journal of Comparative Neurology, 104,* 57–75.

Cohen, S. M. (1972). Electrical stimulation of cortical caudate pairs during delayed successive visual discrimination in monkeys. *Acta Neurobiologiae Experimentalis, 32,* 211–233.

Douglas, R. J., & Pribram, K. H. (1969). Distraction and habituation in monkeys with limbic lesions. *Journal of Comparative and Physiological Psychology, 69,* 473–480.

Estes, W. K. (1959). The statistical approach to learning theory. In S. Koch (Ed.), *Psychology: A study of a science: Vol. 2. General systematic formulations, learning and special processes.* New York: McGraw-Hill.

Ettlinger, G., Morton, H. B., & Moffett, A. (1966). Tactile discrimination performance in the monkey: The effect of bilateral posterior parietal and lateral frontal ablations, and of callosal section. *Cortex, 2,* 5–29.

Ettlinger, G., & Wegener, J. (1958). Somaesthetic alternation, discrimination and orientation after frontal and parietal lesions in monkeys. *Journal of Experimental Psychology, 10,* 177–186.

Gallistel, C. R. (1980). *The organization of action: A new synthesis.* Hillsdale, NJ: Erlbaum.

Gelfand, I. M., Gurfinkel, V. S., Tsetlin, M. L., & Shik, M. L. (1971). Some problems in the analysis of movements. In I. M. Gelfand, V. S. Gurfinkel, S. V. Fromin, & M. L. Tsetlin

(Eds.), *Models of the structural-functional organization of certain biological systems*. Cambridge, MA: MIT Press.
Gentile, A. M. (1972). Movement organization and delayed alternation behavior of monkeys following selective ablation of frontal cortex. *Acta Neurological Biological Experimentalis, 2,* 277–304.
Gentile, A. M., & Stamm, J. S. (1972). Supplementary cues and delayed alternation performance of frontal monkeys. *Journal of Comparative and Physiological Psychology, 80*(2), 230–237.
Goldberg, G. (1985). Supplementary motor area: Review and hypotheses. *Behavioral and Brain Sciences, 8,* 567–588.
Goldman, P. S., & Rosvold, H. E. (1970). Localization of function within the dorsolateral prefrontal cortex of the rhesus monkey. *Experimental Neurology, 27,* 291–304.
Goldman, P. S., Rosvold, H. E., & Mishkin, M. (1970). Selective sparing of function in prefrontal lobectomy in infant monkeys. *Experimental Neurology, 29,* 221–226.
Goldman, P. S., Rosvold, H. E., Vest, B., & Galkin, T. (1971). Analysis of the delayed alternation deficit produced by dorsolateral prefrontal lesions in the rhesus monkey. *Journal of Comparative and Physiological Psychology, 77* (2), 212–220
Goldman-Rakic, P. S. (1978). Neuronal plasticity in primate telencephalon: Anomalous projections induced by prenatal removal of frontal cortex. *Science, 202,* 768–770.
Goldman-Rakic, P. S., & Schwartz, M. L. (1982). Interdigitation of contralateral and ipsilateral columnar projections to frontal association cortex in primates. *Science, 216,* 755–757.
Graham-Brown, T. (1914). On the nature of the fundamental activity of the nervous centres; together with an analysis of the conditioning of rhythmic activity in progression, and a theory of evolution of function of the nervous system. *Journal of Physiology (London), 48,* 18–46.
Gross, C. G. (1963a). A comparison of the effects of partial and total lateral frontal lesions on auditory test performance by monkeys. *Journal of Comparative and Physiological Psychology, 56,* 41–47.
Gross, C. G. (1963b). Discrimination reversal after lateral frontal lesions in monkeys. *Journal of Comparative and Physiological Psychology, 56,* 52–55.
Gross, C. G., & Weiskrantz, L. (1962). Evidence for dissociation of impairment on auditory discrimination and delayed response following lateral frontal lesions in monkeys. *Experimental Neurology, 5,* 453–476.
Grueninger, W., & Pribram, K. H. (1969). The effects of spatial and nonspatial distractors on performance latency of monkeys with frontal lesions. *Journal of Comparative and Physiological Psychology, 68,* 203–209.
Houk, J. C., & Rymer, W. Z. (1981). Neural control of muscle length and tension. In V. B. Brooks (Ed.), *Motor control*. Bethesda, MD: American Physiological Society Handbook of Physiology.
Iversen, S. D., & Mishkin, M. (1970). Perseverative interference in monkeys following selective lesions of the inferior prefrontal convexity. *Experimental Brain Research, 11,* 376–386.
Kaada, B. R., Pribram, K. H., & Epstein, J. A. (1949). Respiratory and vascular responses in monkeys from temporal pole, insular, orbital surface and cingulate gyrus. *Journal of Neurophysiology, 12,* 347–356.
Konorski, J. (1967). *Integrative activity of the brain: An interdisciplinary approach*. Chicago, IL: University of Chicago Press.
Konorski, J. (1972). Some hypotheses concerning the functional organization of prefrontal cortex. *Acta Neurobiologiae Experimentalis, 32,* 595–613.
Konow, A., & Pribram, K. H. (1970). Error recognition and utilization produced by injury to the frontal cortex in man. *Neuropsychologia, 8,* 489–491.
Kovner, R., & Stamm, J. S. (1972). Disruption of short-term visul memory by electrical stimulation of inferotemporal cortex. *Journal of Comparative and Physiological Psychology, 81,* 163–172
Lawicka, W., Mishkin, M., & Rosvold, H. E. (1966). Dissociation of impairment on auditory tasks following orbital and dorsolateral frontal lesions in monkeys. *Proceedings of the Congress of the Polish Physiological Society, 10,* pp. 168ff.

Luria, A. R., Pribram, K. H., & Homskaya, E. D. (1964). An experimental analysis of the behavioral disturbance produced by a left frontal arachnoidal endothelloma (meningioma). *Neuropsychologia, 2,* 257–280.

Malis, L. I., Pribram, K. H., & Kruger, L. (1953). Action potentials in "motor" cortex evoked by peripheral nerve stimulation. *Journal of Neurophysiology, 16,* 161–167.

Malmo, R. B. (1942). Interference factors in delayed response in monkeys after removal of frontal lobes. *Journal of Neurophysiology, 5,* 295–308.

Martinez, J. L. (1983). Endogenous modulators of learning and memory. In S. T. Cooper (Ed.), *Theory in psychopharmacology* (Vol. 2, pp. 48–74). New York: Academic Press.

McEnaney, K. W., & Butter, C. M. (1969). Perseveration of responding and nonresponding in monkeys with orbital frontal ablations. *Journal of Comparative and Physiological Psychology, 69,* 558–561.

McGaugh, J. L., Gold, P. E., Handwerker, M. J., Jensen, R. A., Martinez, J. L., Jr., Meligeni, J. A., & Vasquez, B. J. (1979). Altering memory by electrical and chemical stimulation of the brain. *International Brain Research Organization Monograph Series, 4,* 151–164.

Milner, B., & Petrides, M. (1984). Behavioural effects of frontal-lobe lesions in man. *Trends in Neurosciences, 7*(11), 403–407.

Mishkin, M. (1957). Effects of small frontal lesions on delayed alternation in monkeys. *Journal of Neurophysiology, 20,* 615–622.

Mishkin, M. (1964). Perseveration of central sets after frontal lesions in monkeys. In J. M. Warren & K. Akert (Eds.), *The frontal granular cortex and behavior* (pp. 219–241). New York: McGraw-Hill.

Mishkin, M. (1982). A memory system in the monkey. *Philosophical Transactions of the Royal Society of London, Series B, 298,* 85–95.

Mishkin, M., & Pribram, K. H. (1955). Analysis of the effects of frontal lesions in monkey: I. Variations of delayed alternation. *Journal of Comparative and Physiological Psychology, 48,* 492–495.

Mishkin, M., & Pribram, K. H. (1956). Analysis of the effects of frontal lesions in monkey: II. Variations of delayed response. *Journal of Comparative and Physiological Psychology, 49,* 36–40.

Mishkin, M., Prockop, E. S., & Rosvold, H. E. (1962). One-trial object discrimination learning in monkeys with frontal lesions. *Journal of Comparative and Physiological Psychology, 55,* 178–181.

Mishkin, M., Vest, B., Waxler, M., & Rosvold, H. E. (1969). A re-examination of the effects of frontal lesions on object alternation. *Neuropsychologia, 7,* 357–363.

Nauta, W. J. H. (1964). Some efferent connections of the prefrontal cortex in the monkey. In J. M. Warren & K. Akert (Eds.), *The frontal granular cortex and behavior* (pp. 28–55). New York: McGraw-Hill.

Oscar, M., & Wilson, M. (1966). Tactual and visual discrimination learning in monkeys with frontal lesions. *Journal of Comparative and Physiological Psychology, 62,* 108–114.

Oscar-Berman, M. (1975). The effects of dorsolateral and ventrolateral orbitofrontal lesions on spatial discrimination learning and delayed response in two modalities. *Neuropsychologia, 13,* 237–246.

Passingham, R. E. (1972a). Visual discrimination learning after selective prefrontal ablations in monkeys *(Macaca mulatta). Neuropsychologia, 10,* 27–33.

Passingham, R. E. (1972b). Non-reversal shifts after selective prefrontal ablations in monkeys *(Macaca mulatta). Neuropsychologia, 10,* 41–46.

Passingham, R. E., & Ettlinger, G. (1972). Tactile discrimination learning after selective prefrontal ablations in monkeys *(Macaca mulatta). Neuropsychologia, 10,* 17–26.

Pinsker, H. M., & French, G. M. (1967). Indirect delayed reactions under various testing conditions in normal and midlateral frontal monkeys. *Neuropsychologia, 5,* 13–24.

Pohl, W. G. (1973). Dissociation of spatial and discrimination deficits following frontal and parietal lesions in monkeys. *Journal of Comparative and Physiological Psychology, 82,* 227–239.

Pribram, K. H. (1954). Toward a science of neuropsychology: Method and data. In R. A. Patton

(Ed.), *Current trends in psychology and the behavioral sciences* (pp. 115–142.) Pittsburgh, PA: University of Pittsburgh Press.
Pribram, K. H. (1958a). Comparative neurology and the evolution of behavior. In A. Roe & G. G. Simpson (Eds.), *Behavior and evolution* (pp. 140–164). New Haven, CT: Yale University Press.
Pribram, K. H. (1958b). Neocortical function in behavior. In H. F. Harlow & C. N. Woolsey (Eds.), *Biological and biochemical bases of behavior* (pp. 151–172). Madison: University of Wisconsin Press.
Pribram, K. H. (1960). The intrinsic systems of the forebrain. In J. Field, H. W. Magoun, & V. E. Hall (Eds.), *Handbook of physiology* (Sect. 1, Vol. II, pp. 1323–1344). Washington, DC: American Physiological Society.
Pribram, K. H. (1961a). A further experimental analysis of the behavioral deficit that follows injury to the primate frontal cortex. *Experimental Neurology, 3,* 432–466.
Pribram, K. H. (1961b). Limbic system. In D. E. Sheer (Ed.), *Electrical stimulation of the brain* (pp. 311–320). Austin: University of Texas Press.
Pribram, K. H. (1969a). DADTA III: Computer control of the experimental analysis of behavior. *Perceptual and Motor Skills, 29,* 599–608.
Pribram, K. H. (1969b). The neurobehavioral analysis of limbic forebrain mechanisms: Revision and progress report. In D. S. Lehrman, R. A., Hinde, & E. Shaw (Eds.), *Advances in the study of behavior* (pp. 297–332). New York: Academic Press.
Pribram, K. H. (1971). *Languages of the brain: Experimental paradoxes and principles in neuropsychology*. Englewood Cliffs, NJ: Prentice-Hall.
Pribram, K. H. (1973). The primate frontal cortex—executive of the brain. In K. H. Pribram & A. R. Luria (Eds.), *Psychophysiology of the frontal lobes*. New York: Academic Press.
Pribram, K. H. (1977). Peptides and protocritic processes. In L. H. Miller, C. L. Sandman, & A. J. Kastin (Eds.), *Neuropeptide influences on the brain and behavior* (pp. 213–232). New York: Raven Press.
Pribram, K. H. (1981). Functional organization of the cerebral cortex. In G. Schaltenband & E. Walker (Eds.), *Stereotaxy of the human brain* (pp. 300–328). Stuttgart and New York: Georg Thieme Verlag, Thieme-Stratton.
Pribram, K. H. (1986). The hippocampal system and recombinant processing. In R. Isaacson & K. H. Pribram (Eds.), *The hippocampus* (Vol. IV). New York: Plenum Press.
Pribram, K. H., & Bagshaw, M. H. (1953). Further analysis of the temporal lobe syndrome utilizing frontotemporal ablations in monkeys. *Journal of Comparative Neurology, 99,* 347–375.
Pribram, K. H., & Carlton, E. (1987). *Brain mechanisms in perception and cognition*. Hillsdale, NJ: Erlbaum.
Pribram, K. H., Chow, K. L., & Semmes, J. (1953). Limit and organization of the cortical projection from the medial thalamic nucleus in monkeys. *Journal of Comparative Neurology, 95,* 433–440.
Pribram, K. H., & Fulton, J. F. (1954). An experimental critique of the effects of anterior cingulate ablations in monkey. *Brain, 77,* 34–44.
Pribram, K. H., Gardner, K. W., Pressman, G. L., & Bagshaw, M. H. (1963). Automated analysis of multiple choice behavior. *Journal of the Experimental Analysis of Behavior, 6,* 123–124.
Pribram, K. H., Lim, H., Poppen, R., & Bagshaw, M. H. (1966). Limbic lesions and the temporal structure of redundancy. *Journal of Comparative and Physiological Psychology, 61,* 365–373.
Pribram, K. H., & McGuinness, D. (1975). Arousal, activation and effort in the control of attention. *Psychology Reviews, 82,* 116–149.
Pribram, K. H., & Mishkin, M. (1955). Simultaneous and successive visual discrimination by monkeys with inferotemporal lesions. *Journal of Comparative and Physiological Psychology, 48,* 198–202.
Pribram, K. H., & Mishkin, M. (1956). Analysis of the effects of frontal lesion in monkey: III. Object alternation. *Journal of Comparative and Physiological Psychology, 49,* 41–45.
Pribram, K. H., & Mishkin, M., Rosvold, H. E., & Kaplan, S. J. (1952). Effects on delayed-response performance of lesions of dorsolateral and ventromedial frontal cortex of baboons. *Journal of Comparative and Physiological Psychology, 45,* 565–575.

Pribram, K. H., Plotkin, H. C., Anderson, R. M., & Leong, D. (1977). Information sources in the delayed alternation task for normal and "frontal" monkeys. *Neuropsychologia, 15,* 329–340.

Pribram, K. H., Sherafat, A., & Beekman, G. J. (1984). Frequency encoding in motor systems. In H.T.A. Whiting (Ed.), *Human motor actions: Bernstein reassessed* (pp. 121–156). Amsterdam: North-Holland.

Pribram, K. H., & Tubbs, W. E. (1967). Short-term memory, parsing and the primate frontal cortex. *Science, 156,* 1765–1767.

Pribram, K. H., & Weiskrantz, L. (1957). A comparison of the effects of medial and lateral cerebral resections on conditioned avoidance behavior of monkeys. *Journal of Comparative and Physiological Psychology, 50,* 74–80.

Pribram, K. H., Wilson, W. A., & Connors, J. (1962). The effects of lesions of the medial forebrain on alternation behavior of rhesus monkeys. *Experimental Neurology, 6,* 36–47.

Ruch, T. C. (1951). Motor systems. In S. S. Stevens (Ed.), *Handbook of experimental psychology* (pp. 154–208). New York: Wiley.

Sanides, F. (1966). The architecture of the human frontal lobe and the relation to its functional differentiation. *International Journal of Neurology, 5,* 247–261.

Schwartz, M. L., & Goldman-Rakic, P. S. (1984). Callosal and intrahemispheric connectivity of the prefrontal association cortex in rhesus monkey: Relation between intraparietal and principal sulcal cortex. *Journal of Comparative and Physiological Psychology, 226,* 403–420.

Schwartzbaum, J. S. & Pribram, K. H. (1960). The effects of amygdalectomy in monkeys on transposition along a brightness continuum. *Journal of Comparative and Physiological Psychology, 53,* 396–399.

Settlage, P., Butler, R., & Odoi, H. (1956). Perseverative interference in monkeys following bilateral removal of the prefrontal areas. *Journal of General Psychology, 54,* 255–262.

Settlage, P., Zable, M., & Harlow, H. F. (1948). Problem solution by monkeys following bilateral removal of the prefrontal areas: VI. Performance on tests requiring contradictory reactions to similar and to identical stimuli. *Journal of Experimental Psychology, 38,* 50–65.

Stamm, J. S. (1967). Electrical stimulation of monkeys prefrontal cortex during delayed-response performance. *Journal of Comparative and Physiological Psychology, 67,* 535–546.

Stamm, J. S. (1970). Dorsolateral frontal ablations and response processes in monkeys. *Journal of Comparative and Physiological Psychology, 70,* 437–447.

Stamm, J. S. (1973). Functional dissociation between the inferior and arcuate segments of dorsolateral prefrontal cortex in the monkey. *Neuropsychologia, 11,* 181–190.

Stamm, J. S., & Weber-Levine, M. L. (1971). Delayed alternation impairments following selective prefrontal cortical ablations in monkeys. *Experimental Neurology, 33,* 263–278.

Stepien, I., & Stamm, J. S. (1970). Impairments on locomotor task involving spatial opposition between cue and reward in frontally ablated monkeys. *Acta Neurobiologiae Experimentalis, 30,* 1–12.

Tubbs, W. T. (1969). Primate frontal lesions and the temporal structure of behavior. *Behavioral Science, 14,* 347–356.

von Holst, E. (1948). Von der Mathematik der nervoesen Ordnungsleistungen. *Experientia, 4,* 374–381.

von Holst, E. (1937). Vom Wesen der Ordnung im Zentralnervensystem. *Naturwissenschaften, 25,* 625–631.

Weiskrantz, L., Mihailovic, L. T., & Gross, L. G. (1962). Effects of stimulation of frontal cortex and hippocampus on behavior in the monkey. *Brain, 85,* 487–504.

Weiskrantz, L., & Mishkin, M. (1958). Effect of temporal and frontal cortical lesions on auditory discrimination in monkeys. *Brain, 81,* 406–414.

Weiskrantz, L., & Wilson, W. A. (1958). The effect of ventral rhinencephalic lesions on avoidance thresholds in monkeys. *Journal of Comparative and Physiological Psychology, 51,* 167–171.

Wilson, W. A., Jr. (1962). Alternation in normal and frontal monkeys as a function of response and outcome of the previous trial. *Journal of Comparative and Physiological Psychology, 55,* 701–704.

3

Architecture and Connections of the Frontal Lobe

Deepak N. Pandya and Clifford L. Barnes

INTRODUCTION

The frontal lobe is thought to participate in a wide variety of functions, such as the planning and sequencing of behaviors, decision making, drives, emotional coloring, and abstract thinking (Damasio, 1979; Nauta, 1964, 1971; Stuss & Benson, 1986). For the most part, these functions have been inferred either from studies of patients who have sustained damage to the frontal lobes or from studies of experimental lesions in subhuman primates. Although these investigations have provided us with a great deal of information concerning frontal lobe function, they also have certain limitations. To attribute a particular function to a damaged portion of the brain ignores the normal connections of that region with other areas of the brain. By altering, injuring, or removing portions of the cerebral cortex, one may also cause secondary changes in those areas that send projections to the damaged region and those areas that receive projections from it. In the case of the frontal lobe, these areas include large portions of both the temporal and parietal lobes, as well as limbic areas and a variety of different subcortical regions. Since it is likely that these connections play a vital role in the normal functioning of the frontal lobes, an understanding of the precise organization of frontal lobe interrelations with other cortical and subcortical regions is an indispensable prerequisite to any consideration of frontal lobe function. This chapter will focus on this topic. First, we will summarize available data on the afferent and efferent connections of the frontal lobe. Next, we will present a novel approach that, by relying on an additional analysis of cortical cytoarchitecture, seeks to explain cortical function in light of the evolution of the cerebral cortex. Since only limited connectional information is available for the human brain, and since most of the experimental work describing cortical connections has been gathered from subhuman primates, we will restrict our discussion to the anatomy of the monkey brain *(Macaca mulatta)*.

ISBN 0-936925-00-0

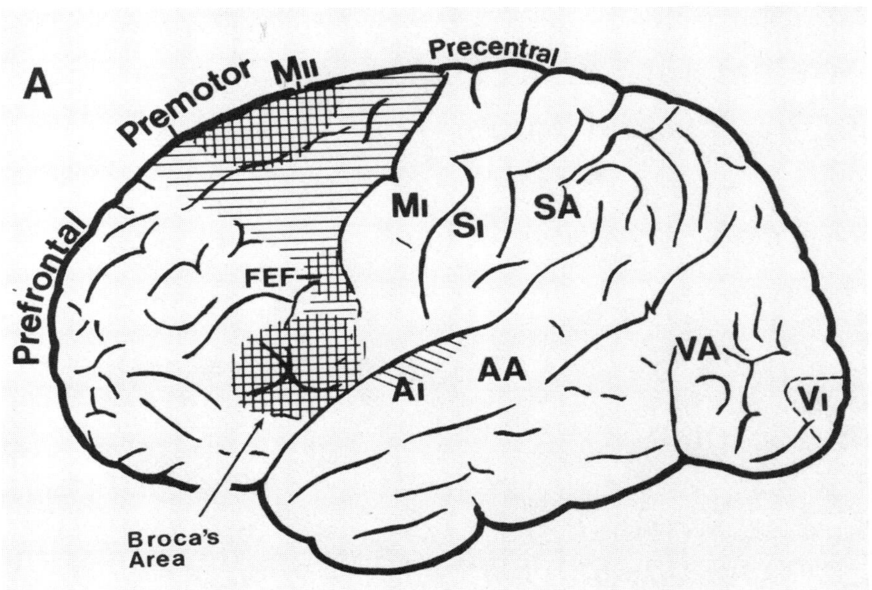
A
Premotor
MII
Precentral
Prefrontal
MI
SI
SA
FEF
VA
AA
AI
VI
Broca's Area
B
RhF
OTS
CF
CC
POMS
Cing S
SA$_3$
MII
SSA
Precentral
Premotor
Prefrontal
M$_1$
S$_1$
SA$_1$
SA$_2$
IPS
SA$_3$
SA$_2$
AS
CS
PS
LS
VA$_1$
AA$_1$
LF
AA$_2$
AA$_3$
VA$_2$
STS
VA$_3$

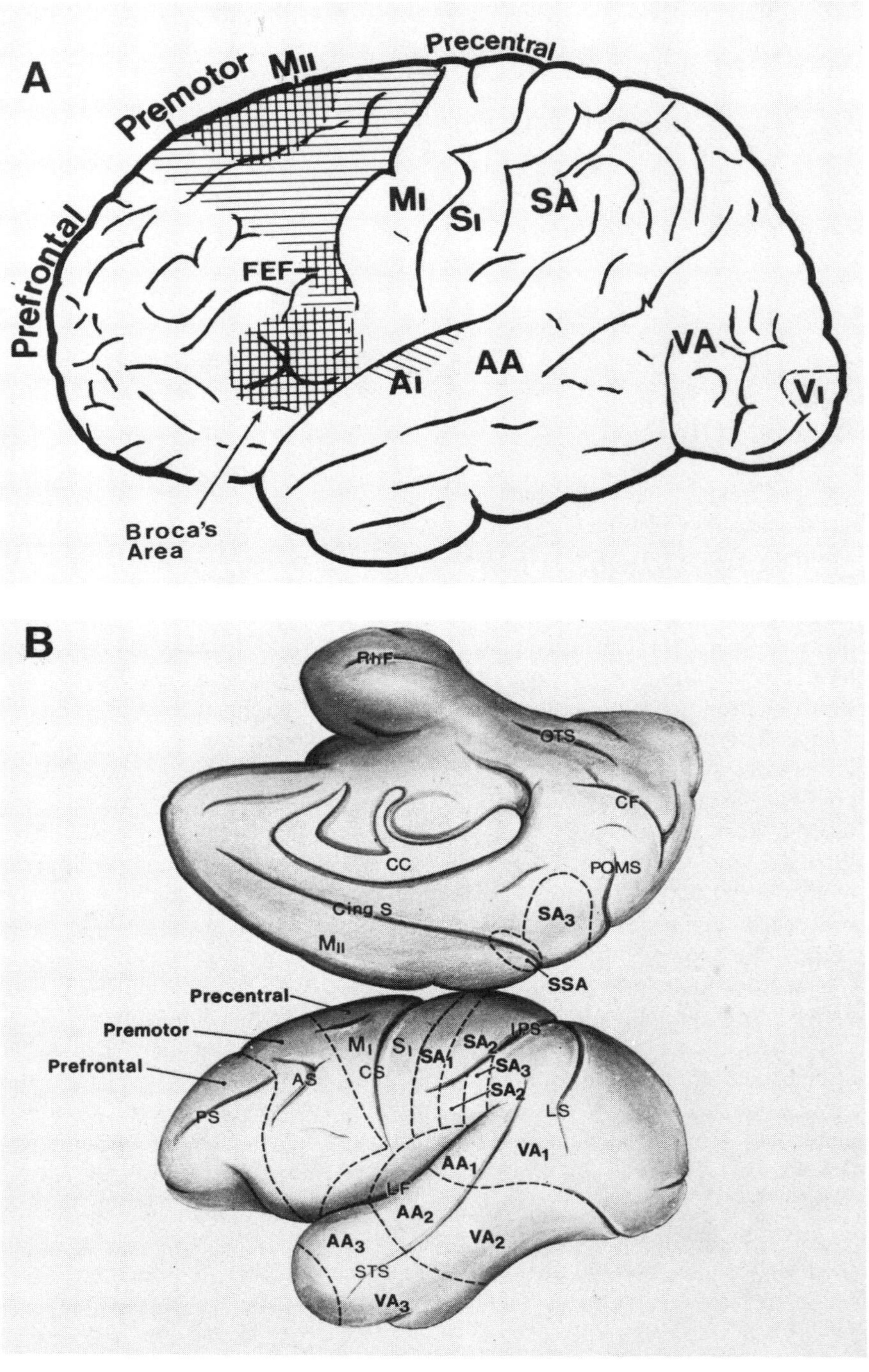

RESULTS AND DISCUSSION

Traditionally, the frontal lobe has been divided into three principal regions: precentral, premotor, and prefrontal. The precentral region is the classic motor cortex that gives rise to the corticobulbar and corticospinal tracts (Kuypers, 1964). Stimulation of this area results in phasic body movements (Wise & Evarts, 1981; Woolsey, 1958). The area lying just in front of the motor cortex is termed the premotor region and contains several functional areas, including the supplementary motor area (MII) on the medial surface in the superior frontal gyrus, the frontal eyefields in the middle frontal gyrus, and Broca's area in the inferior frontal gyrus (Figure 1). The lateral premotor area appears to be involved in postural and orienting movements, whereas MII is thought to contribute to the programming and initiation of body movements (Brinkman & Porter, 1983; Denny-Brown & Botterell, 1948; Freund & Hummelsheim, 1985; Goldberg, 1985; Lilly, 1958; Roland, Larsen, Lassen & Skinhøj, 1980; Tanji & Kurata, 1985; Weinrich, Wise, & Mauritz, 1984; Wiesendanger, 1981). The frontal eyefields maintain a certain amount of control over such eye movements as conjugate deviation (Wagman, Kreiger, Papatheodorou, & Bender, 1961) whereas Broca's area controls voluntary speech. The remainder of the frontal lobe comprises the prefrontal region. This sector is thought to be involved in the more abstract functions mentioned earlier (Fuster, 1980). Embedded in the prefrontal region are both limbic areas, such as the orbitofrontal and anterior cingulate cortices, as well as isocortical regions. All of these areas have specific architectonic characteristics.

Morphological descriptions of neural tissue that are based on the organization of nerve cells are termed *cytoarchitectonics*. A number of investigators have divided the cortex of the human brain, as well as that of other species, into different regions based on the cytoarchitectonic organization of the different cortical layers (Brodmann, 1909; Vogt & Vogt, 1919; von Bonin & Bailey, 1947; Walker, 1940). For instance, the precentral gyrus, or motor cortex, of the rhesus monkey is characterized by having large pyramidal cells in Layer V and a general lack of granular cells in Layer IV. The prefrontal region, by contrast, has a somewhat different mixture of granular cell and pyramidal cell populations.

FIGURE 1 (A) Map of the human brain showing the major functional areas of the frontal lobe. AA, auditory association areas; AI, primary auditory area; FEF, frontal eyefields; MI, motor cortex; MII, supplementary motor cortex; SA, somatosensory association areas; SI, primary somatosensory area; VA, visual association areas; VI, primary visual area. (B) Diagram of the lateral and medial surfaces of the cerebral hemisphere of the rhesus monkey showing three major subdivisions of the frontal lobe. This diagram also shows the divisions of post-Rolandic sensory association areas: auditory, AA1, AA2, AA3; somatosensory, SA1, SA2, SA3; and visual, VA1, VA2, VA3. Abbreviations in this and subsequent figures: AS, arcuate sulcus; CC, corpus callosum; CF, calcarine fissure; Cing. S, cingulate sulcus; CS, central sulcus; IOS, inferior occipital sulcus; IPS, intraparietal sulcus; LF, lateral fissure; LS, lunate sulcus; OTS, occipitotemporal sulcus; POMS, medial parietooccipital sulcus; PS, principal sulcus; RhF, rhinal fissure; STS, superior temporal sulcus.

The premotor region is intermediate between prefrontal and precentral divisions; that is, it lacks the large Layer V pyramidal cells of the motor area, but contains a substantial population of granular cells, especially in its ventral part (Barbas & Pandya, 1981). In several of the best-known schemata, numerical designations have been given to the different regions based on their different cellular compositions (Figure 2). For example, the precentral region, or motor cortex, has been given the number 4, while the more rostral premotor region consists of Area 6 around the arcuate sulcus, and Area 8 corresponds to the frontal eyefields. The prefrontal region includes a large number of different cytoarchitectonic zones: Areas 10, 14, 24, 25, and 32 on the medial surface; Areas 9, 10, 12, and 46 on the lateral surface; and Areas 10, 11, 12, 13, and 14 on the orbitofrontal surface (Walker, 1940). This nomenclature provides a point of reference for the study of connectional anatomy, as well as behavior and physiology; however, it remains purely descriptive. Classic cytoarchitectonics do not provide any theoretical framework for understanding the pattern or organization of the frontal lobes.

Beginning approximately 30 years ago, with the advent of improved techniques for tracing cortical connections, the interconnections of the different cytoarchitectonic areas of the frontal lobe, as well as their extrinsic connections to other areas of the cerebral cortex, began to be investigated (Chavis & Pandya 1976; Jones & Powell, 1970; Kuypers, Szwarcbart, Mishkin, & Rosvold, 1965; Myers, 1967; Nauta, 1964; Pandya, Dye, & Butters, 1971; Pandya & Kuypers, 1969; Pandya & Vignolo, 1971). These studies showed that a major source of cortical input to the frontal lobes was post-Rolandic sensory-related and limbic areas. Thus, the primary somatosensory cortex (Areas 3, 1, and 2: SI), which is the recipient of exteroceptive somatosensory information by way of the specific thalamic relay nuclei, sends major projections to the primary motor area (MI). In addition, it sends projections to the supplementary motor area (MII) and the gustatory region located in the frontal operculum (Figure 3) (Jones & Burton, 1976; Pandya, Mufson, & McLaughlin, 1980). Cortical outflow from SI is not restricted to the frontal lobes, however. It also projects to the so-called "first-order" somatosensory association area (SA1), immediately adjacent to SI in the posterior parietal lobe.[1] Interestingly, SA1 is itself connected with several frontal regions, namely, Dorsal and Ventral Area 6 (premotor cortex), Medial Area 6 (MII), and the pericentral operculum (gustatory region). There are also "second-order" (SA2) and "third-order" (SA3) somatosensory association cortices located

[1]Since the main theme of our presentation is to describe frontal lobe connections, other efferents from the post-Rolandic areas are not mentioned, except for those related to the sequential parasensory association areas.

FIGURE 2 (A) Architectonic map of monkey cerebral hemisphere showing different subdivisions according to Brodmann (1909). (B) Architectonic parcellation of frontal lobe showing subdivisions on the medial, lateral, and orbital (inferior) surfaces according to Walker (1940).

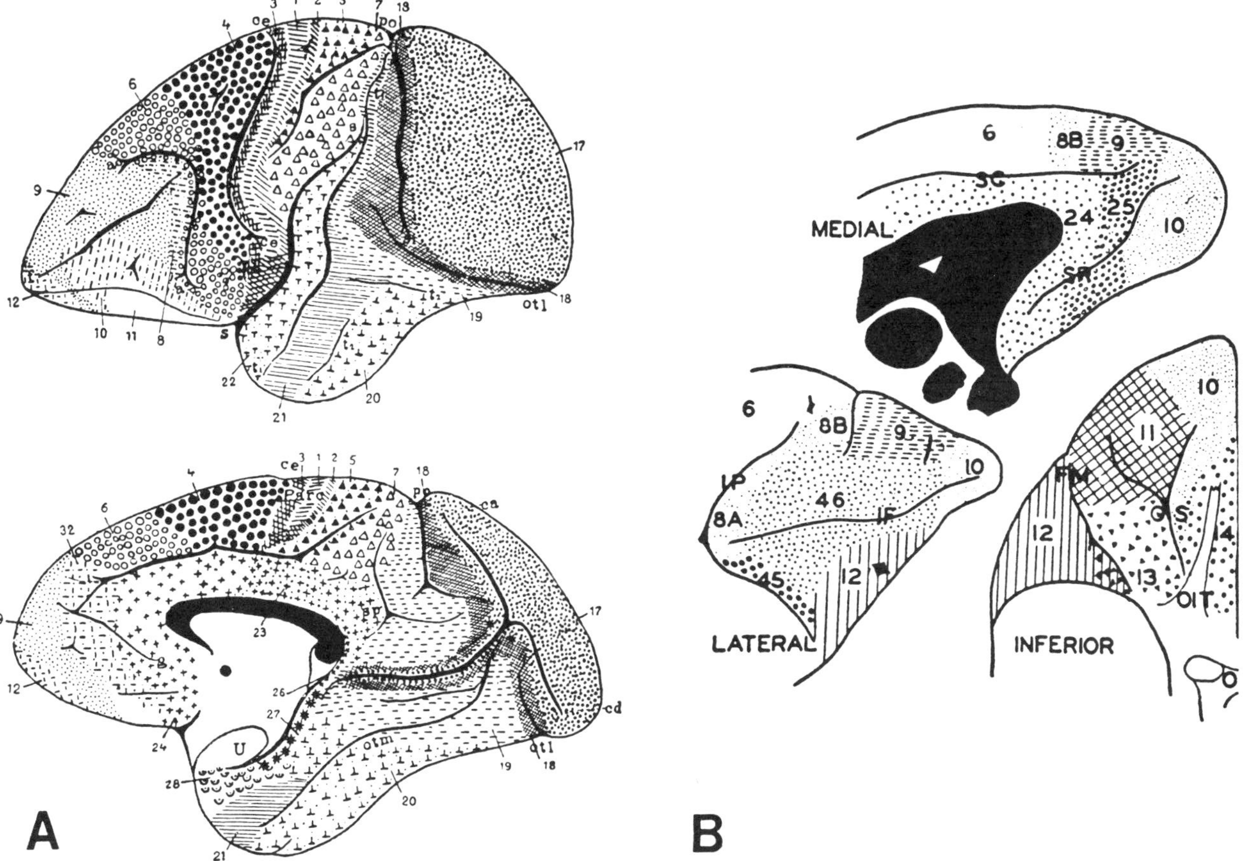
A
B
MEDIAL
LATERAL
INFERIOR

in the most caudal portions of the parietal lobe, connected in sequence with the primary somatosensory area via SA1 (Figure 3). Each has distinctive frontal connections. SA2 sends projections to MII, Dorsal Area 6, as well as prefrontal cortex (Area 46). SA3 is connected with dorsal and ventral prefrontal cortex (Area 46) as well as with the cingulate gyrus (Areas 24 and 23). Thus, there appears to be a direct parallel between the caudal progression of information from the primary somatosensory area through successive somatosensory association areas and its sequential transmittal rostrally to precentral, premotor, and prefrontal regions of the frontal lobe (Barbas & Mesulam, 1981, 1985; Bowker & Coulter, 1981; Chavis & Pandya, 1976; Jones, Coulter, & Hendry, 1978; Jones & Powell, 1970; Petrides & Pandya, 1984; Vogt & Pandya, 1978).

Auditory related cortical areas have a similar pattern with respect to their connections with the frontal lobes (Figure 4). The primary auditory area (Areas 41 and 42: AI), located in the supratemporal plane, although it does not have direct connections with the frontal lobes, projects to a first-order association area (AA1) in the superior temporal gyrus. AA1 projects to Areas 8, 9, and 10 in the frontal lobe, as well as to a second-order auditory association area (AA2) in the superior temporal gyrus. This latter area in turn projects more rostrally in the frontal lobe to Areas 46, 9, and 10 and to a third-order auditory association region (AA3) in the temporal pole. AA3 projects predominantly to the orbital cortex (Areas 12 and 13) and medial prefrontal cortex (Areas 25 and 32) of the frontal lobe (Barbas & Mesulam, 1981, 1985; Chavis & Pandya, 1976; Fitzpatrick & Imig, 1980; Jones & Powell, 1970; Pandya, Hallett, & Mukherjee, 1969).

Visual related areas of the cerebral cortex also have a somewhat similar organization. As shown in Figure 5, one can identify a chain of primary visual cortex and visual association areas—VA1, VA2, and VA3 in occipitotemporal cortex—tied together in an orderly sequence of connections.[2] Like the primary auditory area, primary visual cortex, VI, does not project to the frontal lobe. But it does project to VA1, which in turn sends efferents to the dorsal and ventral portions of Area 8. The second-order visual association area, VA2, by contrast, sends projections to Area 46 in the frontal lobe, whereas VA3 connects with the orbitofrontal region (Area 11) (Barbas & Mesulam, 1981, 1985; Chavis & Pandya, 1976; Jones & Powell, 1970; Kuypers et al., 1965; Mishkin, 1972; Weller & Kass, 1985). Thus, successive parasensory association areas for all three major modalities of sensation send projections, progressively, to premotor, prefrontal, orbital, and medial cortices of the frontal lobe. Furthermore, there are certain regions in the frontal lobe that appear to receive post-Rolandic input from areas relating to all three modalities in an overlapping manner (Figure 6). These putative convergence zones are located in and around the arcuate sulcus in the

[2]In recent years, so-called multiple representations have been described in these visual association areas (Van Essen & Maunsell, 1983; Zeki, 1978). We have maintained, however, our previously proposed classifications of visual association areas for describing the frontal lobe connections.

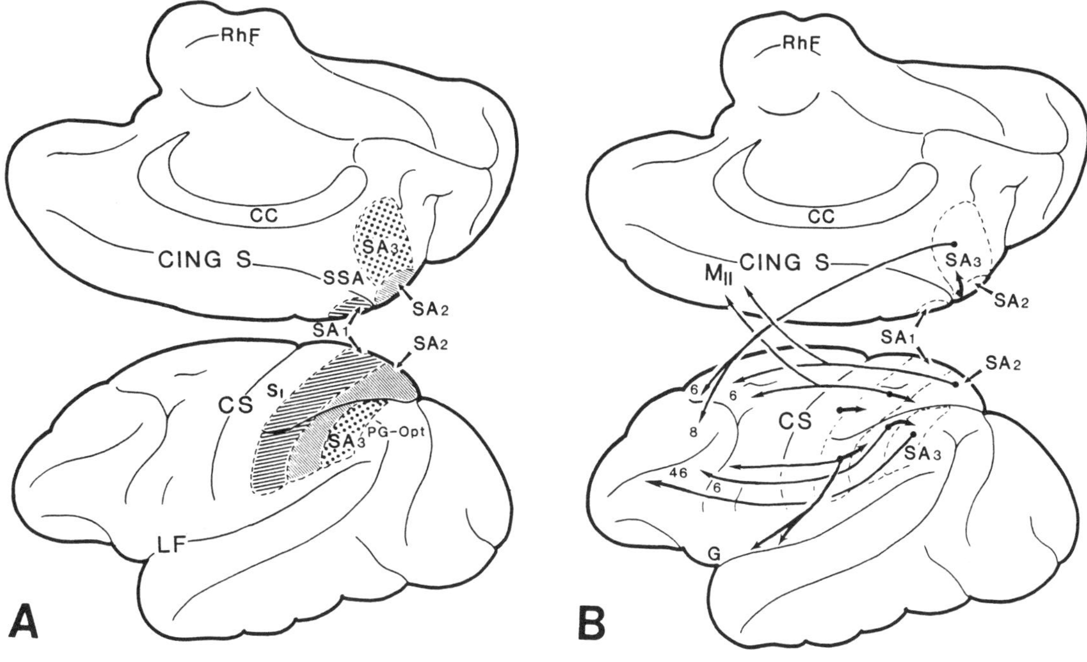

FIGURE 3 Diagrams of the lateral and medial surfaces of the cerebral hemisphere showing three major subdivisions of the somatosensory association areas of the posterior parietal cortex (A), and their frontal lobe connections (B).

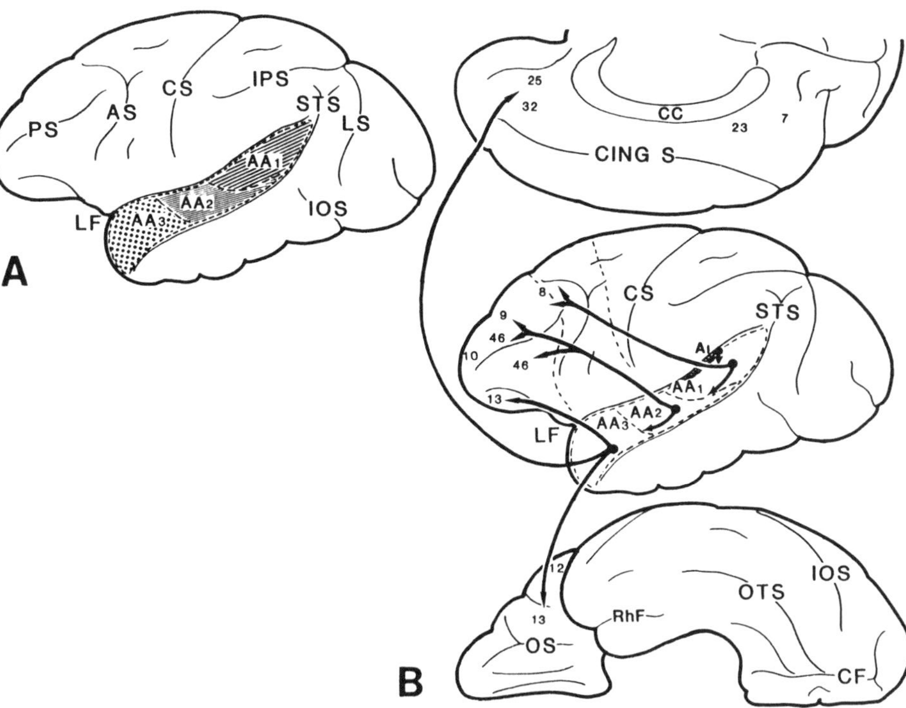

FIGURE 4 Diagrams showing the three major subdivisions of the auditory association area of the superior temporal gyrus (A), and their frontal lobe connections (B).

premotor region, receiving efferents from first-order sensory association areas (SA1, AA1, and VA1), and in the ventral prearcuate area of the prefrontal region, receiving efferents from second-order sensory association areas (SA2, AA2, and VA2) (Chavis & Pandya, 1976; Jones & Powell, 1970). This anatomical convergence of different sensory afferents in the frontal lobe has been corroborated by several physiological and behavioral studies and may be the morphological basis for intermodal and cross-modal exchange of information (Bignall & Imbert, 1969; Nelson & Bignall, 1973; Passingham, 1972; Passingham & Ettlinger, 1972; Petrides, 1982; Petrides & Iversen, 1976, 1978; Van Hoesen, Vogt, Pandya, & McKenna, 1980; Welch & Stuteville, 1958).

In addition to this sequential set of sensory-related afferents, the frontal lobe receives substantial neural input from the limbic cortices (Figure 7A). Thus, the rostral portion of the cingulate gyrus (Area 24) projects to the premotor cortex (Areas 8 and 6), the supplementary motor region (MII), and the orbitofrontal cortex (Area 12). The posterior part of the cingulate gyrus (Area 23) projects to the lateral prefrontal (Area 46) and orbitofrontal (Area 11) regions (Baleydier & Mauguiere, 1980; Pandya, Van Hoesen, & Mesulam, 1981). A ventrally located paralimbic region, the parahippocampal gyrus on the ventral surface of the temporal lobe, also projects to the orbitofrontal region and to the ventrolateral prefrontal areas (Figure 7B) (Van Hoesen, 1982). Most of these connections from limbic and association areas are reciprocal in nature (see below). One may assume that it is the combination of highly processed sensory and limbic input that allows the frontal lobe to integrate both external, or somatic, and internal,

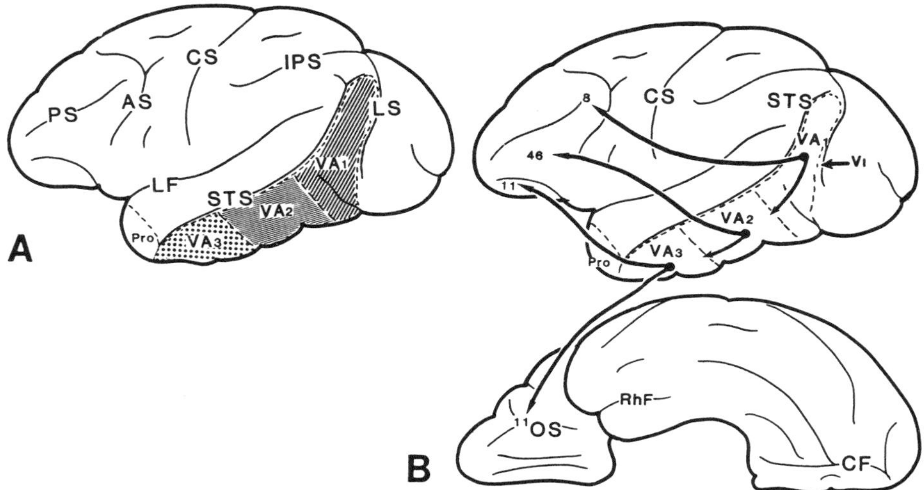

FIGURE 5 Diagrams showing the three major subdivisions of the visual association areas of the occipitotemporal cortex (A), and their frontal lobe connections (B).

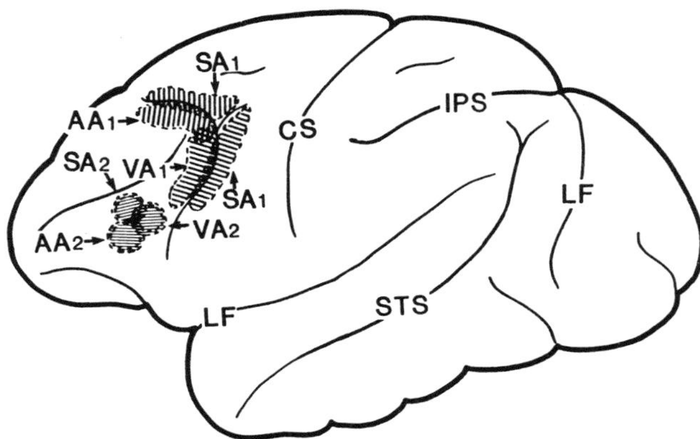

FIGURE 6 Diagram showing the location of multimodal areas of the premotor and prefrontal regions. Note that the premotor area receives converging afferents from first-order sensory association areas (AA1, SA1, VA1), and the prefrontal area from second-order sensory association areas (AA2, SA2, VA2).

or visceral, influences to generate a balanced behavioral output (Nauta, 1971).

There are also substantial subcortical inputs to the frontal lobe over and above the cortical afferents mentioned above. The frontal lobe receives connections from both thalamus and hypothalamus. In terms of thalamocortical connections, the precentral region receives input primarily from the ventrolateral (VLc) and ventral posterior (VPLo) nuclei, while premotor areas are connected with the ventrolateral (VLo) nucleus and nucleus X (Schell & Strick, 1984). Prefrontal cortex, on the other hand, receives widespread projections from dorsomedial, ventrolateral, as well as anterior and intralaminar nuclei of the thalamus (Goldman-Rakic & Porrino, 1985; Kievit & Kuypers, 1977; Tanaka, 1976; Tobias, 1975).

Studies of the sequence of corticocortical connections have led to a great deal of emphasis being placed on the "sequential processing" model of cortical functioning. Clearly, however, this cannot account for all aspects of cerebral function (Van Essen & Maunsell, 1983). Two lines of evidence have recently suggested that "parallel processing" of information may explain some facets of cortical function. One is the observation that association areas of the cortex also receive input from the periphery via the thalamus. The other is the physiological demonstration of multiple sensory and motor representations in the cerebral cortex. These representations are modality specific and located within regions previously considered as association areas. For example, in the visual system, in addition to the primary visual region (VI), several investigators have described other areas of re-representation of the visual field, that is, V2, V3, V4, MT, etc. (Van Essen & Maunsell, 1983; Woolsey, 1981b; Zeki, 1978). Similar re-rep-

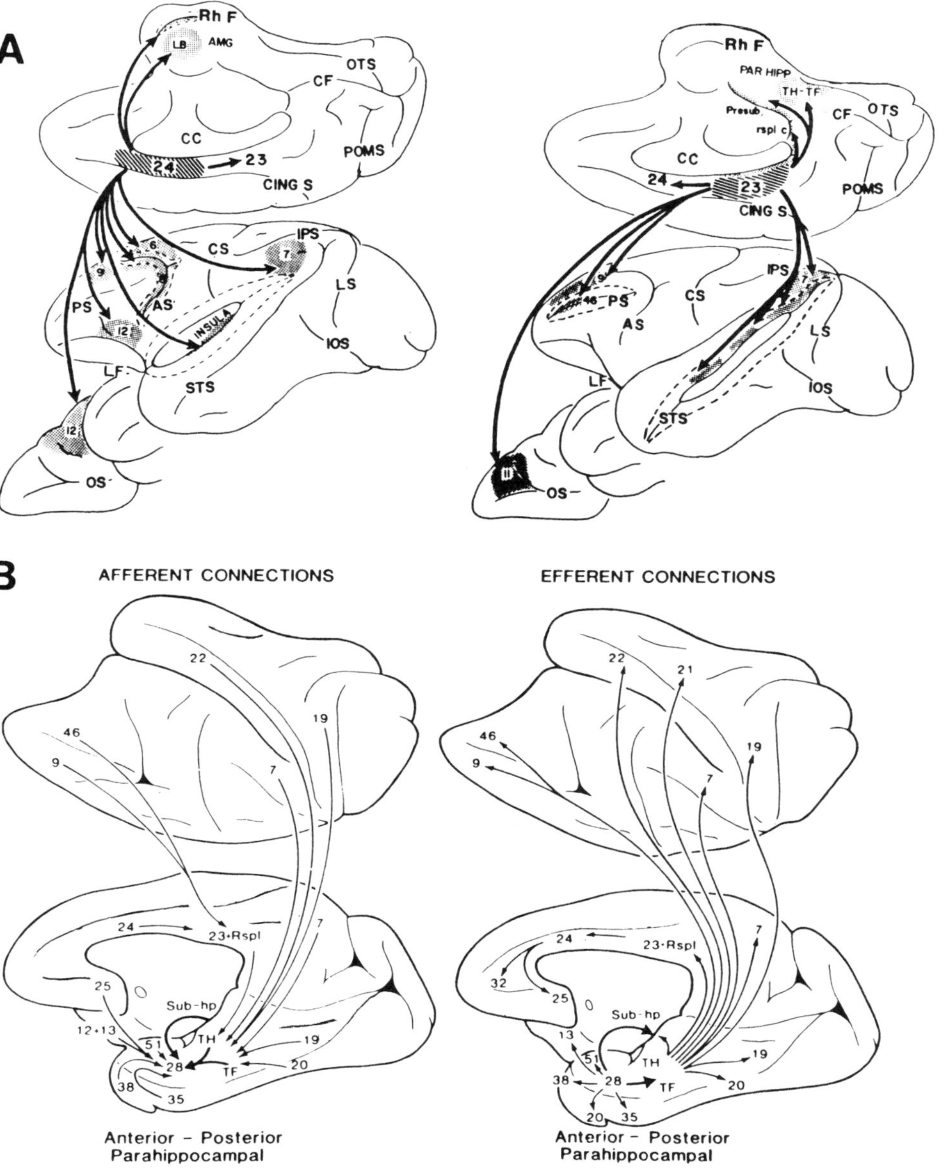

FIGURE 7 (A) Diagrams summarizing the limbic afferents from the cingulate gyrus to the frontal lobe as well as to other areas (Pandya, Van Hoesen, & Mesulam, 1981). (B) Summary diagrams of afferent and efferent connections of the parahippocampal region according to Van Hoesen (1982).

resentations have also been outlined for the auditory and somatosensory systems (Merzenich & Brugge, 1973; Merzenich, Sur, Nelson, & Kaas, 1981; Woolsey, 1981a, 1981c), as well as for the motor system (Maukkassa & Strick, 1979).

All of these notions (i.e., sequential analysis, parallel processing, multiple representations, and even the modular concept [Goldman-Rakic, 1984]) have undoubtedly enhanced our knowledge and understanding of cortical functions. Nevertheless, we still have to rely on general postulates to design experiments that unravel function or interpret clinical deficits. It seems that there is a need for a more detailed and deeper understanding of the morphological substrate in order to better understand the underlying mechanisms for various complex functions embedded within the frontal lobes.

Since cortical function undoubtedly changes and becomes more complex as the brain evolves, another way of approaching the question of cortical function may be to consider it in terms of evolution. Moreover, since cross-species differences in cortical organization are manifested in morphological differences, principally in cytoarchitecture and connectional patterns, it is reasonable to attempt to correlate functional differences in the central nervous system with differences in architectonics. The basis for this evolutionary approach can be traced back to the studies of Dart (1934) and Abbie (1940), who advanced the notion of dual origin of cerebral cortex. More recently, Sanides (1971, 1972) has proposed a more comprehensive theory of cortical architectonics based on comparative studies in primitive insectivores and in prosimians and other primates. Sanides came to a similar conclusion of dual origin of cerebral cortex from his own studies. Basic to Sanides's thinking is the notion that the six-layered isocortex ultimately evolves from two prime moieties (primordial areas), namely, the hippocampal formation, an archicortical moiety, and the olfactory region, a paleocortical moiety (Figure 8A). Both of these primitive regions give rise to an adjacent "periallocortex," which in turn is succeeded by a "proisocortex." This proisocortex then gives rise to a true six-layered isocortex (Figure 8B). The progression toward isocortex passes through two major cortical regions, the cingulate gyrus and the parinsular area of the lateral sulcus (Figure 8C). These belong to the archi- and paleocortical trends, respectively. The cingulate trend shows predominant emphasis on pyramidal cells and gives rise to both the supplementary motor area (MII) and the supplementary sensory association area (SSA) located on the medial surface of the hemisphere (Murray & Coulter, 1981; Woolsey, 1958). Primary motor (MI) and somatosensory (SI) cortices are hypothesized to stem from this trend. The parinsular trend, by contrast, shows a progressive emphasis on granular cells as it differentiates into a second somatosensory area (SII), a second auditory area (AII), a gustatory area, a vestibular area, and a presumptive second visual (VII or MT) area (Figure 8C). Further development from these regions is thought to lead to a stage in each sensory modality from which the primary cortices originate. From both the pyramidal and granular trends also evolve the so-called post-Rolandic sensory associ-

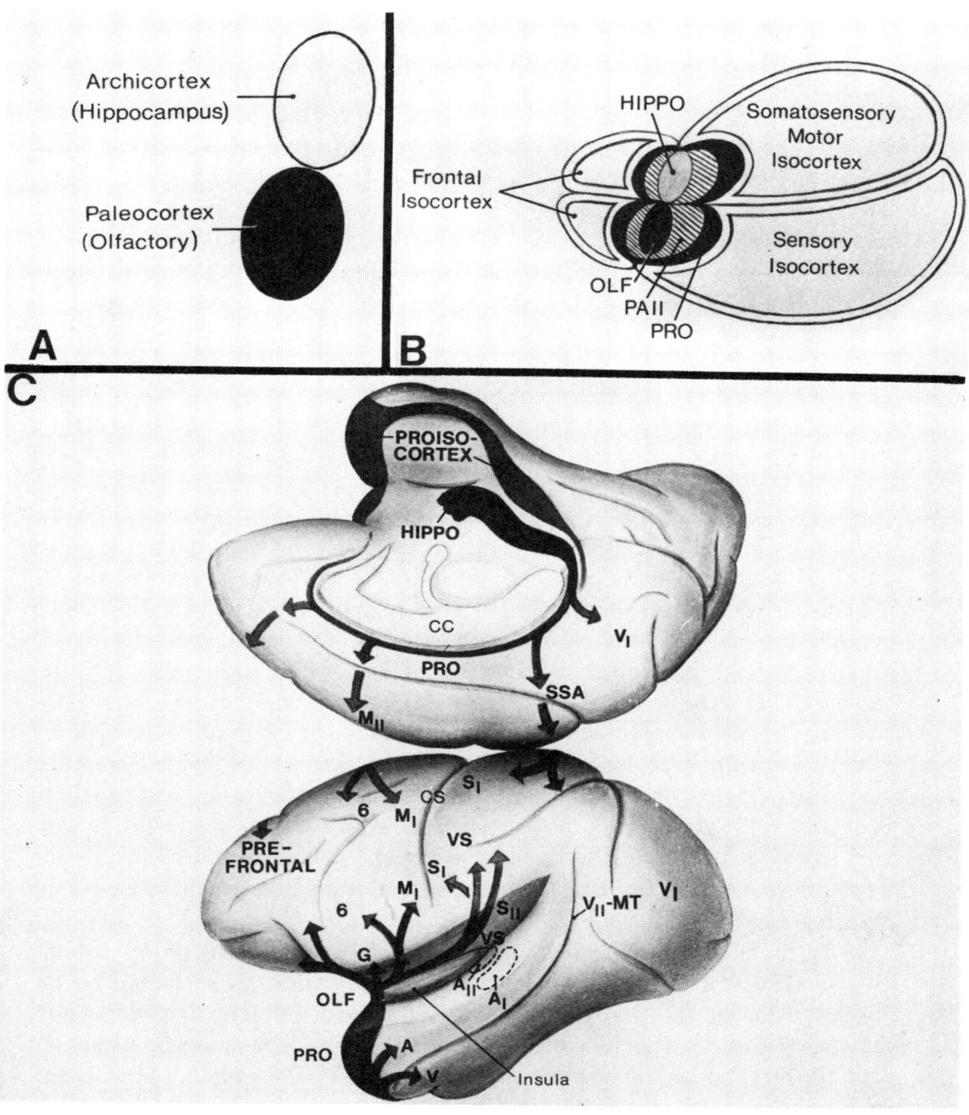

FIGURE 8 (A–C) Schematic diagrams showing progressive development of the cortical areas from two primordial moieties (archicortical and paleocortical) through successive steps: periallocortex (PAll) to proisocortex (PRO), culminating in pre- and post-Rolandic sensory, motor, and association areas. Abbreviations: A, auditory areas; AI, primary auditory area; AII, second auditory area; G, gustatory area; MI, primary motor cortex; MII, supplementary motor area; MT, middle temporal visual area; OLF, olfactory cortex; PRO, proisocortex; SI, primary somatosensory area; SII, second somatosensory area; SSA, supplementary sensory area; V, visual areas; VI, primary visual area; VII, visual area MT in the superior temporal sulcus; VS, vestibular area.

ation areas as well as the frontal association cortices (Pandya & Yeterian, 1985).

According to the notion of dual origin of the cortex presented above, the premotor and precentral areas of the frontal lobe in the rhesus monkey may be conceptualized as having evolved, by successive architectonic differentiation, from archicortical (hippocampal) and paleocortical (olfactory) moieties (Figures 8 and 9) (Barbas & Pandya, 1981; Pandya & Barbas, 1985; Sanides, 1971). Thus, the premotor cortex may be broadly subdivided into dorsal and ventral sectors with the spur of the arcuate sulcus being the dividing point. The dorsal premotor region extends medially as far as the upper bank of the cingulate sulcus. Basically, it is an agranular cortex. The ventral premotor region, by contrast, extends up to the frontal operculum and is characterized by an incipient layer of granular cells in Lamina IV. According to the evolutionary architectonic approach, the dorsal premotor region originates from the proisocortex of the cingulate gyrus (Area 24), the archicortical moiety. From the cingulate cortex, a trend of increasing laminar differentiation can be traced dorsolaterally up to Area 4 of the precentral gyrus (Figure 9). The ventral premotor region, on the other hand, shows a trend of increasing laminar differentiation that begins in the insular proisocortex (paleocortical moiety) and progresses toward the spur of the arcuate sulcus and ventral precentral region (Area 4). Thus, in this scheme, the supplementary motor region comprises one step in the dorsal trend and contains a rather crude re-representation of the entire body. The lateral premotor area is another step in the dorsal trend and contains predominantly the trunk re-representation. The dorsal trend also includes that portion of the precentral gyrus that contains the representations of the extremities and the trunk of the opposite side of the body (Woolsey, 1958). In the ventral trend, the frontal opercular region appears to be analogous to MII in architectonic terms and has been designated "ProM" (Sanides, 1972). The ventral premotor area contains, in part, a re-representation of the head, face, and neck. This region is abutted by the ventral precentral region, also belonging to the ventral trend, which contains the face representation.

The architectonically based notion that the frontal lobe may be divided into two fundamental divisions, namely, dorsal and ventral, is supported by the intrinsic connections (Barbas & Pandya, 1981; Pandya & Barbas, 1985). Thus, the rostral portion of the dorsolateral premotor cortex is reciprocally connected with the neighboring dorsal prefrontal cortex, supplementary motor area, cingulate gyrus, and dorsal premotor region, all parts of the proposed "dorsal trend" (Figure 10A). On the other hand, the caudal premotor region has direct connections with the motor cortex as well as with the rostral premotor and MII areas. Similarly, the ventral premotor area is reciprocally connected with motor cortex and the ventral prefrontal and frontal opercular regions, all parts of the proposed "ventral trend" (Figure 10B).

Recent architectonic analysis has shown that, like the premotor region, the prefrontal region can be traced from the two basic trends (Figure 11) (Barbas &

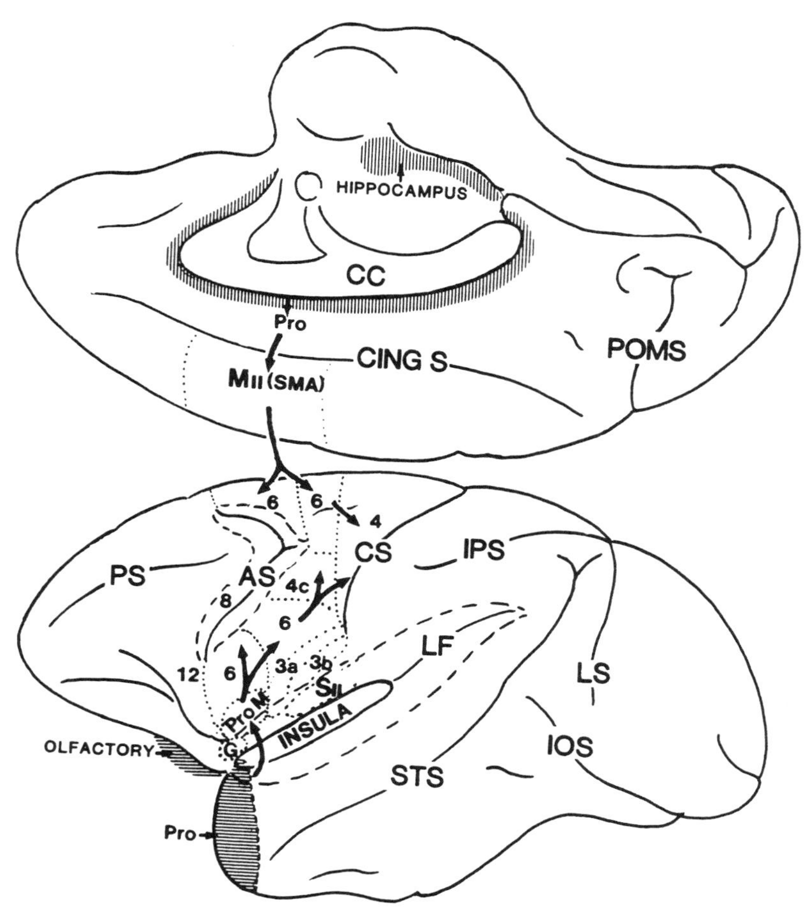

FIGURE 9 Diagrammatic representation of dorsal (hippocampal-cingulate) and ventral (olfactory-insular) architectonic trends to show architectonic steps leading to the dorsal and ventral sectors of the premotor (Area 6) and motor (Area 4) cortices.

Pandya, 1982). The dorsal trend starts in the medial periallocortical region around the rostrum of the corpus callosum, proceeds through proisocortical Areas 25 and 32, and leads to a dorsal architectonic sequence: Area 9, Dorsal Area 10, Dorsal Area 46, and Dorsal Area 8 (Figure 11A). This dorsal sequence is characterized by successive "granularization" of Layer IV and the acquisition of pyramidal neurons in Layer III along with changes in other layers (Figure 12A). The ventral trend begins in the periallocortex around the olfactory tubercle on the orbital surface and differentiates into proisocortex, which further develops into a series of isocortical areas (Figure 11B). These areas show successive

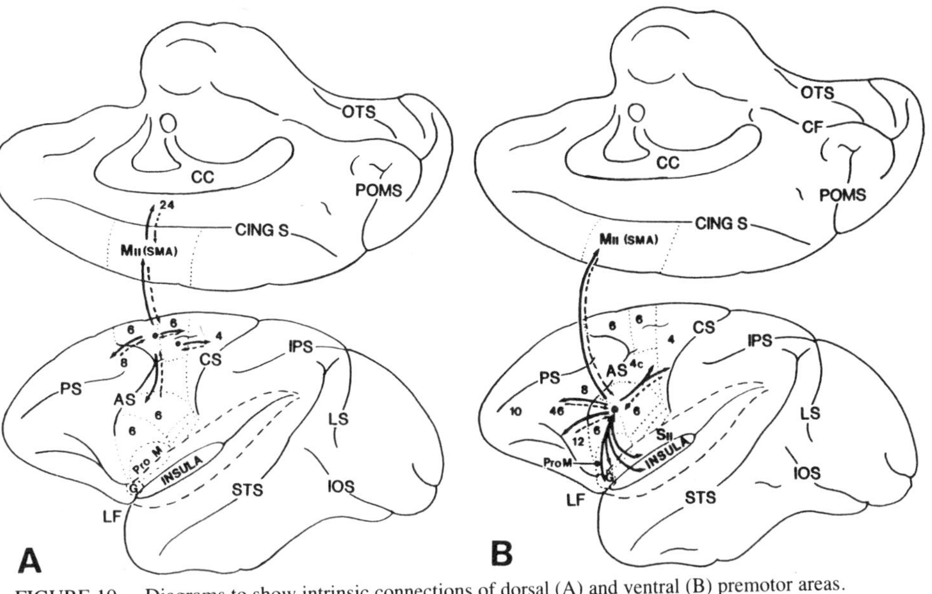

FIGURE 10. Diagrams to show intrinsic connections of dorsal (A) and ventral (B) premotor areas.

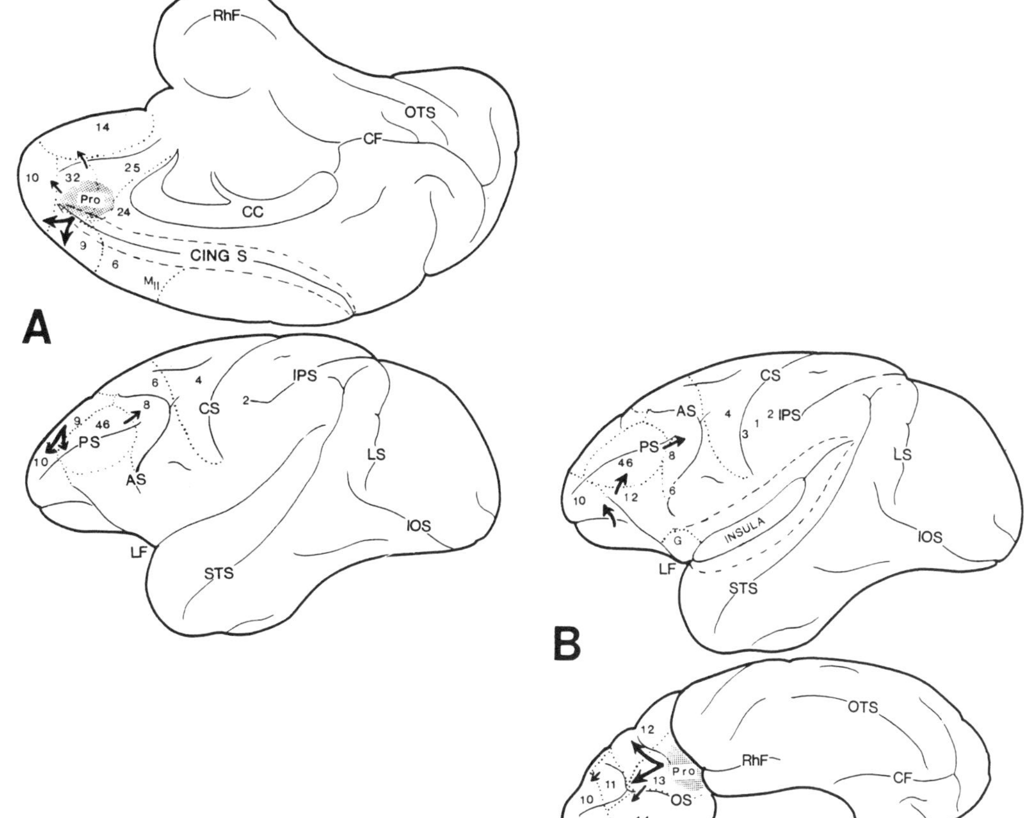

FIGURE 11 Diagram of cerebral hemisphere showing progressive architectonic steps from medial proisocortex leading to Dorsal Area 8 (dorsal trend) (A). Similar steps from orbital proisocortex leading to Ventral Area 8 (ventral trend) (B).

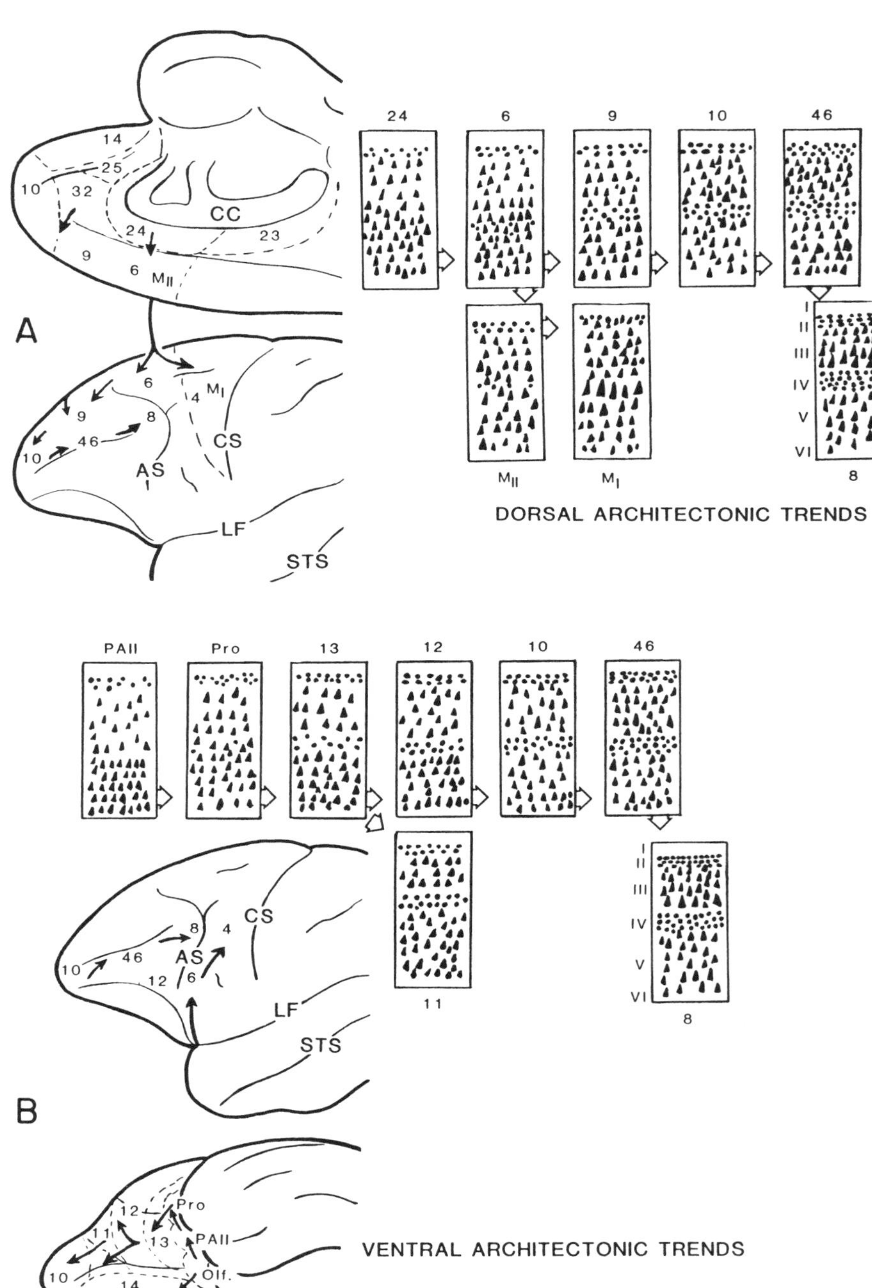
14
25
10
32
CC
24
23
9
6
M_{II}
A
6
M_I
4
9
8
46
10
CS
AS
LF
STS
24
6
9
10
46
I
II
III
IV
V
VI
M_{II}
M_I
8
DORSAL ARCHITECTONIC TRENDS
PAII
Pro
13
12
10
46
8
4
CS
46
AS
10
12
6
LF
STS
11
I
II
III
IV
V
VI
8
B
12
Pro
11
13
PAII
10
14
Olf.
VENTRAL ARCHITECTONIC TRENDS

changes in all cortical layers, particularly with a progressive acquisition of granular cells in Layer IV and pyramidal neurons in Layer III, and correspond to the architectonic sequence: Areas 13, 12, 11, Ventral Area 10, Ventral Area 46, and Ventral Area 8 (Figure 12B).

The intrinsic connections of prefrontal cortex also conform to the proposed notion of dual architectonic trends (Barbas & Pandya, 1982). Thus, in the dorsal trend, the medial proisocortical region projects to Area 14 ventrally and to Areas 9 and 10 dorsally (Figure 13A). Area 9, in turn, has connections with the medial proisocortical areas and Dorsal Areas 10 and 46, laterally. Area 46 projects back to Areas 9 and 10, on the one hand, and to Dorsal Area 8, on the other. Finally, Dorsal Area 8 projects back to its precursor region, Dorsal Area 46, rostrally, and to Dorsal Area 6, caudally.

The ventral prefrontal areas have a similar pattern of intrinsic connectivity. Thus, the ventral proisocortical area projects mainly to Areas 13 and 12, on the one hand, and to Area 14, on the other (Figure 13B). Area 13, in turn, projects back to the proisocortical area as well as to Areas 12 and 10. In a similar manner, Area 12 projects to its precursor regions, Areas 10 and 13, and to Ventral Area 46 as well. Ventral Area 46 sends connections back to Areas 12 and 10 and, in the opposite direction, to Ventral Area 8. Area 8 projects to the ventral portion of Area 46, rostrally, and to the ventral sector of Area 6, caudally. These patterns of connections suggest that, within each trend, a given cortical region projects both to an architectonically less well differentiated area and to a region with more developed cortical laminar organization. It should be pointed out, however, that at certain points these two trends are interconnected; for example, Dorsal Area 8 and Ventral Area 8 are interconnected, as are Areas 9 and 12 and the medial and orbital proisocortices (Figure 14).

The frontal lobe also has long efferent connections to other areas of the cerebral cortex. These projections appear to follow the dual organization described above (Deacon, Rosenberg, Eckert, & Shank, 1982; Godschalk, Lemon, Kuypers, & Ronday, 1984; Jones & Powell, 1970; Künzle, 1978; Künzle & Akert, 1977; Murray & Coulter, 1981; Nauta, 1964; Pandya et al., 1971; Pandya & Vignolo, 1971). Thus, Dorsal Area 6 projects preferentially to MII and to the superior and medial parietal cortices (SA1 and SSA), whereas Ventral Area 6 projects to the rostral inferior parietal lobule (SA1) and to parietal operculum (Figure 15A). With regard to prefrontal cortex, Dorsal Area 46 projects to the caudal superior parietal lobule and to the medial surface (SA2 and SA3) of the parietal lobe, while Ventral Area 46 projects to the caudal inferior parietal lobule (SA2 and SA3). The temporal lobe projections of the prefrontal region also have a dual organization. The dorsal sector of the prefrontal region projects to the superior temporal region, whereas ventral prefrontal cortex sends fibers to the

---

FIGURE 12 Camera lucida drawing of differential cytoarchitectonic patterns within the dorsal (A) and ventral (B) trends of the prefrontal cortex. Note the progressive changes in cortical laminations starting from proisocortical areas up to Area 8.

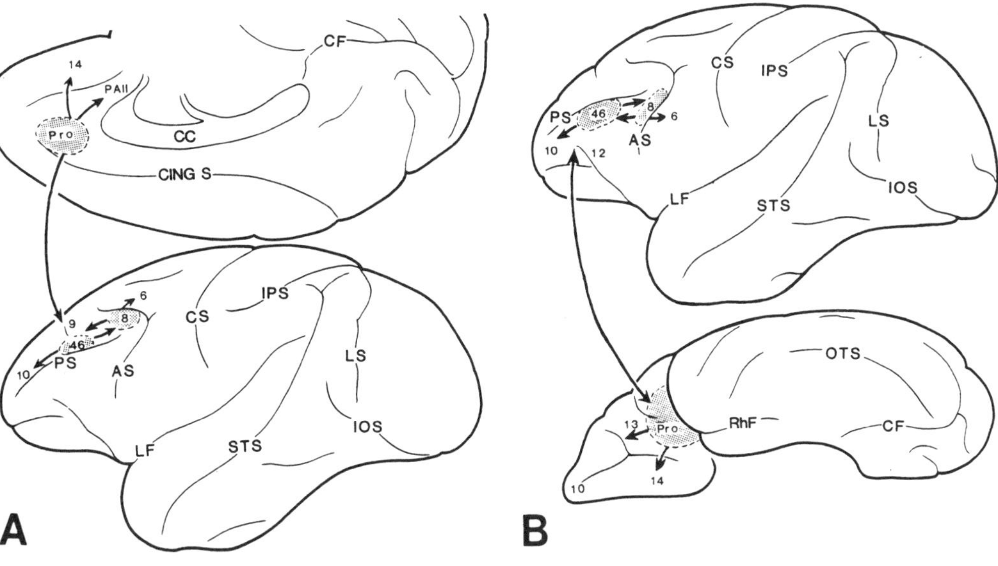

FIGURE 13 Diagram showing the intrinsic connections of subregions within dorsal (A) and ventral (B) trends of the prefrontal regions.

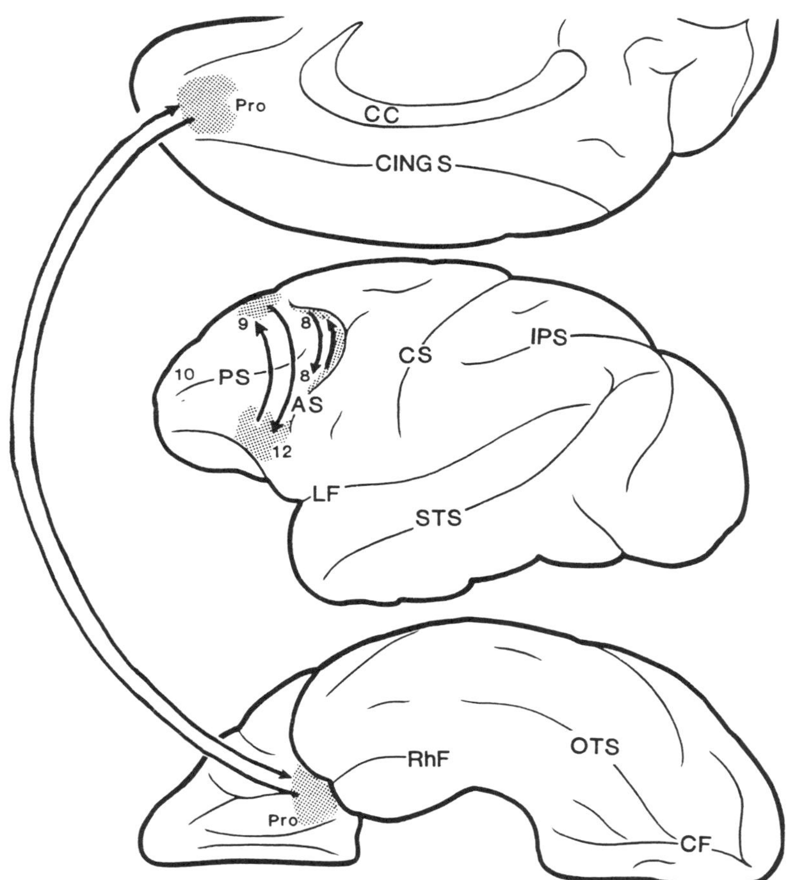

FIGURE 14 Diagram showing the interconnections between dorsal and ventral cytoarchitectonic trends. Note that such connections are found at proisocortical, prefrontal (Areas 9 and 12), and premotor (Area 8) levels.

inferotemporal region (Figure 15B). In addition, the dorsal prefrontal area sends substantial connections to cingulate gyrus and retrosplenial cortex (Baleydier & Mauguiere, 1980; Jones & Powell, 1970; Nauta, 1964; Pandya et al., 1971; Pandya & Kuypers, 1969), whereas the ventral prefrontal and orbitofrontal areas project preferentially to the temporal pole (Pro), perirhinal region, and parahippocampal gyrus (area TH) (Van Hoesen, 1982; Van Hoesen, Pandya, & Butters, 1972). The long efferent connections of the prefrontal regions therefore appear to be directed to those sensory association areas that project to the frontal region as described above. It is interesting to note that the dorsal prefrontal regions are connected preferentially with the superior parietal and cingulate regions, parts of the dorsal, or archicortical trend. In contrast, the ventral prefrontal region projects to those areas of parietal and temporal lobes (and ventral limbic areas) that are themselves considered to belong to the ventral, or paleocortical trend. Such a morphological dichotomy is in agreement with the assertion of Nauta (1964) that there is a dual nature to the prefrontal limbic connections.

The dual organization of the frontal lobe is also reflected in the pattern of frontothalamic connections. For instance, from the thalamic connectional studies of a number of different investigators (Akert, 1964; Goldman-Rakic & Porrino, 1985; Kievit & Kuypers, 1977; Siwek & Pandya, 1984; Tanaka, 1976; Tobias, 1975), it can be said that prefrontal projections to the dorsomedial nucleus (MD) follow the lateromedial and rostrocaudal topography of the frontal lobe (Figure 16). Thus, the medial prefrontal and orbitofrontal proisocortical areas project to the most medial portion of MD, maintaining their respective dorsal and ventral topographies in this nucleus. The lateral prefrontal region, above and below the principal sulcus, projects to the middle part of MD, again showing a dorsoventral topography. Finally, Dorsal Area 8 and Ventral Area 8, within the concavity of the arcuate sulcus, project to dorsal and ventral portions of the most lateral parts of MD, respectively. Thus, these frontal lobe projections to MD correspond to the patterns of cytoarchitectonic differentiation of the prefrontal cortex. The three sectors of the thalamus correspond to the three subdivisions of MD as outlined by Olszewski (1952). The corticothalamic connections follow the progressive architectonic organization based on the hypothesis of dual origins of the frontal lobe.

The projections to the different subdivisions of the frontal lobe from the various post-Rolandic sensory-related association areas were described above. It is interesting to note that these connections also correlate closely with the architectonics. Thus, the first-order association areas of the different sensory modalities (SA1, AA1, and VA1) project preferentially to periarcuate areas (Figure 17), and all of the parasensory association areas that give rise to these connections and the periarcuate area have prominent third and fourth cortical cell layers. Likewise, the third-order parasensory association areas (SA3, AA3, and VA3), which send projections predominantly to proisocortical and surrounding areas on the orbital and medial frontal cortices and to the rostral prefrontal cortex (Figure 17), have similar basic architectonic characteristics, namely, prominent infragranular neurons with an unclear separation of Laminae V and VI as well as a lack of granular cells in Layer IV. The second-order sensory association areas (SA2, AA2, and VA2) send their connections preferentially to the lateral prefrontal regions (Figure 17). The prefrontal cortices that receive these connections and second-order sensory association areas that project to them have cytoarchitectonic features intermediate between those of the premotor regions and first-order association areas and those of proisocortical areas and third-order association areas. It is important to point out, however, that the areas of the frontal lobe and post-Rolandic sensory association areas that are mutually in-

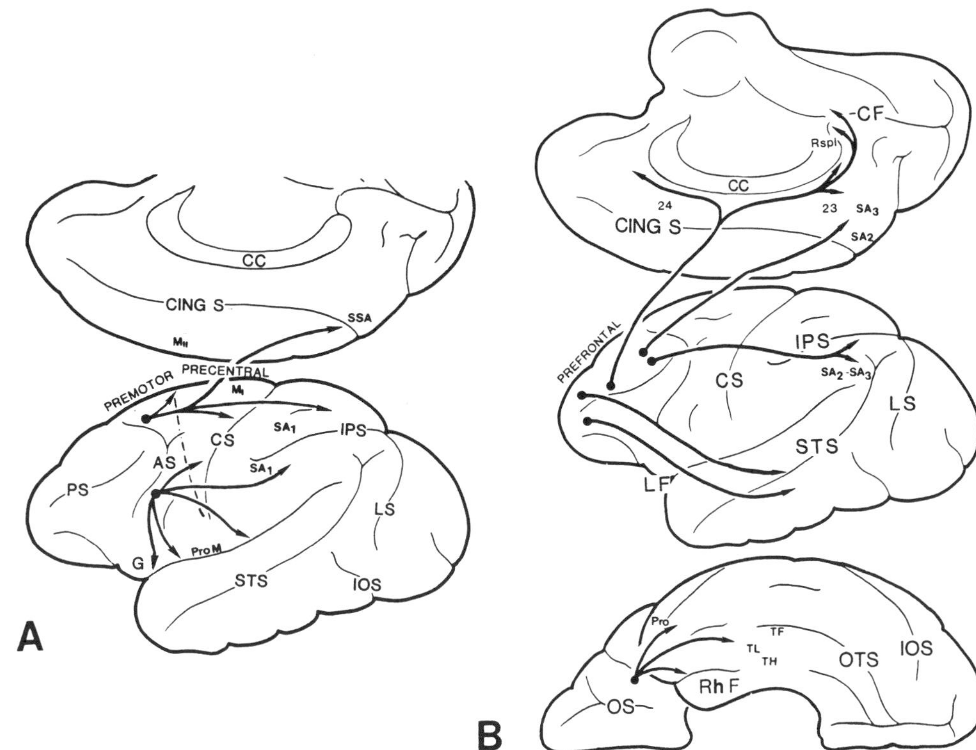

FIGURE 15 Diagrams showing the long association connections of premotor (A) and prefrontal (B) regions.

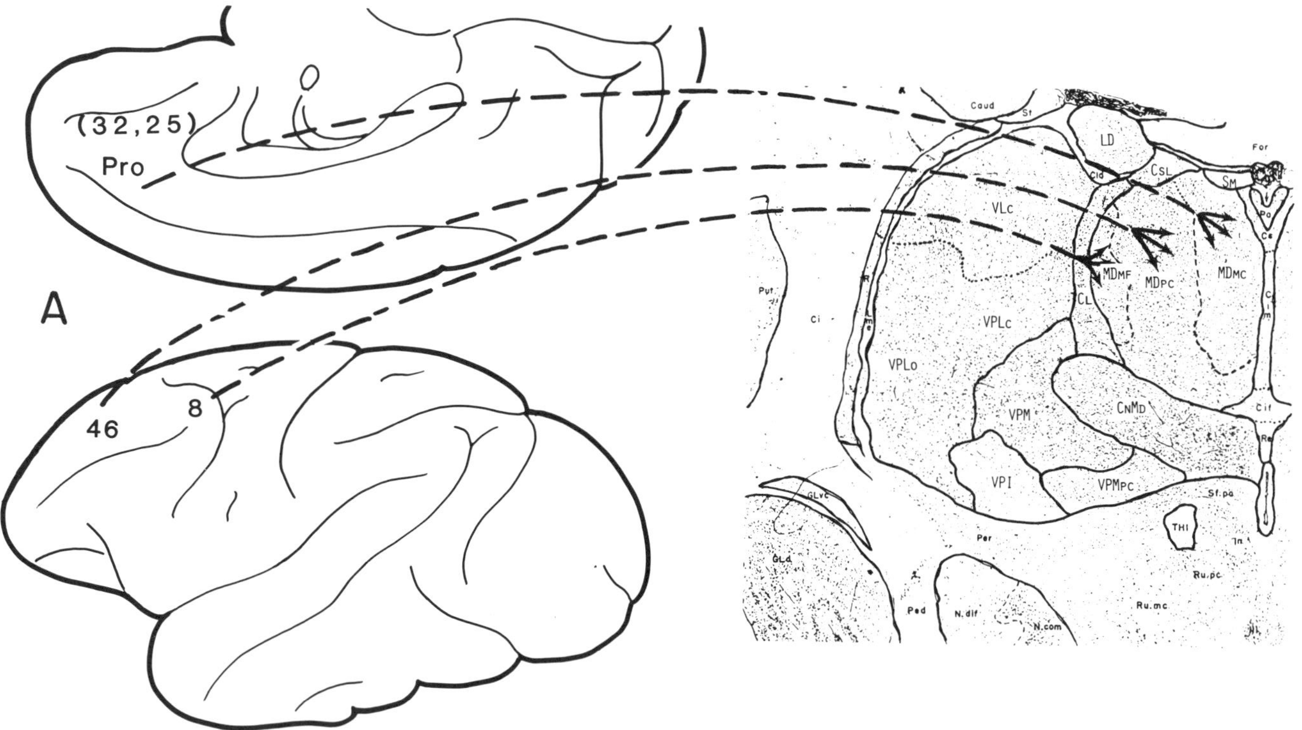

FIGURE 16. Diagram summarizing the corticothalamic projections from the dorsomedial (dorsal trend—A) and ventromedial (ventral trend—B) regions of the prefrontal cortex to the different subdivisions of the dorsomedial thalamic nucleus (MD). Note that the cortical areas of the dorsal and ventral trends project respectively to the dorsal and ventral parts of MD. Caud, Nucleus caudatus; Ci, Capsula interna; Cif, nucleus centralis inferior; Cim, nucleus centralis intermedialis; Cl, nucleus centralis lateralis; Cld, capsule of the nucleus lateralis dorsalis; CnMd, nucleus centrum medianum; Cs, nucleus centralis superior; Csl, nucleus centralis superior lateralis; For, fornix (continued on facing page).

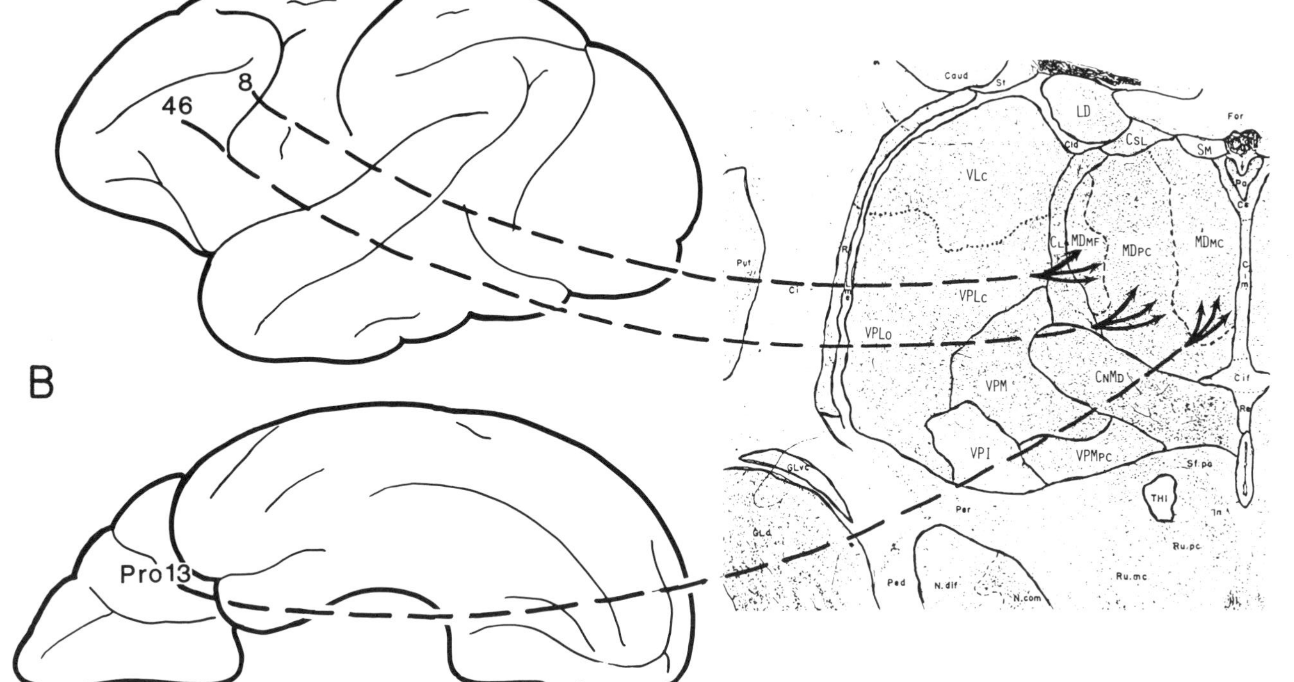

FIGURE 16 (Continued).
GLd, nucleus geniculatus lateralis dorsalis; GLvc, nucleus geniculatus ventralis, pars caudalis; In, nucleus interstitialis; LD, nucleus lateralis dorsalis; MDmf, nucleus medialis dorsalis, pars multiformis; MDpc, nucleus medialis dorsalis, pars parvocellularis; MDmc, nucleus medialis dorsalis, pars magnocellularis; N. com, substantia nigra, pars compacta; N. dif, substantia nigra, pars diffusa; Pa, nucleus paraventricularis; Ped, pes pedunculi; Per, nucleus peripeduncularis; Put, nucleus putamen; Re, nucleus reuniens; Ru. mc, nucleus ruber magnocellularis; Ru. pc, nucleus ruber parvocellularis; Sf. pc, nucleus subfascicularis, pars parvocellularis; SM, stria medullaris, St, stria terminalis; THI, tractus habenulo interpeduncularis; VLc, nucleus ventralis lateralis, pars caudalis; VPI, nucleus ventralis posterior inferior; VPLc, nucleus ventralis posterior lateralis, pars caudalis; VPLo, nucleus ventralis posterior lateralis, pars oralis; VPM, nucleus ventralis posterior medialis; VPMpc, nucleus ventralis posterior medialis, pars parvocellularis (Olszewski, 1952).

terconnected are not identical in architectonic terms; rather, they are at a similar stage in architectonic evolution. Furthermore, as shown in Figure 17, they have distinctive limbic and subcortical (i.e., thalamic) patterns of connectivity. By virtue of their interconnections, the related cortical and subcortical regions may comprise an overall unit involved in a particular behavior or function.

CONCLUSIONS

Knowledge of basic morphology, in particular, cytoarchitectonics and connections, is a fundamental requirement to the understanding of cortical function. This chapter provides a hypothesis that the connectional anatomy and cytoarchitectonic morphology of the frontal lobe are intimately related to each other, and that the basis of the connections can be understood in terms of the evolutionary development of the cerebral cortex. Each stage in development is marked by a more differentiated cytoarchitecture and a new set of connections, which together might reasonably be expected to subserve a new, and more advanced, behavior. Intrinsic to this hypothesis is the concept that the cortex has dual origins, namely, archi- and paleocortical. One portion of the frontal lobe

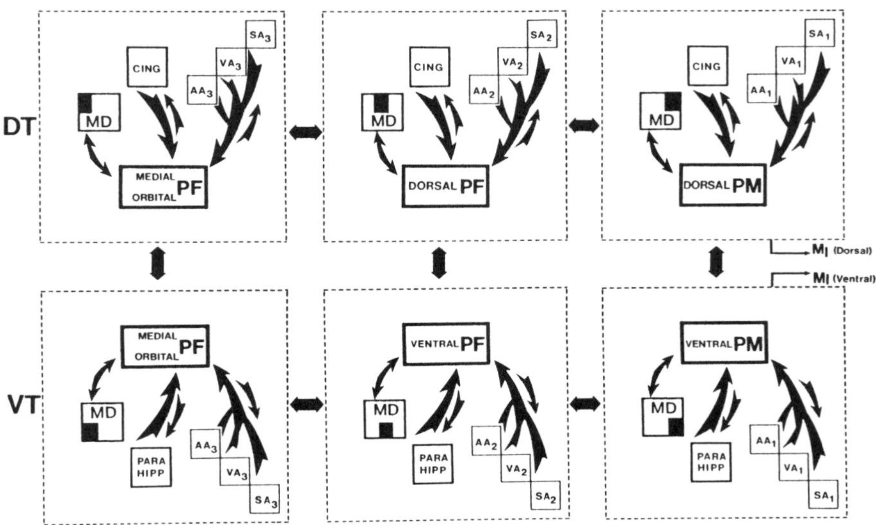

FIGURE 17 Summary diagram showing connections (afferent and efferent) of the three major subdivisions of the frontal lobe (proisocortical, prefrontal, and premotor) related to the dorsal (DT) and ventral (VT) trends. Note that thalamic (MD), limbic (cingulate and parahippocampal gyri), and association area connections form a unit.

develops from the rudimentary hippocampal formation and differentiates through the cingulate gyrus. This dorsal trend would thus be responsible for the cortex of the medial surface of the frontal lobe and the dorsolateral surface of the prefrontal cortex down to the level of the principal sulcus, as well as the dorsal premotor and precentral regions. The other portion takes origin from a ventral or paleocortical trend, with its origin in or near the olfactory cortex, and differentiates through the insular proisocortex. This trend would thus give rise to the cortex of the orbital surface of the frontal lobe and the ventrolateral surface up to the level of the principal sulcus, as well as the ventral premotor and precentral regions (Figure 8).

The first, or dorsal, system appears to be preferentially involved in the spatial analysis of sensory information. It has been shown that this processing is transferred to the frontal lobe via the posterior parietal lobe and the cingulate gyrus. Both of these latter regions have strong connectional relationships with those frontal lobe regions belonging to the dorsal trend. The second, or ventral, system is located in the ventral parietotemporal regions and appears to be preferentially concerned with the emotional tone of sensory information. These ventral parietotemporal regions maintain a strong connectional relationship with the ventral frontal lobe trend. The sequential processing of spatially related and motivational information in the dorsal trend and object-related information, as well as the emotional types of information conveyed by the ventral trend, interact in the frontal lobes (Macko & Mishkin, 1985; Mesulam, 1983; Mishkin, 1972; Ungerleider & Mishkin, 1982). The resulting integrated information is then relayed, via premotor regions, to the precentral gyrus, to initiate the proper motor response.

It is important to note, however, that, while these dorsal and ventral systems may have evolved separately and thus process the information separately, they are nonetheless anatomically interconnected (Figure 14). Furthermore, in functional terms, it would appear that they must interact in order to produce the execution of smooth, integrated behavior, which is the outcome of frontal lobe activity. In addition, both cortical and subcortical influences must "come together" so that the motor response occurs in the proper place and sequence, and is performed in harmony with the emotional state of the organism.

We have tried to put forth the concept that the cortex has developed in a series of sequential stages. This is seen in the increasing complexity or differentiation of the frontal lobe areas. Thus, the more primitive stages of cortical development, such as the proisocortical regions of the orbital and medial surfaces, preceded the more developed prefrontal, premotor, and precentral stages of the frontal lobe. These sequential stages developed as two trends from two prime moieties. As an extension of this idea of sequential stages of development, we have shown that these stages are connected preferentially with similar developmental stages of the post-Rolandic sensory-related association areas

(Figure 17). This is noticed in the similarity of the architectonic characteristics of the connected regions; for example, the proisocortical portions of the temporal lobe are connected preferentially with the orbital and medial proisocortical areas of the frontal lobe (Figure 17). The idea of connected areas forming a developmental stage is extended into the subcortical connections. Thus, each stage of development maintains a specific relationship with a specific division of the dorsomedial thalamic nucleus (Figures 16 and 17). This may also be the case with other subcortical connections, such as those of the corticostriate and corticopontine areas.

We would like to propose that, by virtue of interconnections among evolutionarily related regions in a given stage, a unit is formed that may subserve an individual function. Therefore, while considering frontal lobe functions, one must keep in mind the successive contributions of each unit in generating overall frontal lobe function. For example, the process of planning behavior would receive a contribution from each stage or unit: The proisocortical stage would add emotional tone, prefrontal would add spatial tone, and premotor would add attentional tone. By virtue of the interconnectivity among these units, each would contribute a part that would ultimately influence the motor cortex and result in the properly planned behavior. A similar notion has recently been put forth by Goldberg (1985): "Knowledge of biological form and its phylogenetic development can provide an important and valuable context in which to interpret the functional data. Phylogenetically older structures are likely to assume more integral, deep, rudimentary aspects of function whereas those of recent development can be viewed as surface elaborations correlating with the emergence of phylogenetically more recent behaviors" (p. 606). Of course, we fully realize that this is a very simplistic approach to frontal lobe function. However, this line of thinking based on evolving cortical and subcortical morphology relating to the evolving functions may provide a meaningful background for understanding clinical deficits as well as for designing experiments dealing with frontal lobe function.

ACKNOWLEDGMENTS

We wish to express our thanks to Drs. Benjamin Seltzer and Edward Yeterian for their most useful comments and suggestions. We would also like to thank Mr. Brian Buttler for his excellent technical assistance. This study was supported by the Veterans Administration, Edith Nourse Rogers Memorial Hospital, Bedford, Massachusetts 01730, and by NIH Grant 16841.

REFERENCES

Abbie, A. A. (1940). Cortical lamination in the monotremata. *Journal of Comparative Neurology, 72*, 429–467.

Akert, K. (1964). Comparative anatomy of frontal cortex and thalamofrontal connections. In J. M.

Warren & K. Akert (Eds.), *The frontal granular cortex and behavior* (pp. 372–396). New York: McGraw-Hill.

Baleydier, C., & Mauguiere, F. (1980). The duality of the cingulate gyrus in monkey. *Brain, 103,* 525–554.

Barbas, H., & Mesulam, M.-M. (1981). Organization of afferent input to subdivisions of area 8 in the rhesus monkey. *Journal of Comparative Neurology, 200,* 407–432.

Barbas, H., & Mesulam, M.-M. (1985). Cortical afferent input to the principalis region of the rhesus monkey. *Neuroscience, 15,* 619–637.

Barbas, H., & Pandya, D. N. (1981). Frontal lobe afferent input to area 6 in the rhesus monkey. *Society for Neuroscience Abstracts, 7,* 414.

Barbas, H., & Pandya, D. N. (1982). Cytoarchitecture and intrinsic connections of the prefrontal cortex of the rhesus monkey. *Society for Neuroscience Abstracts, 8,* 933.

Bignall, D. E., & Imbert, M. (1969). Polysensory and cortico-cortical projections to frontal lobe of squirrel and rhesus monkeys. *Electroencephalography and Clinical Neurophysiology, 26,* 206–215.

Bowker, R. M., & Coulter, J. D. (1981). Intracortical connectivites of somatosensory and motor areas. Multiple cortical pathways in monkey. In C. N. Woolsey (Ed.), *Cortical sensory organization: Vol. 1. Multiple somatic areas* (pp. 205–242). Clifton, NJ: Humana Press.

Brinkman, C., & Porter, R. (1983). Supplementary motor area and premotor area of monkey cerebral cortex: Functional organization and activities of single neurons during performance of learned movement. In J. E. Desmedt (Ed.), *Motor control mechanisms in health and disease,* (pp. 393–420). New York: Raven Press.

Brodmann, K. (1909). *Vergleichende Lokalisationlehre der Grosshirnrinde in ihren Prinzipien dargestellt auf Grund des Zellenbaues.* Leipzig: Barth.

Chavis, D. A., & Pandya, D. N. (1976). Further observations on corticofrontal connections in the rhesus monkey. *Brain Research, 117,* 369–386.

Damasio, A. (1979). The frontal lobes. In K. M. Heilman & E. Valenstein (Eds.), *Clinical neuropsychology* (pp. 360–412). London & New York: Oxford University Press.

Dart, R. A. (1934). The dual structure of the neopallium: Its history and significance. *Journal of Anatomy, 69,* 3–19.

Deacon, T. W., Rosenberg, P., Eckert, M. K., & Shank, C. E. (1982). Afferent connections of the primate inferior arcuate cortex. *Anatomical Record, 8,* 933.

Denny-Brown, D., & Botterell, E. H. (1948). The motor functions of agranular frontal cortex. *Research Publications—Association for Research in Nervous and Mental Disease, 27,* 235–345.

Fitzpatrick, K. A., & Imig, T. J. (1980). Auditory cortico-cortical connections in the owl monkey. *Journal of Comparative Neurology, 192,* 589–610.

Freund, H.-J., & Hummelsheim, H. (1985). Lesions of premotor cortex in man. *Brain, 108,* 697–733.

Fuster, J. M. (1980). *The prefrontal cortex: Anatomy, physiology, and neuropsychology of the frontal lobe.* New York: Raven Press.

Godschalk, M., Lemon, R. N., Kuypers, H. G. J. M., & Ronday, H. K. (1984). Cortical afferents and efferents of monkey postarcuate area: An anatomical and electrophysiological study. *Experimental Brain Research, 56,* 410–424.

Goldberg, G. (1985). Supplementary motor area structure and function: Review and hypotheses. *Behavioral and Brain Sciences, 8,* 567–616.

Goldman-Rakic, P. S. (1984). Modular organization of prefrontal cortex. *Trends in Neurosciences, 7,* 419–424.

Goldman-Rakic, P. S., & Porrino, L. J. (1985). The primate mediodorsal (MD) nucleus and its projection to the frontal lobe. *Journal of Comparative Neurology, 242,* 535–560.

Jones, E. G., & Burton, H. (1976). Areal differences in the laminar distribution of thalamic afferents in cortical fields of the insular, parietal and temporal regions of primates. *Journal of Comparative Neurology, 168,* 197–248.

Jones, E. G., Coulter, J. D., & Hendry, S. H. C. (1978). Intracortical connectivity of architectonic fields in the somatic sensory, motor and parietal cortex of monkeys. *Journal of Comparative Neurology, 181,* 291–348.

Jones, E. G., & Powell, T. P. S. (1970). An anatomical study of converging sensory pathways within the cerebral cortex of the monkey. *Brain, 93,* 793–820.

Kievit, J., & Kuypers, H. G. J. M. (1977). Organization of the thalamocortical connections to the frontal lobe in the rhesus monkey. *Experimental Brain Research, 29,* 299–322.

Künzle, H. (1978). An autoradiographic analysis of the efferent connections from premotor and adjacent prefrontal regions (areas 6 and 9) in *Macaca fascicularis. Brain, Behavior, and Evolution, 15,* 185–234.

Künzle, H., & Akert, K. (1977). Efferent connections of cortical area 8 (frontal eyefield) in *Macaca fascicularis:* A reinvestigation using the autoradiographic technique. *Journal of Comparative Neurology, 173,* 147–164.

Kuypers, H. G. J. M. (1964). The descending pathways to the spinal cord, their anatomy and function. *Progress in Brain Research, 11,* 178–202.

Kuypers, H. G. J. M., Szwarcbart, M. K., Mishkin, M., & Rosvold, H. E. (1965). Occipitotemporal corticocortical connections in the rhesus monkey. *Experimental Neurology, 11,* 245–262.

Lilly, J. C. (1958). Correlations between neurophysiological activity in the cortex and short-term behavior in the monkey. In H. F. Harlow & C. N. Woolsey (Eds.), *Biological and biochemical bases of behavior* (pp. 83–100). Madison: University of Wisconsin Press.

Macko, K. A., & Mishkin, M. (1985). Metabolic mapping of higher-order visual areas in the monkey. In L. Sokoloff (Ed.), *Brain imaging and brain function* (pp. 73–86). New York: Raven Press.

Merzenich, M. M., & Brugge, J. F. (1973). Representation of the cochlear partition on the superior temporal plane of the macaque monkey. *Brain Research, 50,* 275–296.

Merzenich, M. M., Sur, M., Nelson, R. J., & Kaas, J. H. (1981). Multiple cutaneous representations in areas 3b and 1 of the owl monkey. In C. N. Woolsey (Ed.), *Cortical sensory organization: Vol. 1. Multiple somatic areas* (pp. 67–119). Clifton, NJ: Humana Press.

Mesulam, M.-M. (1983). The functional anatomy and hemispheric specialization for directed attention. *Trends in Neurosciences, 6,* 384–387.

Mishkin, M. (1972). Cortical visual areas and their interactions. In A. G. Karczmar & J. C. Eccles (Eds.), *Brain and human behavior* (pp. 187–208). Berlin & New York: Springer-Verlag.

Muakkassa, K. F., & Strick, P. L. (1979). Frontal lobe inputs to primate motor cortex: Evidence for four somatotopically organized premotor areas. *Brain Research, 177,* 176–182.

Murray, E. A., & Coulter, J. D. (1981). Supplementary sensory area: The medial parietal cortex in the monkey. In C. N. Woolsey (Ed.), *Cortical sensory organization: Vol. 1. Multiple somatic areas* (pp. 167–195.) Clifton, NJ: Humana Press.

Myers, R. E. (1967). Cerebral connectionism and brain function. In C. H. Millikan & F. L. Darley (Eds.), *Brain mechanisms underlying speech and language* (pp. 61–72). New York: Grune & Stratton.

Nauta, W. J. H. (1964). Some efferent connections of the prefrontal cortex in the monkey. In J. M. Warren & K. Akert (Eds.), *The frontal granular cortex and behavior* (pp. 397–409). New York: McGraw-Hill.

Nauta, W. J. H. (1971). The problem of the frontal lobe: A reinterpretation. *Journal of Psychiatric Research, 8,* 167–187.

Nelson, C. N., & Bignall, K. E. (1973). Interactions of sensory and non-specific thalamic inputs to cortical polysensory units in the squirrel monkey. *Experimental Neurology, 40,* 189–206.

Olszewski, J. (1952). *The thalamus of the Macaca mulatta.* Basel: Karger.

Pandya, D. N., & Barbas, H. (1985). Supplementary motor area structure and function: Review and hypotheses. Commentary: Architecture and connections of the premotor areas in the rhesus monkey. *Behavioral and Brain Sciences, 8,* 595–596.

Pandya, D. N., Dye, P., & Butters, N. (1971). Efferent cortico-cortical projections of the prefrontal cortex of the rhesus monkey. *Brain Research, 31,* 35–46.

Pandya, D. N., Hallett, M., & Mukherjee, S. K. (1969). Intra- and interhemispheric connections of the neocortical auditory system in the rhesus monkey. *Brain Research, 14,* 49–65.

Pandya, D. N., & Kuypers, H. G. J. M. (1969). Cortico-cortical connections in the rhesus monkey. *Brain Research, 13,* 13–36.

Pandya, D. N., Mufson, E. J., & McLaughlin, T. J. (1980). Some projections of the frontal operculum (gustatory area) in the rhesus monkey. *Anatomical Record, 196,* 143A.

Pandya, D. N., Van Hoesen, G. W., & Mesulam, M.-M. (1981). Efferent connections of the cingulate gyrus in the rhesus monkey. *Experimental Brain Research, 42,* 319–330.

Pandya, D. N., & Vignolo, L. A. (1971). Intra- and interhemispheric projections of the precentral, premotor and arcuate areas in the rhesus monkey. *Brain Research, 26,* 217–233.

Pandya, D. N., & Yeterian, E. H. (1985). Architecture and connections of cortical association areas. In A. Peters & E. G. Jones (Eds.), *Cerebral cortex* (Vol. 4, pp. 3–61). New York: Plenum.

Passingham, R. E. (1972). Visual discrimination learning after selective prefrontal ablations in monkeys *(Macaca mulatta). Neuropsychologia, 10,* 27–39.

Passingham, R. E., & Ettlinger, G. (1972). Tactile discrimination learning after selective prefrontal ablations in monkeys *(Macaca mulatta). Neuropsychologia, 10,* 17–26.

Petrides, M. (1982). Motor conditional associative-learning after selective prefrontal lesions in the monkey. *Behavioural Brain Research, 5,* 407–413.

Petrides, M., & Iversen, S. D. (1976). Cross-modal matching and the primate frontal cortex. *Science, 192,* 1023–1024.

Petrides, M., & Iversen, S. D. (1978). The effect of selective anterior and posterior association cortex lesions in the monkey on performance of a visual-auditory compound discrimination task. *Neuropsychologia, 16,* 527–538.

Petrides, M., & Pandya, D. N. (1984). Projections to the frontal cortex from the posterior parietal region in the rhesus monkey. *Journal of Comparative Neurology, 228,* 105–116.

Roland, P. E., Larsen, B., Lassen, N. A., and Skinhøj, E. (1980). Supplementary motor area and other cortical areas in organization of voluntary movements in man. *Journal of Neurophysiology, 43,* 118–136.

Sanides, F. (1971). Functional architecture of motor and sensory cortices in primates in the light of a new concept of neocortex development.In C. R. Noback & W. Montana (Eds.), *Advances in primatology,* (Vol. I, pp. 137–208). New York: Appleton-Century-Crofts.

Sanides, F. (1972). Representations in the cerebral cortex and its areal lamination patterns. In G. F. Bourne (Ed.), *The structure and function of nervous tissue* (Vol. 5, pp. 329–453). New York: Academic Press.

Schell, G. R., & Strick, P. L. (1984). The origin of thalamic inputs to the arcuate premotor and supplementary motor areas. *Journal of Neuroscience, 4,* 539–560.

Siwek, D. F., & Pandya, D. N. (1984). Cortico-thalamic connections of prefrontal cortex in the rhesus monkey. *Anatomical Record, 208,* 188–189.

Stuss, D. T., & Benson, F. D. (1986). *The frontal lobes.* New York: Raven Press.

Tanaka, D., Jr. (1976). Thalamic projections to the dorsomedial prefrontal cortex in the rhesus monkey *(Macaca mulatta). Brain Research, 110,* 21–48.

Tanji, J., & Kurata, K. (1985). Contrasting neuronal activity in supplementary and precentral motor cortex of monkeys. 1. Responses to instructions determining motor responses to forthcoming signals of different modalities. *Journal of Neurophysiology, 53,* 129–141.

Tobias, T. J. (1975). Afferents to prefrontal cortex from the thalamic mediodorsal nucleus in the rhesus monkey. *Brain Research, 83,* 191–212.

Ungerleider, L. G., & Mishkin, M. (1982). Two cortical visual systems. In D. J. Ingle,

M. A. Goodale, & R. J. W. Mansfield (Eds.), *Advances in the analysis of visual behavior* (pp. 549–586). Cambridge, MA: MIT Press.

Van Essen, D. C., & Maunsell, J. H. R. (1983). Hierarchical organization and functional streams in the visual cortex. *Trends in Neurosciences, 6,* 370–375.

Van Hoesen, G. W. (1982). The parahippocampal gyrus. *Trends in Neurosciences, 5,* 345–350.

Van Hoesen, G. W., Pandya, D. N., & Butters, N. (1972). Cortical afferents to the entorhinal cortex of the rhesus monkey. *Science, 175,* 1471–1473.

Van Hoesen, G. W., Vogt, B. A., Pandya, D. N., & McKenna, T. M. (1980). Compound stimulus differentiation behavior in the rhesus monkey following periarcuate ablation. *Brain Research, 186,* 365–378.

Vogt, B. A., & Pandya, D. N. (1978). Corticocortical connections of somatic sensory cortex (areas 3, 1 and 2) in the rhesus monkey. *Journal of Comparative Neurology, 177,* 179–192.

Vogt, C., & Vogt, O. (1919). Allgemeinere Ergebnisse unserer Hirnforschung. *Journal fuer Psychologie und Neurologie, 25,* 279–461.

von Bonin, G., & Bailey, P. (1947). *The neocortex of Macaca mulatta.* Urbana: University of Illinois Press.

Wagman, I. H., Kreiger, H. P., Papatheodorou, C. A., & Bender, M. B. (1961). Eye movements elicited by surface and depth stimulation of the frontal lobe of *Macaca mulatta. Journal of Comparative Neurology, 117,* 179–188.

Walker, A. E. (1940). A cytoarchitectural study of the prefrontal area of the macaque monkey. *Journal of Comparative Neurology, 73;* 59–86.

Weinrich, M., Wise, S. P., & Mauritz, K.-H. (1984). A neurophysiological study of the premotor cortex in the monkey. *Brain, 107,* 385–414.

Welch, K., & Stuteville, P. (1958). Experimental production of neglect in monkeys. *Brain, 81,* 341–347.

Weller, R. E., & Kaas, J. H. (1985). Cortical projections of the dorsolateral visual area in owl monkey: The prestriate relay to inferior temporal cortex. *Journal of Comparative Neurology, 234,* 35–59.

Wiesendanger, M. (1981). Organization of secondary motor areas of cerebral cortex. In V. B. Brooks (Ed.), *Nervous system: Vol. 2, Part 2. Motor control* (pp. 1121–1147). Bethesda, MD: American Physiological Society.

Wise, S. P., & Evarts, E. V. (1981). The role of the cerebral cortex in movement. *Trends in Neurosciences, 4,* 297–300.

Woolsey, C. N. (1958). Organization of somatic sensory and motor areas of the cerebral cortex. In H. F. Harlow & C. N. Woolsey (Eds.), *Biological and biochemical bases of behavior* (pp. 63–81). Madison, WI: University of Wisconsin Press.

Woolsey, C. N. (1981a). *Cortical sensory organization: Vol. 1. Multiple somatic areas.* Clifton, NJ: Humana Press.

Woolsey, C. N. (1981b). *Cortical sensory organization: Vol. 2. Multiple visual areas.* Clifton, NJ: Humana Press.

Woolsey, C. N. (1981c). *Cortical sensory organization: Vol. 3. Multiple auditory areas.* Clifton, NJ: Humana Press.

Zeki, S. M. (1978). Functional specialization in the visual cortex of the rhesus monkey. *Nature (London), 274,* 423–428.

4

The Riddle of the Monkey's Delayed-Response Deficit Has Been Solved

John S. Stamm

INTRODUCTION

Jacobsen's (1936) discovery of delayed-response (DR) impairments after bilateral prefrontal resections in primates has become a major landmark in the history of brain research. In retrospect, his contributions were twofold: establishment of an intimate and lasting association between the monkey's frontal lobe and delayed-response performance, and the search for an explanation of the underlying deficit. Jacobsen's additional findings of the frontally ablated monkey's impairment on delayed-alternation (DA) performance, but not on visual discriminations, and its hyperdistractable behavior had relatively little impact on subsequent investigations. His explanation of the DR deficit as a defect in "immediate memory" was first challenged by his collaborators. Finan (1939) found that frontally ablated monkeys remained unimpaired on a difficult maze discrimination between preresponse delays of 30 and 120 sec, while they responded at chance level on DR with 2-sec delays. Malmo (1942) reported reductions in the DR impairment with darkening of the apparatus. These and other experimental variations led to differing explanations for the DR deficit: (1) the monkey's inadequate attention to cue properties (Nissen, Riesen, & Nowliss, 1938; Pribram, 1950); (2) its susceptibility to interference effects during the delay period (Malmo, 1942); and (3) deficient regulation of motoric processes (Konorski & Lawicka, 1964; Rosvold & Szwarcbart, 1964; Wegener & Stamm, 1966).

The progress made during the early decades of research was reported in the 1962 symposium on frontal lobe functions (Warren & Akert, 1964). Comparisons among experimental findings were possible because of the use of consistent testing procedures and of demarcations for the intended lesions. Most experiments were conducted with the Wisconsin General Test Apparatus (WGTA) in which the monkey is placed in a portable cage (about 50 × 50 × 50

ISBN 0-936925-00-0

cm) with vertical bars in front. It faces a vertical opaque screen that, when opened, reveals a test tray that contains two food wells (40-cm horizontal separation between centers) that are covered by slides or objects. At the start of the DR trial the monkey observes the experimenter placing a reward (peanut) in one food well. The screen is then interposed for a constant (5- to 10-sec) delay (the food wells are covered) and again opened for the monkey's choice response. For successive trials, the left and right food wells are baited according to a pseudorandom sequence. For the DA task the first response of each session is always rewarded (not scored) and for subsequent trials the reward is shifted between the two food wells. After a wrong response (counted) a correction procedure is employed, with the reward remaining in the food well until it is retrieved. The correction responses are not counted as a trial, but are usually scored separately as repetitive errors. Intertrial intervals are 5–10 sec. The demarcations for the bilateral dorsolateral frontal ablations are from midline to the orbital ridge and from frontal pole to the depth of arcuate sulcus, including the banks and floor of the principal sulcus and the anterior arcuate bank.

At the 1962 symposium the effects of bilateral frontal lesions in monkey, dog, and cat on a wide variety of tasks were reported. Severe impairments were found with many variations for DR and DA tasks and for place-discrimination reversals. Also, there were transitory postoperative deficits on visual and auditory discriminations. However, there was no consensus in explaning the animal's underlying dysfunctions. This problem was considered by Teuber (1964), who, after presenting his solution to "the riddle of frontal lobe functions in man," stated: "Is it too much to hope that the delayed response deficit, as seen in the bifrontal macaque, might yield to a similar interpretation? Perhaps it is too much to expect that, since it would be compounding a riddle with an enigma" (p. 441).

The lack of a satisfactory explanation may be attributed to two aspects of the monkey's frontal lobe disorder: (1) The lesions result in a syndrome that includes hyperactivity, hyperreactivity, response perseveration, and deficient spatial-response differentiations, and (2) the cues that guide the monkey's choice responses had not been identified. Research during the subsequent years was aimed toward clarification of these issues.

KINESTHETIC-MOTOR PROCESSES

Konorski (1967) considered the prefrontal cortical areas as the locus for kinesthetic gnosis of spatial relations, so that the cues that guide the animal in frontal lobe task performance are provided by the "spatio-kinesthetic image" toward the appropriate food box. The task for which performance is most dependent on kinesthetic-motor processes is delayed alternation, because the response to one manipulandum provides the cues for the subsequent choice response in a different direction. According to Konorski's interpretation, experimental procedures that would enhance the vividness of the spatio-kinesthetic images should result in more rapid DA acquisition by normal monkeys and more severe impairments after frontal lesions. This hypothesis was examined with the following experiments.

In the WGTA the monkey's differential choice responses are arm movements toward the food wells and sometimes shifts in its body position. More pronounced response processes are required with locomotor movements in a maze apparatus, as shown in Figure 1 (Stamm, 1970). The maze trial starts with raising of the opaque screen (D-1) and at the choice point the monkey must pass through the left (D-3) or right (D-4) swinging door. Groups of eight monkeys each were trained on DA (30 trials per session) in the WGTA with 10-sec intertrial intervals and in the maze with 15-sec intervals. Initial and repetitive errors were scored separately. Criterion performance (90% correct) was attained significantly faster in the maze than the WGTA, with group medians of 150 and 725 trials, respectively. All monkeys were then trained on a simple visual discrimination between cross and triangle patterns, which were painted on the WGTA food-box slides or on the doors from the choice compartment. Median trials to criterion were 490 in the WGTA and 1,880 in the maze.

Four monkeys in each group received bilateral resections of dorsolateral prefrontal cortex. Postoperative DA retention scores (initial errors) were 48% correct in the WGTA and 36% in the maze, and prolonged training (840 trials) resulted in improvements to only 65% correct by the WGTA and 52% by the maze group. Visual-discrimination retention was 69% correct in the WGTA and

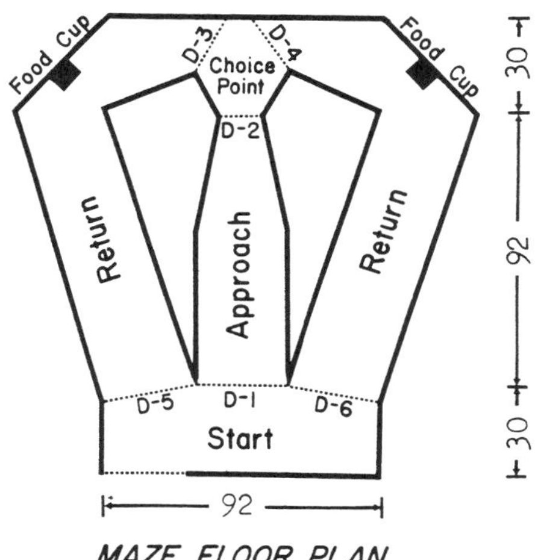

FIGURE 1 Floor plan of the locomotor maze. D-1 is an opaque sliding panel that is raised at the start of the DA trial. D-3, D-4, D-5, and D-6 are swinging doors that can be pushed open by the monkey (D-2 is not used for DA). Dimensions in centimeters.

53% correct in the maze, with most errors resulting from responses in one direction. Criterion performance was reattained after 135 and 255 trials, respectively, for the WGTA and maze groups. The most impressive findings were the high rates of repetitive DA errors by the maze monkeys, especially during the first postoperative session when several monkeys responded to the same side 40 times (unrewarded) during the 10-min session. Median scores of repetitive errors per trial were 12.0 in the maze and .78 in the WGTA and declined at the end of training to .60 and .023, respectively. Finally, the monkeys were tested without delay, with all doors and panels in open position. The frontally ablated monkeys rapidly learned the task and made continuous runs through the maze, with alternations in the choice compartment. However, brief interruption (.5 sec) of their locomotion by lowering the panel from the start box (D-1, Figure 1) resulted in performance at chance level. These tests demonstrate the ablated monkey's ability for sequential movements that include spatial alternations and the effects of brief interruption of the locomotion.

The findings support the view of the importance of kinesthetic cues in guiding the DA responses and identify two distinct forms of behavioral impairments: spatial-response differentiations in the absence of exteroceptive cues, and inhibitions of interfering response tendencies. The latter, as expressed by response perseverations in one direction, is exaggerated with locomotor tasks.

FRACTIONATION OF MORPHOLOGY AND FUNCTION

An important advance in frontal lobe research was the demarcation of the principal sulcus as the cortical locus for DR and DA performance (Goldman & Rosvold, 1970). This led to investigations for functional dissociations among the principalis and other segments within the dorsolateral prefrontal area.

In the subsequent experiment (Stamm & Weber-Levine, 1971), monkeys were trained on DA in the locomotor maze and bilateral lesions were made in principalis cortex (PRIN), the surrounding superior-anterior arcuate-inferior (SAI) segment, or the combined area (TOTAL), as seen in Figure 2. The main postoperative results were (1) reattainment of criterion performance by the SAI group after several sessions, but permanent impairment by the other lesion groups, and (2) high rates of repetitive errors during the initial sessions by the TOTAL group (11.0 errors per trial), but significantly lower rates by the PRIN (1.5 per trial) and SAI (1.0 per trial) groups. These errors declined during the course of testing (1,000 trials). The findings confirm the principalis focus for the DA task and the exceedingly high rates of response perseverations by monkeys with total prefrontal ablations. The subsequent testing phase examined the effects of pronounced prechoice differential postural cues on the ablated monkeys' DA performance. These cues were elicited by insertion of a 28-cm-high barrier in the approach alley (Figure 1) that was raised or lowered, so that the monkeys had to

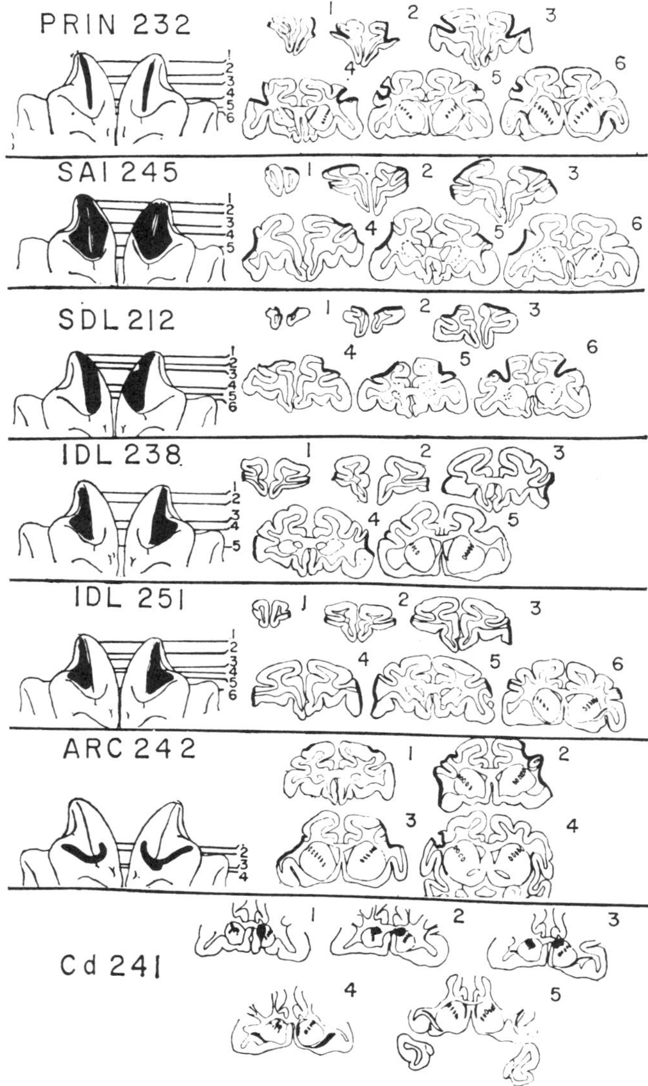

FIGURE 2 Reconstructions of representative dorsolateral frontal lesions. Cortical or subcortical damage is indicated by heavy black lines. (In the cross sections the left side represents the right hemisphere.) Lesion groups: PRIN, principal sulcus; SAI, cortex superior, posterior, and inferior to PRIN, inclusive of anterior arcuate bank; SDL, cortical strip superior to PRIN; IDL, inferior to PRIN; ARC, both banks of arcuate sulcus; Cd, head of caudate nucleus. The numbers refer to individual monkeys.

jump over it for a choice response in one direction and crawl under it for the opposite response. After 450 trials on this crawl/jump (C/J) DA variation, 150-trial blocks were alternated between it and the standard DA task. All lesion groups performed better on the C/J than on the standard task, with above 90% correct responses by the PRIN and SAI groups during the final trials and 83% correct by the TOTAL group. However, with the standard task, performance scores rose to 92% correct for the PRIN, but remained at 63% correct for the TOTAL group. Thus, the prechoice C/J kinesthetic cues were effective in overcoming the DA impairment following principalis, ablation but not after the traditional TOTAL ablation.

In search for the prefrontal focus for perseverative interference, monkeys were trained in the WGTA on visual discriminations with the successive method (Stamm, 1973). Two identical patterns (either crosses or triangles) were displayed on the food-box slides and the rewarded response was to the left with one pair of patterns and to the right with the other pair. This method was found to result in greater transitory deficits than did the simultaneous display of both patterns (Wegener & Stamm, 1966). Following preoperative training the monkeys received five different prefrontal or caudate lesions (Figure 2). During postoperative retraining to 90% criterion the most severe deficits were found by the SAI and IDL lesion groups, with respective mean errors of 133 and 106. These were significantly higher than the error scores for any other group, which were 47 for PRIN, 16 for ARC (resection of cortex in both banks of the sulcus), 6 for SDL, and 35 for caudate (Cd) lesions. Since almost all errors were perseverative responses toward one food box, the cortical strip inferior to principal sulcus seems to be the focus for inhibitions of such response tendencies. The dissociation between this and the PRIN segment was, however, not complete, because during the first 100 trials the PRIN-lesioned group responded at only 73% correct and 3 of the 4 monkeys made more errors than any in the SDL or ARC groups. Lesions of the cortical strip superior to principal sulcus (SDL) did not affect correct responses, which were 93% correct during the first 100 trials. In other experiments such lesions did not impair performance on DR, DA, place-reversal, or conditional position-response tasks, so that the functional property of SDL has not been determined.

Cortex in the arcuate sulcus has been delineated as the frontal focus for performance on the conditional position-response (CPR) task, where the location of an auditory stimulus (above or below the testing cage; Goldman & Rosvold, 1970) or visual stimulus (Podbros, Stamm, & Denaro, 1980) signals the concurrent choice response toward the right or left food dispenser. On the visual tasks two variations were used, with the directions for correct responses signaled by cues located either on the top and bottom or on the left and right edges of a vertical display panel. In both experiments bilateral arcuate lesions severely disrupted correct CPR performance, whereas principalis-lesioned monkeys showed no deficits. A corresponding dissociation had been found with a locomo-

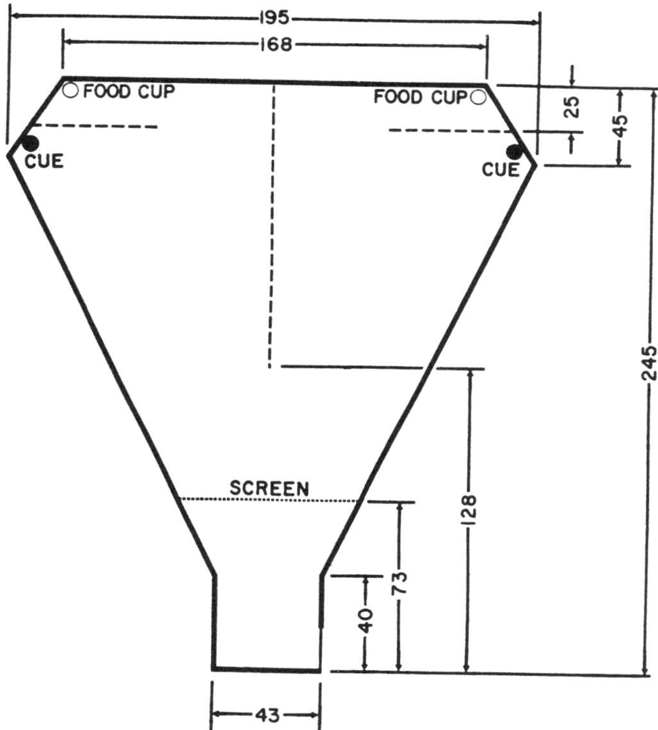

FIGURE 3 Floor plan of open field testing apparatus. The "screen" is a translucent panel that is raised to permit the monkey to leave the start box. The dashed lines represent rigid transparent panels. At the cue locations are diffuse plastic disks (6.3 cm in diameter) that may be rear-illuminated by red light and loudspeakers are mounted above them. Dimensions in centimeters.

tor CPR task, in which a visual or auditory cue signaled a food reward in the opposite direction (Stepien & Stamm, 1970a). Ablations of principalis cortex did not affect correct performance, whereas monkeys with SAI ablations were severely impaired. In a variation of the task (Stepien & Stamm, 1970b), with a 5-sec delay after termination of the 2-sec cue, the principalis-lesioned monkeys also were severely impaired and their response scores did not rise above chance level during 900 trials. In the apparatus (Figure 3) each food cup and adjacent cue location were separated by a transparent panel so that different error responses could be determined. On the concurrent CPR task, 22% of the SAI monkeys' errors were to the cue location, where they remained for the remainder of the trial. No such responses were observed with PRIN-lesioned monkeys.

The CPR task permits an analysis of the required response processes. The cue elicits an orienting response (OR) which was observed during the early stages of preoperative learning by the monkeys' movements in its direction. The

OR activates kinesthetic receptors of limb, neck, and eye musculature, which serve as stimuli for the appropriate choice response in a different direction. Thus, the crucial CPR processes are (1) formation of associations between the OR and the choice response and (2) rapid termination of the OR. The unimpaired CPR performance by principalis-lesioned monkeys indicates that these processes remain intact and do not contribute to the DR deficit.

The Riddle of DR

The numerous ablation experiments have clarified some issues about functions of the monkey's prefrontal cortex. The cortical focus for DR and DA performance has been delineated to the principal sulcus, and the critical features for the tasks are spatial response differentiations and temporal separation between the cue and the choice response. This has led to the conclusion (Goldman & Rosvold, 1970) that principalis cortex is the neural substrate for memory specifically for spatial information. The mnemonic explanation, however, is inadequate in several respects: Konorski (1972), with a three-choice locomotor DR apparatus, found that after the prefrontally ablated dog made an erroneous run it often immediately approached the correct feeder, but not the other, incorrect one. Also, in our maze experiments, the impaired DA performance with very brief delays cannot be explained by a deficient mnemonic trace. Furthermore, the spatial memory explanation provides no answers with regard to underlying functional processes. These seem to be movement-induced kinesthetic cues that regulate the animal's responses, including inhibitions of disrupting preferences. Thus, the most adequate explanation for the principalis deficit is that it reflects a disturbance of kinesthetic gnosis of spatial relations (Konorski, 1967).

However, this explanation does not specify the involvement of kinesthetic processes in meeting the several demands of the tasks. DR is a complex task that requires the monkey's identification of the location and significance of the cue, maintenance of a short-term memory, and execution of the appropriate choice response. The answer for the temporal implication of principalis cortex during the DR trial cannot be obtained with the irreversible ablation technique. Therefore, we attempted to solve this riddle with methods of electrocortical stimulation and recordings during task performance.

FRACTIONATION OF THE DR TRIAL

An automated apparatus was used for these experiments. The monkey was tested in a restraining chair, with one arm attached by a wristcuff to the shelf of the chair and its head movements restricted by fitted plastic shields. The monkey faced a vertical panel that contained three circular display windows, each 3.5 cm in diameter. Two windows, which also served as manipulanda, were separated horizontally (7 cm between centers) and the third was located above and midway between them. A plastic food cup was mounted below midway between the bottom windows. The DR trial started with white illumination of either the left or right bottom window (cue), followed by a blackout period (delay), and then illumination of both bottom windows with blue light until the monkey pressed lightly on one of them (response). This started a second blackout period (intertrial interval). A correct response resulted in delivery of a sugar pellet and brief illumination of the food cup. For a comparison, a visual delayed match-to-sample (DMS) task was programmed. The DMS trial started with illumination of the upper window by one pattern (sample) and for the choice response the bottom windows displayed this and another pattern. In some experiments four different colors were used.

Electrocortical Stimulation

Arrays of stimulating electrodes were chronically implanted on both banks of the principal sulcus and, in some experiments, on the ventral surface of the temporal lobes. Monkeys were trained on DR, generally with 2-sec cues and 8-sec delay. Electrical stimulations consisted of 2-sec or 1-sec trains of 50/sec pulses, applied across the principal sulcus of one hemisphere. The voltage was gradually increased until motor or EEG epileptic signs were elicited. For the testing sessions the voltage was set at 80–90% of this threshold and was applied during 120-trial sessions, with the onset of stimulation shifted to differing epochs of the trial.

Consistent results were obtained with principalis stimulation in 12 monkeys (Stamm & Rosen, 1969). As shown in Figure 4, correct DR performance was disrupted only with stimulus application during the early delay period and, in some monkeys, at the end of cue presentation, but remained near criterion level with stimulation during the subsequent portion of the delay. This performance decrement was unaffected by variations in durations of the cue or the delay periods, or by shifts of the responding hand. By contrast, inferotemporal stimulation disrupted DR performance only when applied throughout the cue presentation. The task specificity of these effects was demonstrated with DMS (Kovner & Stamm, 1972). On this task, principalis stimulation, even at convulsive levels, had little effect on correct performance. Inferotemporal stimulation disrupted DMS performance most markedly when applied toward the end of the delay period, but not during sample presentation or during the early portion of the delay.

Event-Related Potentials

For recordings of cortical slow potential (SP) shifts, pairs of nonpolarizable Ag-AgCl electrodes were implanted on the pial surface (active) and in subjacent

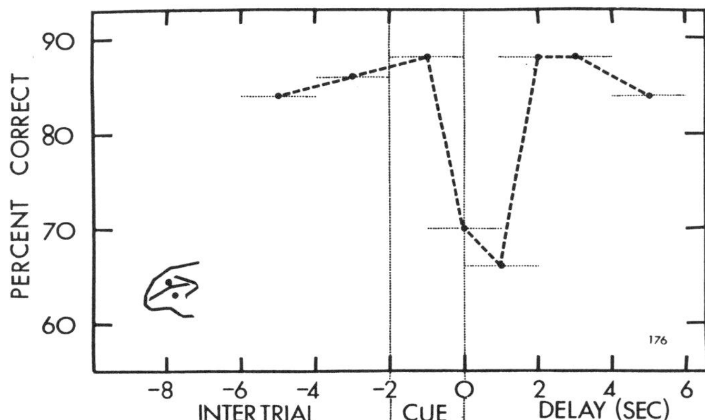

FIGURE 4 A monkey's delayed-response performance (2-sec cue presentation, 8-sec delay) during 2-sec electrocortical stimulation (1-msec pulses, 50 pulses/sec; 4 mAp) applied across the principal sulcus of one hemisphere (see inset at left). Horizontal lines indicate stimulation periods. Each point on the graph represents a mean score for 50–110 trials.

white matter (reference) in principalis (depth of sulcus), precentral, and occipital regions. Miniature nonpolarizable electrodes were placed subcutaneously across one eye for recordings of lateral eye movements (Stamm & Rosen, 1972; Stamm, Rosen, & Gadotti, 1977). Averaged EEG recordings during DR performance revealed several event-related potentials, of which two seemed to reflect specific frontal lobe functions, as shown in Figure 5. The positive cue-evoked potentials (CEP) were related to cue position, since the amplitudes from principalis electrodes in the right and left hemispheres were larger to the contralateral than to the ipsilateral light. This effect was found for each of four monkeys and was expressed by an average amplitude enhancement of 65% to the contralateral light. No corresponding amplitude differences were found from occipital or precentral electrode locations.

Of special relevance to our research was the subsequent surface-negative SP wave that attained maximum amplitude at the start of the delay period and then declined to baseline level. The time course and magnitude of this SP wave remained unaffected by variations of the cue (.06–8.0 sec) and the delay (4–20 sec) periods or by intramanual transfer of the responding hand. However, with four partially trained monkeys the magnitude of the SP wave (area above baseline) was significantly correlated with correct response scores ($r = .74–.90$). Corresponding correlations for precentral and occipital SP waves were small and insignificant. Also, for monkeys trained on DMS, no appreciable correlations were found between SP shift magnitudes and response scores. The posttrial SP wave was a function of the reinforcement, since it disappeared concurrently from all electrode locations with omission of the sugar pellet and reinforcement light.

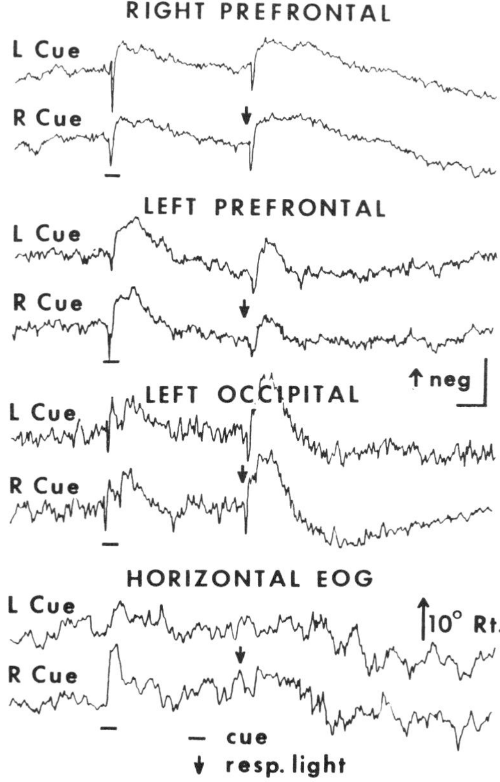

FIGURE 5 Averaged recordings (40 trials) of prefrontal (depth of principal sulcus) and occipital electrocorticograms and horizontal electrooculograms (EOG) during a monkey's performance on 8-sec DR. Trials with left (L) and right (R) cues are averaged separately. Horizontal bars indicate cue presentations and arrows the onset of the response lights. Calibrations: vertical bar, 100 μV (upward deflection indicates surface negativity); horizontal bar, 2 sec. Note: Amplitudes of the cue-evoked responses are larger in the prefrontal recordings contralateral to location of the cue light.

These findings are consistent with those obtained with single-unit recordings during DR performance. Thus, Fuster (1973; this volume, Chapter 6) identified several classes of prefrontal neurons that were activated during the cue and delay epochs, with highest overall rates occurring during the early delay period. These and other physiological investigations have provided evidence that surface-negative SP events reflect activation of the underlying neuronal system. The present CEP enhancements seem related to the finding of differential prefrontal unit activations to left and right DR cues (Niki, 1974). The latencies of the principalis CEPs (85–165 msec) are shorter than those for onset of lateral eye movements (185–235 msec). Therefore, the CEPs do not reflect the activations of neurons in the frontal eyefield that occur during saccadic and slow pursuit eye movements (Bizzi & Schiller, 1970). Also, the present recordings (Figure 5) show no simple relationship between CEP amplitudes and direction of eye movements, which had differing amplitudes to right and left cues. The EOG recordings and our observations indicate that most monkeys had visual orientations toward one display window during the intertrial interval, so that pronounced eye deviations occurred only when the opposite cue was displayed. Therefore, we interpret the enhanced CEP amplitudes as expressions of cortical processing for the cue location.

The findings from the cortical stimulation and recording experiments delineate the late cue and early delay period as the *crucial epoch* for functions of principalis cortex in DR performance.

ACTIVATION OF PRINCIPALIS CORTEX

With the method for SP recordings the EEGs during rest periods showed continuous slow baseline fluctuations of several seconds per cycle. Since the negative phase of these fluctuations seems indicative of heightened cortical excitation, we hypothesized that initiation of the DR trial during this phase would result in faster than normal task acquisition. In these experiments (Sandrew, Stamm, & Rosen, 1977; Stamm & Gillespie, 1980) 16 monkeys with implanted nonpolarizable electrodes were pretrained, with the right hand for responding, on the DR task with 1-sec cues and 0-sec delay. During subsequent training on 2-sec DR, the trial was started when one of several preconditions was met. For one group (FN), the ongoing EEG from left principalis cortex was monitored by a computer that generated a voltage window for a surface-negative shift of 50–100 μV (for different monkeys) over a 2.5-sec epoch. When the sampled EEG points met a criterion (86% within the voltage window), the programmed cue light was displayed for the DR trial. After 88% criterion performance in a 100-trial session, the delay was increased in steps to 4, 8, and 12 sec. Other monkey groups were trained under pretrial conditions of surface negativity from left precentral cortex (MN), 5-sec near-baseline SP from principalis cortex (FB), or rightward eye deviations (LEM). Yoked controls (YC) were trained without pretrial requirements, with the intertrial intervals that had been recorded from experimental monkeys. After a rest period, this procedure was replicated for DMS acquisition (four different colors).

The results, as shown by Figure 6, were impressive. Every FN monkey learned 12-sec DR faster than any monkey in the other groups. Total mean errors (including criterion trials) were 53.2 for the FN, compared with 308 for the YC

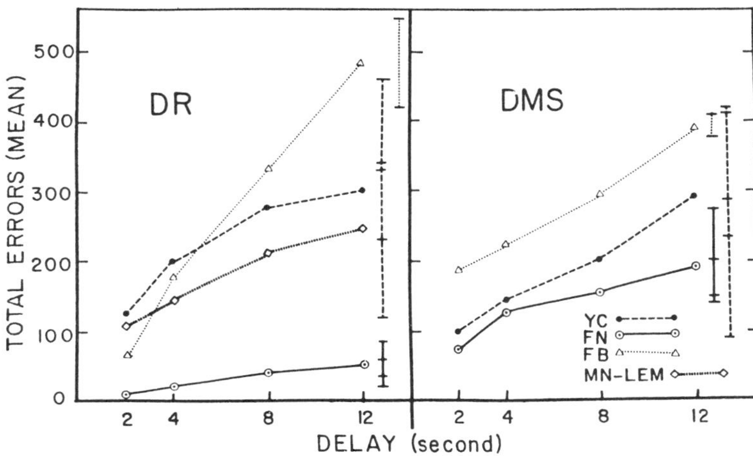

FIGURE 6 Acquisition of spatial delayed-response (DR) and visual delayed matching-to-sample (DMS) tasks, with successive intratrial delays of 2, 4, 8, and 12 sec. The ordinate indicates mean cumulative errors on each delay setting, including those for the 90% correct criterion sessions. The pretrial requirements for cue onset are FN ($N = 4$), a 2.5-sec surface-negative steady potential (SP) shift from left principalis cortex; MN ($N = 2$), a similar SP shift from left precentral cortex; LEM ($N = 2$), rightward eye deviations; FB ($N = 2$), 5-sec near-baseline SP from left principalis cortex; YC ($N = 5$), intertrial intervals yoked to those of monkeys in other groups. The data for the MN and LEM groups are combined for DR and not shown for DMS. The vertical lines at the right of the graphs present cumulative errors for individual monkeys (not shown for MN-LEM monkeys).

group (respective ranges of 19–98 and 121–480 errors). The fastest FN monkey responded above criterion during the first session on each delay and another required only one additional session. Possible state dependence of the rapid acquisition was examined by noncontingent test sessions with constant intertrial intervals. The mean transfer scores for correct responses from the previous acquisition session of above 90% indicate that the FN monkeys had indeed learned the task. Training on DMS did not result in significantly faster acquisition by the FN than by the control group, so that the rapid-learning effect was specific to a principalis-mediated task.

The effectiveness of the pretrial negative SP shifts was demonstrated, furthermore, with DR cues of brief durations. During the final testing phase the monkeys were tested on 12-sec DR with randomly programmed cues lasting .5, .2, or .1 sec. As shown by Figure 7, criterion DR performance with the shorter cues continued only for the monkeys with pretrial negative SP shifts (FN), whereas the response scores for the other groups declined significantly. However, on DMS the FN group's correct performance also dropped significantly below criterion with .1-sec cues. The control groups' DMS scores were below

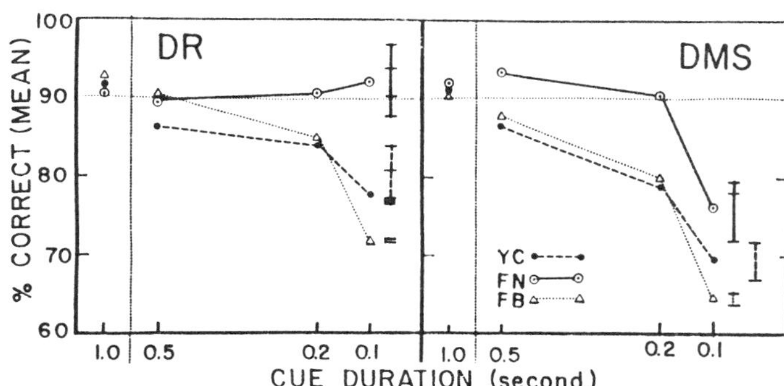

FIGURE 7 Correct performance on 12-sec DR and 12-sec DMS tasks with cues of .5-, .2-, or .1-sec durations, presented randomly during two sessions (98 trials each). The performance scores with 1.0-sec cues were obtained during the preceding sessions. The vertical lines at the right of the graphs present individual scores. For designation of monkey groups see legend to Figure 6.

those they had obtained with 1.0-sec cues and declined markedly with .1-sec cues.

The EEGs, averaged backward and forward with reference to cue onset, showed the required SP shifts with maximum negativity (50–100 μV) at cue onset and a decline during the course of the delay interval. The SP shift amplitudes are comparable to the post-cue negative waves that were obtained in ERP experiments (Figure 5). However, the negative wave remained localized to the criterion electrode and was not seen from other recording locations, including contralateral principalis cortex.

The results from these experiments provide remarkable evidence for the capability of the activated principalis cortex. The average DR acquisition at 5.8 times the normal rate, as determined by the error ratio between the yoked control and FN groups, indicates the effectiveness of cortical activation on task performance. Also, the transfer of correct performance with short cues indicates the monkey's ability for rapid attention to the task demands. It should be noted that the present technique utilizes endogenous SP fluctuations and that no evidence was found for the monkey's acquisition of self-regulation for SP events, because the highly variable intertrial intervals (20 to 67 sec) were not reduced during the course of training.

SOLUTION TO THE DR RIDDLE

During the decades of monkey research substantial progress has been reported in investigations of human frontal lobe functions. The several specific prefrontal functions that have been delineated (Stuss & Benson, this volume, Chapter 8; Stuss & Benson, 1984) seem consonant, to a remarkable degree, with those derived from monkey research. According to Luria (1966), the frontal lobes regulate the active state of the subject, control the essential elements of his intentions, and are essential to the programming and execution of complex sequences of actions. Furthermore, self-regulation of these several functions is by verbal processes. Consequently, destruction of the frontal self-regulatory system "results in marked deterioration of the highest forms of attention as well as in disturbance of the most complicated control of memory processes" (Luria & Homskaya, 1964, p. 371).

Application of this explanation to the monkey's prefrontal functions poses the question about the nature of its self-regulatory process. The experimental findings provide evidence for their kinesthetic characteristics. The crucial demands of the DR task—recognition of the significance of the spatial location of the cue and subsequent execution of the appropriate choice response—are met by kinesthetic processes. During cue presentation the relevant information becomes internalized by an orienting response, which, with the restraining chair, seems restricted to a brief eye deviation. The orienting response establishes "kinesthetic gnosis" (Konorski, 1967), that is, kinesthetic stimuli that guide the subsequent choice response. For DA tasks the guiding stimuli are derived from the response movements of the previous trial. This guidance system also requires suppression of responses to interfering exteroceptive (distracting) and interoceptive (response preference) stimuli. The fractionation experiments have delineated a prefrontal focus for inhibitions of inappropriate responses to the inferior prefrontal strip. However, principalis-lesioned monkeys also exhibit moderate transitory response perseverations. Therefore, inhibition of interfering responses seems to be a general function of the dorsolateral prefrontal area.

The task demand during the critical period of the DR trial, just before and after delay onset, is recognition of the cue location and selection of the appropriate delayed choice response, or, in Luria's terminology, the programming for self-regulation of future actions. This requires formation of a kinesthetic guidance system. This process, which has a duration of several seconds (negative SP wave), is not simple since it requires the monkey's attention to cue location, and formation of internalized stimulus-response associations that are resistant to distracting stimuli. Furthermore, the frontal lobe's function in regulation of its active state is supported by the rapid DR learning during its activated phase.

The solution to the monkey's DR riddle, therefore, is the remarkable function of principalis cortex in the formation of self-regulating kinesthetic processes that guide its subsequent choice responses.

REFERENCES

Bizzi, E., & Schiller, P. H. (1970). Single unit activity in the frontal eye fields of unanesthetized monkeys during eye and head movement. *Experimental Brain Research, 10,* 151–158.

Finan, J. L. (1939). Effects of frontal lobe lesions on temporally organized behavior in monkeys. *Journal of Neurophysiology, 2,* 208–226.

Fuster, J. M. (1973). Unit activity in prefrontal cortex during delayed-response performance: Neural correlates of transient memory. *Journal of Neurophysiology, 36,* 61–78.

Goldman, P. S., & Rosvold, H. E. (1970). Localization of function within dorsolated prefrontal cortex of the rhesus monkey. *Experimental Neurology, 27,* 291–304.

Jacobsen, C. F. (1936). Studies of cerebral functions in primates: I. The functions of the frontal association areas in monkeys. *Comparative Psychology Monographs, 13,* 3–60.

Konorski, J. (1967). *Integrative activity of the brain. An interdisciplinary approach.* Chicago, IL: Chicago University Press.

Konorski, J. (1972). Some hypotheses concerning the functional organization of prefrontal cortex. *Acta Neurobiologiae Experimentalis, 32,* 595–613.

Konorski, J., & Lawicka, W. (1964). Analysis of errors by prefrontal animals on the delayed-response test. In J. M. Warren & K. Akert (Eds.), *The frontal granular cortex and behavior.* New York: McGraw-Hill.

Kovner, R., & Stamm, J. S. (1972). Disruption of short-term visual memory by electrical stimulation of inferotemporal cortex in the monkey. *Journal of Comparative and Physiological Psychology, 81,* 163–172.

Luria, A. R. (1966). *Higher cortical function in man.* New York: Basic Books.

Luria, A. R., & Homskaya, E. D. (1964). Disturbance in the regulative role of speech with frontal lobe lesions. In J. M. Warren & K. Akert (Eds.), *The frontal granular cortex and behavior.* New York: McGraw-Hill.

Malmo, R. B. (1942). Interference factors in delayed response in monkeys after removal of frontal lobes. *Journal of Neurophysiology, 5,* 295–308.

Niki, H. (1974). Differential activity of prefrontal units during right and left delayed response trials. *Brain Research, 70,* 346–349.

Nissen, H. W., Riesen, A. H., & Nowlis, V. (1938). Delayed response and discrimination learning by chimpanzees. *Journal of Comparative Psychology, 26,* 361–386.

Podbros, L. Z., Stamm, J. S., & Denaro, F. J. (1980). Associative function of the arcuate segment of the monkey's prefrontal cortex. *Physiology and Behavior, 24,* 103–109.

Pribram, K. H. (1950). Some physical and pharmacological factors affecting delayed response performance of baboons following frontal lobotomy. *Journal of Neurophysiology, 13,* 373–382.

Rosvold, H. E., & Szwarcbart, M. K. (1964). Neural structures involved in delayed-response performance. In J. M. Warren & K. Akert (Eds.), *The frontal granular cortex and behavior.* New York: McGraw-Hill.

Sandrew, B., Stamm, J. S., & Rosen, S. (1977). Steady potential shifts and facilitated learning of delayed response in monkeys. *Experimental Neurology, 55,* 43–55.

Stamm, J. S. (1970). Dorsolateral frontal ablations and response processes in monkeys. *Journal of Comparative and Physiological Psychology, 70,* 437–447.

Stamm, J. S. (1973). Functional dissociation between the inferior and arcuate segments of dorsolateral prefrontal cortex in the monkey. *Neuropsychologia, 11,* 181–190.

Stamm, J. S., & Gillespie, O. (1980). Task acquisition with feedback of steady potential shifts from monkey's prefrontal cortex. In H. H. Kornhuber & L. Deecke (Eds.), *Motivation, motor and sensory processes of the brain: Electrical potentials, behavior and clinical use.* Amsterdam: Elsevier.

Stamm, J. S., & Rosen, S. C. (1969). Electrical stimulation and steady potential shifts in prefrontal cortex during delayed response performance by monkeys. *Acta Biologia Experimentalis, 29,* 385–399.

Stamm, J. S., & Rosen, S. C. (1972). Cortical steady potential shifts and anodal polarization during delayed response performance. *Acta Neurobiologiae Experimentalis, 32,* 193–209.

Stamm, J. S., Rosen, S. C., & Gadotti, A. (1977). Lateralization of functions in the monkey's frontal cortex. In S. R. Harnad (Ed.), *Lateralization in the Nervous System.* New York: Academic Press.

Stamm, J. S., & Weber-Levine, M. (1971). Delayed alternation impairments following selective prefrontal cortical ablations in monkeys. *Experimental Neurology, 33,* 263–278.

Stepien, I., & Stamm, J. S. (1970a). Impairments on locomotor task involving spatial opposition between cue and reward in frontally ablated monkeys. *Acta Neurobiologia Experimentalis, 30,* 1–12.

Stepien, I., & Stamm, J. S. (1970b). Locomotor delayed response in frontally ablated monkeys. *Acta Neurobiologia Experimentalis, 30,* 13–18.

Stuss, D. T., & Benson, D. F. (1984). Neuropsychological studies of the frontal lobes. *Psychological Bulletin, 95,* 3–28.

Teuber, H. L. (1964). The riddle of frontal lobe function in man. In J. M. Warren & K. Akert (Eds.), *The frontal granular cortex and behavior.* New York: McGraw-Hill.

Warren, J. M., & Akert, K. (Eds.). (1964). *The frontal granular cortex and behavior.* New York: McGraw-Hill.

Wegener, J. G., & Stamm, J. S. (1966). Behavior flexibility of the frontal lobes. *Cortex, 2,* 188–201.

5

Conditional Learning and the Primate Frontal Cortex

Michael Petrides

By the early 1970s, a number of investigations of the behavioral effects of frontal lobe lesions in experimental animals had demonstrated severe impairments on various tasks in which the animals had to make particular directional responses, such as approaching the left or right food wells, when the appropriate visual or auditory cues were presented (Goldman & Rosvold, 1970; Konorski, 1975; Lawicka, Mishkin, & Rosvold, 1975; Stamm, 1973). It had also been demonstrated that, in the monkey, this impairment could be observed after lesions restricted to the periarcuate region (Area 8 and Rostral Area 6) of the frontal cortex (Goldman & Rosvold, 1970; A. D. Milner, Foreman and Goodale, 1978; Stamm, 1973). In interpreting these findings, emphasis was often placed on the spatial nature of the stimuli and the required responses (e.g., Konorski, 1975; Stamm, 1973). It is possible, however, that this impairment may reflect a more general difficulty in the learning and performance of conditional responses to visual, auditory, and somaesthetic cues. Such an interpretation would be in agreement with the anatomical evidence demonstrating that this region of the frontal cortex is connected with visual, auditory, and somaestetic "association" cortex, as well as with the motor cortex and various subcortical regions involved in response control (Petrides, 1982). It would also be consistent, in a general sense, with the clinical impression that environmental stimuli do not appear to regulate the behavior of patients with damage to the frontal lobes to the same extent as that of normal individuals.

STUDIES WITH PATIENTS

An investigation of the effects of damage to the human frontal cortex on the learning of spatial and nonspatial conditional tasks has now been completed (Petrides, 1981, 1985b). This work examined the performance of patients with

ISBN 0-936925-00-0

unilateral frontal or temporal lobe excisions, carried out for the relief of pharmacologically intractable epilepsy, in learning various conditional tasks designed to be similar to those that had previously been used with experimental animals.

In one of these experiments, performance on a spatial conditional task was investigated. The subjects were faced with six white response cards, arranged in a horizontal row, and six identical blue lamps, placed in an irregular array behind the row of response cards. When one of these lamps was turned on, the subject had to touch the card that he thought was the correct one. If he touched the correct card, he was told that his response was correct and the lamp was turned off. If he touched an incorrect card, he was told that his response was wrong, the lamp remained lit, and he continued to touch other cards until he found the correct one. As can be seen in Figure 1, damage to either the left or the right frontal cortex resulted in a severe impairment in learning this task. In marked contrast, patients with excisions from the left or right anterior temporal lobe learned this task at a normal rate, except for the patients with right temporal lobe excisions that included extensive damage to the hippocampal region. The impair-

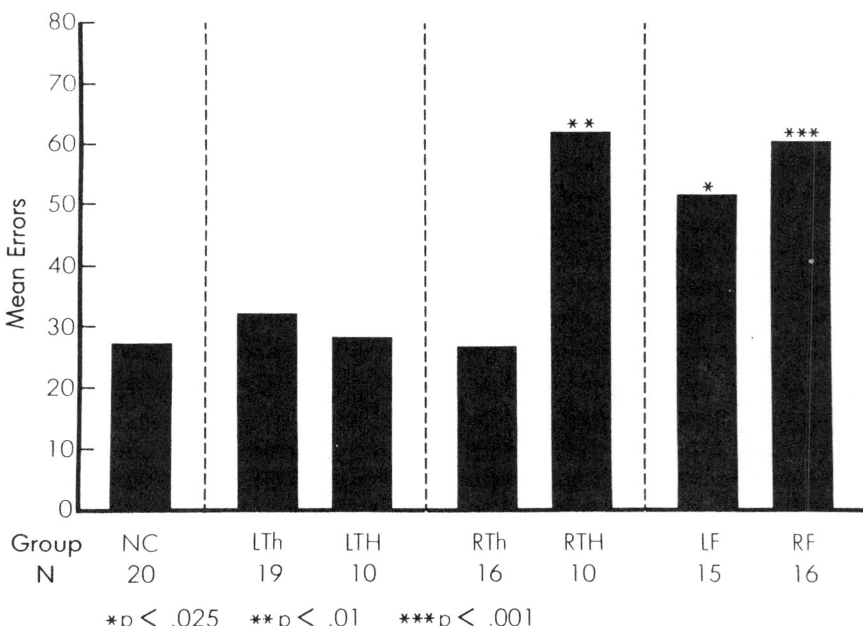

FIGURE 1 Mean error scores for the various groups on the spatial conditional task. NC, normal control group; LTh, left temporal lobe group with little hippocampal involvement; LTH, left temporal lobe group with extensive hippocampal involvement; RTh, right temporal lobe group with little hippocampal involvement; RTH, right temporal lobe group with extensive hippocampal involvement; LF, left frontal lobe group; RF, right frontal lobe group. (From Petrides, 1985b.)

ment after right hippocampal damage is consistent with other investigations that have clearly demonstrated the involvement of this region in spatial learning and memory (Corkin, 1965; B. Milner, 1965, 1971; Smith & Milner, 1981).

In another experiment, the question whether patients with frontal lobe lesions would also be impaired on a comparable task requiring nonspatial responses was investigated. In this experiment, the subjects were first shown six different hand postures and, when they could reproduce all of these postures from memory, six differently colored stimuli were placed on the table and the subjects were told that their task was to learn the correct response to each one of those stimuli. Throughout testing, the stimuli remained on the table in full view of each subject (see Figure 2) and, on any given trial, one of the stimuli was placed in front of the others, the subject having to respond by producing the appropriate hand posture. If an incorrect posture was made, the subject had to try the other hand postures until she found the correct one. In this task, patients with either left or right frontal lobe excisions were again severely impaired, whereas patients with unilateral temporal lobe excisions were not impaired, except for the group with left temporal lobe lesions that involved extensive damage to the hippocampal region (see Figure 3). The deficit of patients with left hippocampal damage is most probably due to the verbal memory component of this task resulting from the tendency of many subjects to verbalize the associations between the colored stimuli and the hand postures; alternatively, it may reflect the greater contribution of the left hemisphere in the control of certain motor

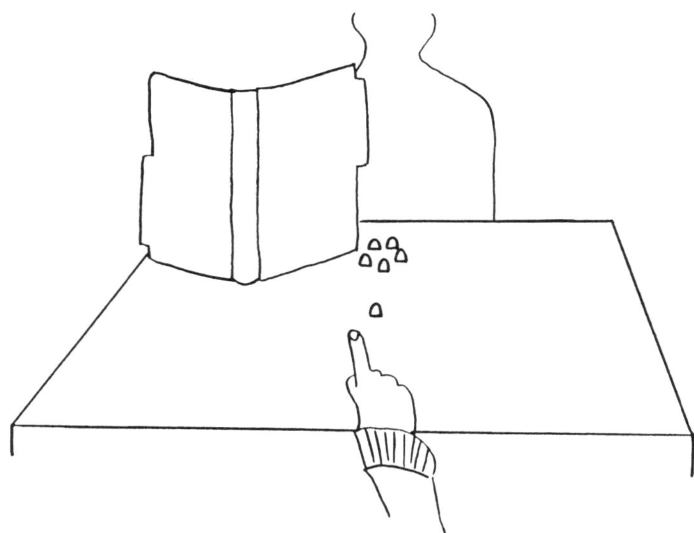

FIGURE 2 Schematic diagram of the experimental arrangement in the nonspatial conditional task. (From Petrides, 1985b.)

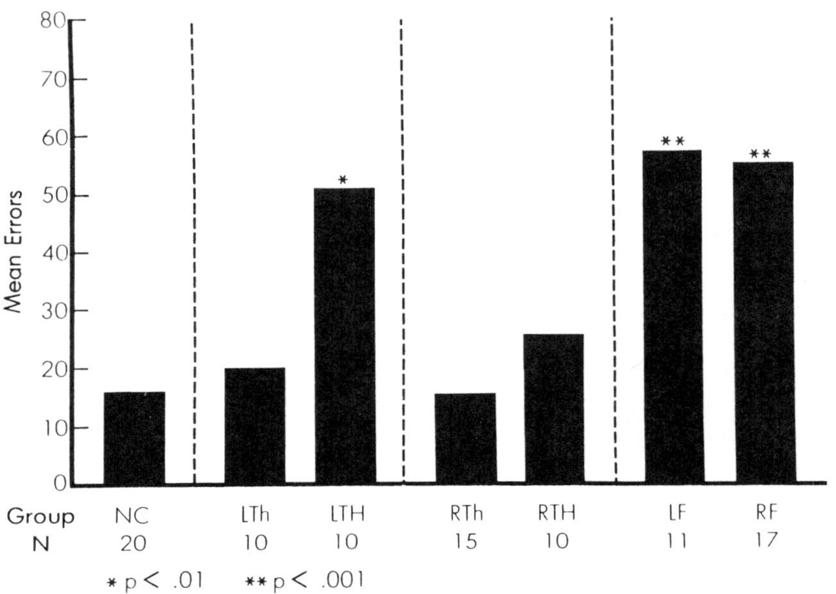

FIGURE 3 Mean error scores for the various groups on the nonspatial conditional task. The abbreviations are the same as those used in Figure 1. (From Petrides, 1985b.)

tasks (DeRenzi, Motti, & Nichelli, 1980; Geschwind, 1967; Kimura & Archibald, 1974).

The work with patients has shown that conditional learning is subserved by a neural circuit that includes the frontal cortex and the hippocampal region, the hippocampal contribution being material specific. The impairment on the conditional tasks after damage to the frontal cortex does not appear to be due to difficulties in discriminating between the stimuli or in making the responses, but rather in learning to select the appropriate response to a given stimulus. For instance, in the motor conditional task, patients with damage to the frontal cortex could discriminate between the stimuli (e.g., they could easily name the color of each stimulus), and they had learned without difficulty all six hand postures before testing began; they also continued, throughout testing, to produce all the hand postures, even though they were severely impaired in learning to select the correct posture for each one of the various stimuli.

STUDIES WITH NONHUMAN PRIMATES

The frontal cortex is a large and heterogeneous area of the brain, as has been demonstrated by a number of anatomical (see Pandya & Yeterian, 1985) and behavioral (see Fuster, 1980) investigations. In work with patients, it is difficult to establish the critical regions within the frontal cortex involved in conditional learning, because the excisions are rarely confined to anatomically distinct regions. This problem can, however, be overcome in work with nonhuman primates. In a series of studies with monkeys, I investigated the hypothesis that the periarcuate region of the dorsolateral frontal cortex is critically involved in the learning and performance of conditional responses to visual and auditory cues (Petrides, 1982, 1985a, 1986). This work examined the effect of lesions restricted to the periarcuate or to the periprincipalis region of the frontal cortex on conditional learning (see Figure 4). The reason for selecting the periprincipalis region as the control lesion site was the fact that it had previously been demonstrated to be a critical region subserving performance on the traditional delayed-response and delayed-alternation tasks (see Fuster, 1980).

The animals with periarcuate or periprincipalis lesions and a normal control group were tested on tasks that required conditional learning as well as on various control tasks (e.g., standard visual discriminations) that did not require such learning. It is important to emphasize at this point the fundamental difference between the learning requirements of the conditional and the control tasks that were used. In the conditional situations, the animal was faced with a set of stimuli and a set of arbitrary responses, and had to learn to perform according to the conditional rule: If Stimulus A is presented, select Response X, and if Stimulus B is presented, select Response Y. By contrast, in the control tasks, the animal was rewarded when it made a certain response to the "positive" but not to

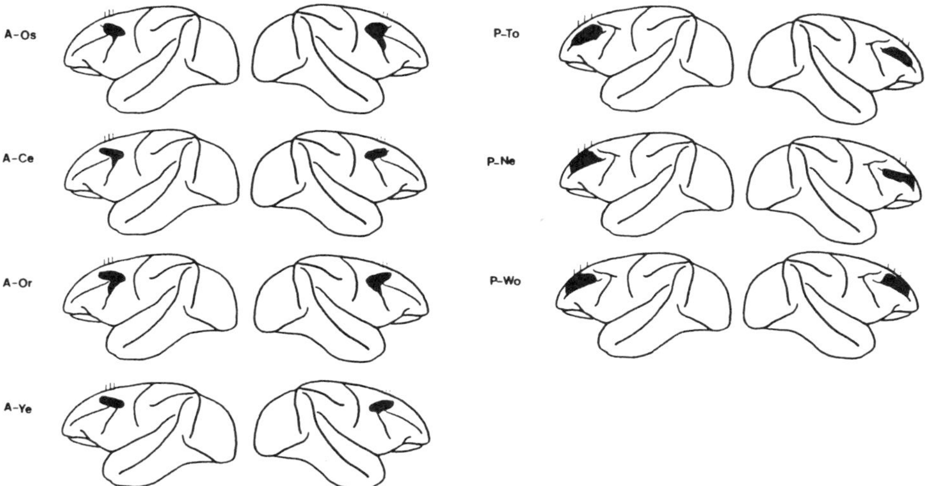

FIGURE 4 Representation of the periarcuate (A) and periprincipalis (P) lesions, drawn on standard diagrams of the lateral surface of the brain of the rhesus monkey.

the "negative" stimulus. Thus, responding in the presence of the positive stimulus was strengthened through reinforcement, whereas responding to the negative stimulus was gradually extinguished as a result of the absence of reinforcement.

In one of the experiments with nonhuman primates, the effect of periarcuate lesions on a motor conditional task designed to be similar to the motor task that had previously been administered to the patients was examined (Petrides, 1982). In this experiment, the monkeys were faced with a box covering the food well and with two manipulanda attached to it: a stick that they could grip and a button they could touch with the palm facing downward (see Figure 5). After the monkeys had mastered these two movements, they had to learn to perform one of them when one of two stimuli was shown, and to perform the other movement in the presence of the other stimulus. As can be seen in Figure 6, none of the animals with periarcuate lesions was able to reach criterion within the limits of testing. However, even though these animals could not consistently select the correct movement in the presence of the appropriate stimulus, they continued to

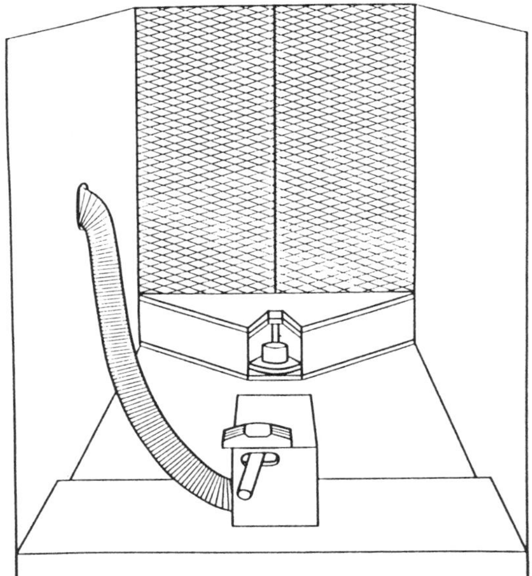

FIGURE 5 Schematic diagram of the monkey's view of the experimental arrangement in the motor conditional task. The animal faced a test board on which there was a box covering the food well. This box could be pushed back to collect the reward, which was delivered through a tube attached to it. The box was fixed to the test board by means of a spring hinge and thus, it automatically returned to its closed position when the monkey had retrieved the reward and had stopped pushing it. A triangular apparatus with an opening at the front through which a stimulus could be presented was located behind the test board and immediately below the one-way vision screen that hid the experimenter from the monkey. (From Petrides, 1982.)

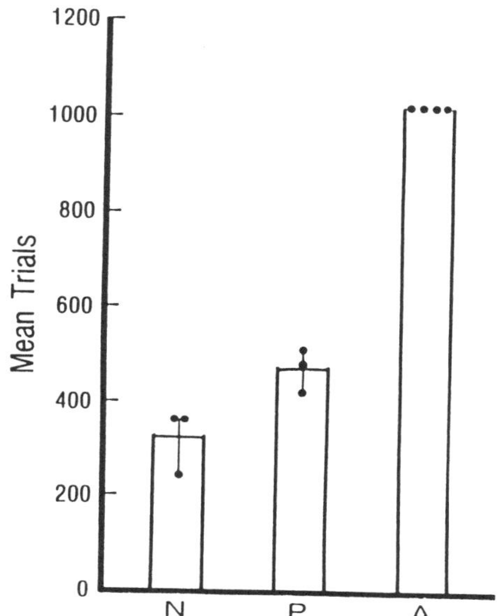

FIGURE 6 Trials to criterion in the motor conditional task. N, normal monkeys; P, monkeys with lesions to the periprincipalis region; A, monkeys with lesions to the periarcuate region. The monkeys with periarcuate lesions (A) failed to reach criterion within the limits of testing (1,020 trials).

choose between these two movements equally well throughout testing. In a control task administered immediately after the motor conditional task, the monkeys were faced with the same response box but with the button now removed from it. Two new stimulus objects were used and the animals were rewarded for responding (i.e., gripping the stick) when one of those two objects was presented, but not when the other stimulus was presented. No significant difference between the periarcuate and the control animals was found in this task. Thus, animals with periarcuate lesions can perform as well as normal controls if they are not required to select between alternative responses but simply have to learn to perform a single response in the presence of a stimulus leading to reward. The normal performance of monkeys with periarcuate lesions on this control task, and the normal performance of these animals on various other nonconditional tasks (see below), rule out the possibility that the deficit observed in the motor conditional task might have resulted from a difficulty in discriminating between the visual stimuli used or from a nonspecific impairment in motivation or attention. In a similar investigation, Halsband and Passingham (1982) have shown that monkeys with lesions to Area 6 were severely impaired in the postoperative retention of a motor conditional task in which the animals had to pull or rotate a handle in response to the appropriate visual cue.

Further evidence that the periarcuate cortex plays a critical role in conditional learning was provided by a series of experiments that investigated the performance of these animals on symmetrically and asymmetrically reinforced go/no-go tasks (Petrides, 1986). In these tasks, the animals faced a single response box that covered the food well (see Figure 7). In the symmetrically reinforced go/no-go tasks, the animals had to learn that, to receive the reward, they had to push open the box within 5 sec of presentation of Stimulus A, and to delay their response for this period of time when Stimulus B was presented; the withdrawal of the stimulus together with the sound of a peanut being delivered down the tube signaled to the animal that the delay period was over and that the box could now be opened to retrieve the reward. Thus, on any given trial, the animals had to decide between responding immediately or delaying their response, depending on the stimulus that was shown. The requirements of this task were therefore comparable to those of a conditional task. There were two responses, both of which led to reward, and the animal had to learn to select the appropriate one according to the conditional rule: If Stimulus A is shown, select Response X (go immediately), but if Stimulus B is shown, select Response Y (go at the end of the delay period). The monkeys with periarcuate lesions exhibited

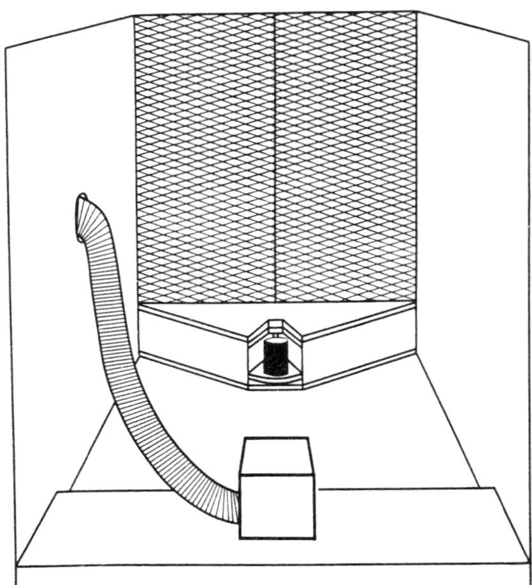

FIGURE 7 Schematic diagram of the monkey's view of the experimental arrangement in the go/no-go tasks. A box covered the food well. This box tilted back, when pushed, to reveal the food well. The reward was delivered to the food well through a tube that was attached to the box. (From Petrides, 1986.)

significant impairments on such tasks (see Figure 8). By contrast, these animals performed as well as normal control subjects on asymmetrically reinforced go/no-go tasks (see Figure 9) in which they were rewarded if they responded (i.e., opened the box) in the presence of positive stimuli, but they were *never* rewarded if they responded in the presence of negative stimuli. In the latter situation, learning can be the result of strengthening a response to the positive stimuli through reinforcement and extinguishing that response to the negative stimuli through lack of reinforcement.

In another set of experiments, the effect of lesions to the periarcuate cortex on the learning of a different nonspatial conditional task was investigated (Petrides, 1985a). In this task, the animal faced two white Perspex boxes placed close to each other (see Figure 10). Inside each of these boxes was a small light bulb that could be turned on or off by the experimenter, who was sitting behind the one-way vision screen. On any given trial one of the boxes, chosen according to a random sequence, was lit and the other remained unlit. The monkeys were rewarded if they opened the lit box when Object A was shown and if they opened the unlit box when Object B was presented. As can be seen in Table 1, the animals with periarcuate lesions were severely impaired in learning this nonspa-

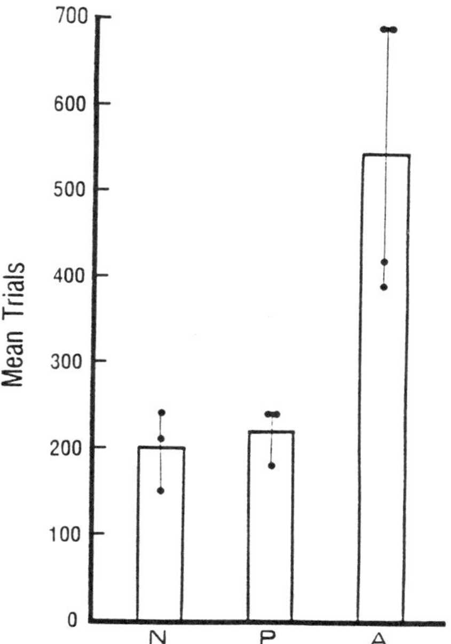

FIGURE 8 Trials to criterion on a symmetrically reinforced go/no-go task. In this experiment the subject was rewarded if he responded within 5 sec when one of the two stimuli was shown and if he delayed responding for 5 sec when the other stimulus was shown. The abbreviations are the same as those used in Figure 6. (Experiment 2 from Petrides, 1986.)

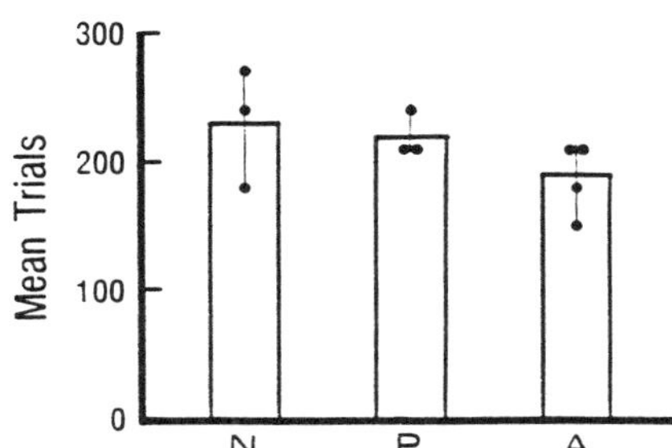

FIGURE 9 Trials to criterion on an asymmetrically reinforced go/no-go task. In this experiment the stimuli were 10 objects. Five of these objects were designated as the positive and the other 5 as the negative stimuli. If the monkey responded by pushing back the box covering the food well when one of the positive stimuli was shown, a reward was delivered to the food well. No reward was delivered, however, if the monkey responded when one of the negative stimuli was shown. The abbreviations are the same as those used in Figure 6. (Experiment 5 from Petrides, 1986.)

tial conditional task. They were, however, able to learn, at a normal rate, two control tasks administered before the conditional task. In the control tasks (visual discrimination and its reversal), the monkeys were again faced with the lit and the unlit box, but now only one response was rewarded, that is, opening the lit box in the discrimination task and the unlit box in the reversal task. In these tasks, unlike the conditional task, learning can be the result of strengthening the rewarded response and extinguishing the unrewarded one.

THE IMPORTANCE OF STIMULUS–RESPONSE SEPARATION

In the work carried out with nonhuman primates, damage to the periarcuate cortex has resulted in severe impairments in various conditional tasks in which one or another response (e.g., Movement X or Y, selection of Stimulus X or Y) had to be produced when the appropriate cue that was physically separate from the responses was given. The physical separation between the cues and the responses is important because, in tasks in which the response manipulandum is also the stimulus, animals are often not faced with conditional learning situations but rather with situations that require learning to approach, avoid, or manipulate individual stimuli in particular ways. For instance, in the various tasks that I used, the monkeys with periarcuate lesions had no problem in learning that the stick was an object to grip and the button an object to place the hand on, that response boxes could be pushed back to open, and that plaques could be displaced to uncover rewards. Clearly, these animals can learn how to manipulate any given object; that is, they can use the visual, tactile, and other sensory

TABLE 1
Number of Trials to Criterion in the Visual Discrimination, Reversal, and Nonspatial Conditional Tasks

Subjects[a]	Visual discrimination task	Reversal task	Nonspatial conditional task
N-He.	270	240	330
N-Bo.	360	210	270
N-Sa.	360	270	300
P-To.	240	240	330
P-Ne.	360	240	330
A-Os.	330	270	1020[b]
A-Ce.	300	270	1020[b]
A-Or.	510	270	1020[b]
A-Ye.	120	240	1020[b]

[a]N = normal monkeys; P = monkeys with lesions of the periprincipalis area; A = monkeys with lesions of the periarcuate area. Criterion trials are not included in the numbers given above. (From Petrides, 1985a.)

[b]Failure to reach criterion within the limits of testing.

features that define an object as cues indicating *how* it should be handled. The importance of the separation between the stimuli and the responses can also be seen in a number of other situations, such as, for example, in two-choice successive discrimination tasks. In such tasks, the animals typically encounter, on each trial, two identical stimuli that cover the two response locations (food wells). For explanatory purposes, let us assume that, on each trial, either two red stimuli or two blue stimuli cover the food wells and that when the red stimuli cover the food wells the reward is on the left, but when the stimuli are blue the reward is on the right. The solution to this task is ambiguous in the sense that the animals could reach criterion performance in two distinct ways. They could learn the conditional solution; that is, when Configuration A (two red stimuli) is present, go left, but when Configuration B (two blue stimuli) is present, go right. Alternatively, the animals may treat the *red* stimulus in the *right* position as one compound stimulus (defined by its color in conjunction with its position), the red stimulus in the *left* position as a different compound stimulus, and so on. In the latter case, the animals have to deal with four stimuli, only two of which are rewarded, and they learn to approach the two rewarded stimuli and to avoid the two unrewarded ones. Thus, for the animals, the successive discrimination task may not be different from the usual simultaneous visual discrimination tasks in which they learn to approach certain stimuli because they are rewarded and to avoid others because approaching them does not lead to reward (Spence, 1952).

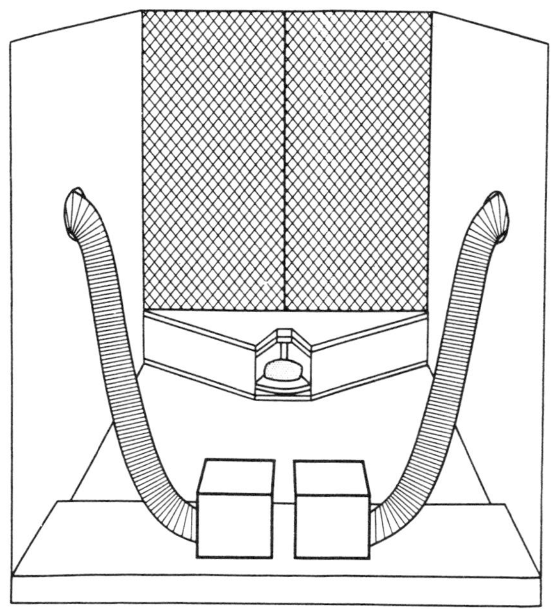

FIGURE 10 Schematic diagram of the monkey's view of the experimental arrangement in the nonspatial conditional task in which the animal had to select between a lit and an unlit box. (From Petrides, 1985a.)

A considerable amount of research has been carried out to find out whether animals solve successive discrimination tasks by learning to approach or avoid particular stimuli or by learning according to the conditional rule: If Configuration A is present, go left; if Configuration B is present, go right (see Mackintosh, 1974, and Sutherland & Mackintosh, 1971, for an excellent review of this issue). It is clear from this work that in situations where there is stimulus–response contiguity, that is, the stimuli occupy the response location, animals tend to solve successive discrimination problems by developing approach or avoidance responses to compound stimuli rather than by employing a conditional solution. It is therefore to be expected that, in many such tasks, monkeys with periarcuate lesions will perform normally.

At the completion of the conditional learning investigations (Petrides, 1982, 1985a, 1986), some of which were summarized above, the monkeys with periarcuate lesions, as well as the operated and unoperated control animals, were tested on a visual successive-discrimination task and, subsequently, on a spatial conditional task that did require a conditional solution. In the successive discrimination task, when the opaque screen, which separated the monkey's compartment from the testing area, was raised, the animal was faced with a test board with two food wells (25.5 cm apart). Each food well was covered with one of two identical objects that were stuck on white plaques (6 × 6 cm). Thirty trials were administered per day. On half the trials, a red toy soldier was stuck on each of the two plaques that covered the food wells and the reward was available only in the left food well. On the other half of the trials, a blue bottle top was stuck on each of the plaques covering the food wells and the reward was under the right plaque. The order of presentation of the two different types of trials was determined according to a random but balanced order. A trial was initiated when the opaque screen was raised, and, after the monkey had responded by uncovering one of the two food wells, the trial was terminated and the screen was lowered. The correction procedure was used throughout testing; that is, incorrect trials were repeated until the animal had corrected the response. Testing continued until the animals reached criterion, which was defined as 90% correct responses on each of three consecutive days. The results of this experiment are shown in Table 2. There were no significant differences between the animals with periarcuate lesions and the periprincipalis and normal control animals on this task.

Following this experiment, the animals were tested on a spatial task that did require conditional learning. In this task, the animals were now faced with a test board on which there were two identical boxes (25 cm apart) covering the food wells. The boxes could be pushed back to collect the reward, which was delivered through a tube attached to each one of the boxes. The boxes were fixed to the test board by means of spring hinges and thus returned to their original

TABLE 2
Number of Trials to Criterion in the Successive Discrimination and Spatial Conditional Tasks

Subjects[a]	Successive discrimination task	Spatial conditional task
N-He.	330	210
N-Bo.	150	60
N-Sa.	300	210
P-To.	360	240
P-Ne.	300	180
A-Os.	360	480
A-Ce.	240	390
A-Or.	330	450
A-Ye.	300	390

[a]N = normal monkeys; P = monkeys with lesions of the periprincipalis area; A = monkeys with lesions of the periarcuate area. Criterion trials are not included in the numbers given above.

positions when the monkey stopped pushing them. The apparatus for presenting the stimuli, located at a distance of 26 cm behind the test board, was the same as that used in the other conditional experiments described above. It consisted of a triangular box with an opening at the front through which the stimulus could be presented. In this experiment, a trial was initiated when a stimulus object was presented, and terminated when the animal had responded by opening one of the two boxes. On half of the 30 daily trials, determined according to a random schedule, a green purse was shown, and on the remaining trials a red cylinder. When the purse was shown, the correct response, resulting in delivery of the reward, was to push open the left box; when the cylinder was presented, the correct response was to open the right box. The correction procedure was used throughout testing. The learning criterion was defined as 90% correct responses on each of 3 consecutive days of testing. In this task, the animals with periarcuate lesions exhibited significant impairments in comparison with the operated and unoperated control animals (see Table 2). The findings of the last two experiments (i.e., the impairment in performance of the spatial conditional task together with the normal performance on the successive discrimination task after periarcuate lesions) are consistent with other related investigations on the effects of damage to the periarcuate cortex (A. D. Milner et al., 1978; Passingham, 1985; Stamm, 1973).

The work described above has clearly demonstrated that the periarcuate cortex, that is, the cortex lying within and around the arcuate sulcus, is critically involved in conditional learning. In conditional learning, the subjects have a set of responses available to them and have to learn to perform the correct response to each of a set of stimuli. The subjects can be said to have the responses available to them since it can be demonstrated that they know the possible responses that they must select from and that they can produce them without any difficulty. It must be emphasized that the responses are not simply particular sets of muscle contractions but rather actions that lead to particular end results and are thus best defined in terms of these end results. For example, even though, in some tasks, the responses may be distinct movements, they can also be responses such as uncover the left or right food well or push open the lit or the unlit box. In the case of situations requiring uncovering the left or right food well, a wide range of movements can achieve the same result, especially in a situation in which the animal is not restrained but is relatively free to move within the testing cage. In the situation in which the animals are required to select between the lit and unlit boxes, the responses can *only* be coded in terms of the goal that must be achieved.

DIFFERENTIAL EFFECTS OF SELECTIVE LESIONS WITHIN THE PERIARCUATE REGION

Although the periarcuate cortex can be distinguished from other frontal cortical regions on the basis of certain anatomical characteristics, such as the fact that this region is directly linked with the modality-specific parasensory "association" cortical areas, there are a number of differences in the pattern of these connections within this region of the frontal lobe (e.g., Barbas & Mesulam, 1981; Chavis & Pandya, 1976; Petrides & Pandya, 1984). The anatomical findings suggest that there may be some separation, within the periarcuate cortex, of the mechanisms subserving conditional learning in terms of the sensory modality through which the stimuli are presented and the types of responses that must be produced.

In a recent investigation, I have examined the effect of selective lesions within the periarcuate region on the performance of two visual nonspatial conditional tasks that differ only in terms of the responses required (Petrides, 1985c). Nine monkeys were preoperatively trained on the nonspatial conditional task in which the animals, on any given trial, were faced with a lit and an unlit box (see Figure 10) and had to learn to select the lit box when one of the two stimulus objects was shown and to select the unlit box in the presence of the second object. When the animals had mastered this task, three monkeys received bilateral ablations restricted to the anterior part of the periarcuate cortex (Area 8), which is closely linked to the visual "association" cortex, and three monkeys

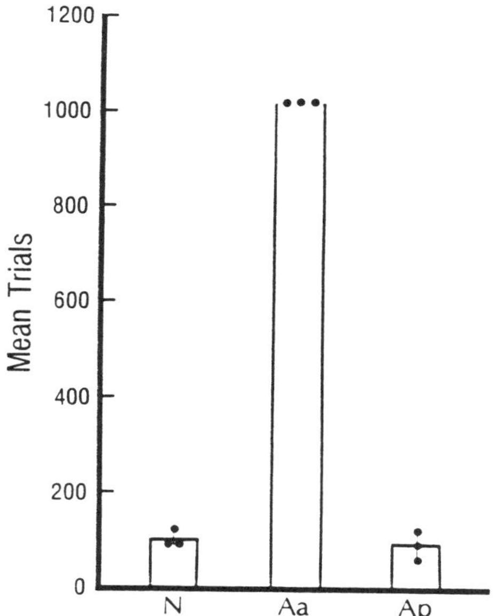

FIGURE 11 Trials to criterion on the nonspatial conditional task requiring selection between a lit and an unlit response box; postoperative retention. N, normal control monkeys; Aa, monkeys with lesions to the anterior arcuate cortex (Area 8); Ap, monkeys with lesions to the posterior arcuate cortex (Rostral Area 6). Note that none of the three monkeys with lesions to the anterior arcuate cortex could relearn the task within the limits of testing (1,020 trials).

received ablations of the posterior part of the periarcuate region (Rostral Area 6), which is closely linked to somatosensory "association" cortex as well as to the motor cortex; the remaining three animals served as unoperated control subjects. Two weeks after surgery, all the animals were retested on this task until they reached the preoperative criterion of 90% correct responses on each of three consecutive days of testing, or until 1,020 trials had been completed. As can be seen in Figure 11, the monkeys with damage to the anterior arcuate cortex were severely impaired in comparison with the normal controls, whereas those with damage to the posterior arcuate cortex were not.

After completion of this experiment, the monkeys were tested on a visual go/no-go task with symmetrical reinforcement. In this task, the monkey was faced with a single response box (see Figure 7) and had to learn to respond (push open the box) when one stimulus was presented and to withhold responding for 5 sec when the second stimulus was shown. In contrast to the findings on the previous task, monkeys with damage to Area 8 performed as well as normal control subjects, the animals with damage to the posterior periarcuate cortex now being impaired (see Figure 12). These results are consistent with the known anatomical connections of particular areas within the periarcuate region. Damage to the anterior part of the periarcuate cortex, which is preferentially connected with the visual system, resulted in a severe impairment on the conditional task in which the appropriate response (select the lit or the unlit box) could only be determined on the basis of the visual characteristics of the manipulanda. By contrast, damage to the posterior part of the periarcuate cortex (Rostral Area 6), which is closely linked to the motor cortex and the somatosensory system, caused a severe impairment in the postoperative acquisition of a conditional task that required selection between two kinesthetically distinct responses, that is,

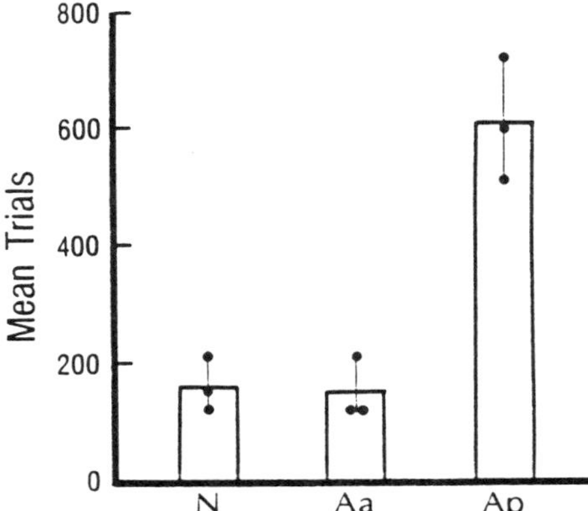

FIGURE 12 Trials to criterion on the symmetrically reinforced go/no-go task in which the animal had to respond immediately or delay responding depending on the stimulus presented; postoperative acquisition. Abbreviations are the same as those in Figure 11.

responses that can be differentiated on the basis of differences in the motor programs (sets of commands to muscle groups) needed to activate them. The work on the effects of selective lesions within the periarcuate region has provided evidence that there is some degree of separation, within this part of the frontal cortex, of mechanisms underlying different conditional tasks, but considerably more work will have to be carried out before it can become clear how the various subdivisions of the periarcuate cortex are organized with respect to conditional learning.

REFERENCES

Barbas, H., & Mesulam, M.-M. (1981). Organization of afferent input to subdivisions of area 8 in the rhesus monkey. *Journal of Comparative Neurology, 200,* 407–431.

Chavis, D. A., & Pandya, D. N. (1976). Further observations of cortico-frontal connections in the rhesus monkey. *Brain Research, 117,* 369–386.

Corkin, S. (1965). Tactually-guided maze learning in man: Effects of unilateral cortical excisions and bilateral hippocampal lesions. *Neuropsychologia, 3,* 339–351.

De Renzi, E., Motti, R., & Nichelli, P. (1980). Imitating gestures: A quantitative approach to ideomotor apraxia. *Archives of Neurology (Chicago), 37,* 6–10.

Fuster, J. M. (1980). *The prefrontal cortex: Anatomy, physiology, and neuropsychology of the frontal lobe.* New York: Raven Press.

Geschwind, N. (1967). The apraxias. In E. W. Straus & R. M. Griffith (Eds.), *Phenomenology of will and action* (pp. 91–102). Philadelphia, PA: Duquesne University Press.

Goldman, P. S., & Rosvold, H. E. (1970). Localization of function within the dorsolateral prefrontal cortex of the rhesus monkey. *Experimental Neurology, 27,* 291–304.

Halsband, U., & Passingham, R. (1982). The role of premotor and parietal cortex in the direction of action. *Brain Research, 240,* 368–372.

Kimura, D., & Archibald, Y. (1974). Motor functions of the left hemisphere. *Brain, 97,* 337–350.

Konorski, J. (1975). The role of prefrontal control in the programming of motor behavior. In J. D. Maser (Ed.), *Efferent organization and the integration of behavior* (pp. 175–201). New York: Academic Press.

Lawicka, W., Mishkin, M., & Rosvold, H. E. (1975). Dissociation of deficits on auditory tasks following partial prefrontal lesions in monkeys. *Acta Neurobiologiae Experimentalis, 35,* 581–607.

Mackintosh, N. J. (1974). *The psychology of animal learning.* New York: Academic Press.

Milner, A. D., Foreman, N. P., & Goodale, M. A. (1978). Go-left go-right, discrimination performance and distractibility following lesions of prefrontal cortex or superior colliculus in stumptail macaque. *Neuropsychologia, 16,* 381–390.

Milner, B. (1965). Visually guided maze learning in man: Effects of bilateral hippocampal, bilateral frontal, and unilateral cerebral lesions. *Neuropsychologia, 3,* 317–338.

Milner, B. (1971). Interhemispheric differences in the localization of psychological processes in man. *British Medical Bulletin, 27,* 272–277.

Pandya, D. N., & Yeterian, E. H. (1985). Architecture and connections of cortical association areas. In A. Peters & E. G. Jones (Eds.), *Cerebral cortex* (Vol. 4, pp. 3–60). New York: Plenum Press.

Passingham, R. E. (1985). Cortical mechanisms and cues for action. *Philosophical Transactions of the Royal Society of London, Series B, 308,* 101–111.

Petrides, M. (1981). Paper presented at the annual meeting of the International Neuropsychology Symposium, Monastir, Tunisia.

Petrides, M. (1982). Motor conditional associative-learning after selective prefrontal lesions in the monkey. *Behavioral Brain Research, 5,* 407–413.

Petrides, M. (1985a). Deficits in non-spatial conditional associative learning after periarcuate lesions in the monkey. *Behavioral Brain Research, 16,* 95–101.

Petrides, M. (1985b). Deficits on conditional associative-learning tasks after frontal- and temporal-lobe lesions in man. *Neuropsychologia, 23,* 601–614.

Petrides, M. (1985c). The effects of selective lesions to the periarcuate cortex on the performance of two nonspatial conditional tasks. *Society for Neuroscience Abstracts, 11,* 460.

Petrides, M. (1986). The effect of periarcuate lesions in the monkey on the performance of symmetrically and asymmetrically reinforced visual and auditory go, no-go tasks. *Journal of Neuroscience, 6,* 2054–2063.

Petrides, M., & Pandya, D. N. (1984). Projections to the frontal cortex from the posterior parietal region in the rhesus monkey. *Journal of Comparative Neurology, 228,* 105–116.

Smith, M. L., & Milner, B. (1981). The role of the right hippocampus in the recall of spatial location. *Neuropsychologia, 19,* 781–793.

Spence, K. W. (1952). The nature of the response in discrimination learning. *Psychological Review,* 59, 89–93.

Stamm, J. S. (1973). Functional dissociation between the inferior and arcuate segments of dorsolateral prefrontal cortex in the monkey. *Neuropsychologia, 11,* 181–190.

Sutherland, N. S., & Mackintosh, N. J. (1971). *Mechanisms of animal discrimination learning.* New York: Academic Press.

6

Single-Unit Studies of the Prefrontal Cortex

Joaquin M. Fuster

INTRODUCTION

This chapter will present a brief survey of contributions from behavioral electrophysiology, more specifically, single-unit studies, to our understanding of frontal lobe functions in the primate. Before summarizing the evidence, I will point to a few general concepts that should help establish the background for discussion of that evidence.

One general concept worthy of mention is the principle of cortical function enunciated, probably for the first time, by the Russian anatomist Vladimir Betz in 1874. Briefly, according to that principle, the cortex in front of the central sulcus is primarily devoted to action, while the cortex behind the central sulcus is mainly devoted to receptive functions and perception. Phylogenetically, this anteroposterior dichotomy of functions is older and better established than the dichotomy of the two hemispheres; the former prevails throughout the nerve axis and is, of course, most distinct at its lowest level, the spinal cord.

Another relevant concept is that of a certain symmetry in the neural processing taking place on the two sides of the central sulcus. In postcentral cortex there are, as we now know, hierarchies of ascending processing steps from the primary sensory areas toward the higher polysensory associative areas. Within each sensory sector there is apparently a progression of analysis from primary sensory to polysensory cortex through a series of interconnected cortical areas. Through those ascending hierarchies of cortical areas, the analysis of sensory information develops progressively, from the concrete aspects of sensation to the more general aspects of perception (editor's note: But see Brown, 1983, and this volume, Chapter 14). Conversely, in anterior (precentral) cortex, the pattern of neural processing seems to progress in the opposite direction: from the general to the concrete, that is, from the general scheme of the action to the concrete

ISBN 0-936925-00-0

aspects of behavior ["the microgenesis of action" (Brown, 1977)]. The organization of action would successively involve the prefrontal cortex, the premotor cortex, including the supplementary motor area, and the primary motor cortex; subcortical connective loops, involving such structures as the basal ganglia, the thalamus, and the cerebellum, would intervene at every step along the way.

THE INTEGRATIVE FUNCTION OF PREFRONTAL CORTEX

Consequently, there is a degree of symmetry in the hierarchical cortical processes of sensory analysis and organization of behavior. The descending hierarchy of motor processing appears to be in some respects the mirror image of the ascending hierarchy of sensory processing. Of course, the two cortices—anterior and posterior—do not work in isolation from one another. On the contrary, they most probably work in close cooperation, especially in the sensorimotor integration of complex behavior. The anatomy alone suggests such cooperation, for we know, from investigations of the past few decades, that there is profuse connectivity between the two general sectors of primate cortex separated by the central sulcus, most clearly between the associative areas of postcentral and those of precentral cortex. From the functional point of view, the reciprocal connections between posterior and anterior associative cortex constitute, most likely, the substrate for the cybernetic "perception-action cycle" (Arbib, 1985; Neisser, 1976), the *Gestaltkreis* of Von Weizsäcker, (Weizsäcker, 1950).

Because of its abundant connections with posterior association areas, the prefrontal cortex—that is, the associative cortex of the frontal lobes—cooperates closely with sensory cortex. To a large extent, its integrative functions are probably determined by a variety of impulses from sensory areas (as well as from subcortical structures). If that is the case, it seems implausible to consider the prefrontal cortex as the sole initiator of action. Attributing to it—or to any part of the brain—such independence almost invariably leads to an infinite regress, much as the argument about free will and the origin of willed action.

However, since there are profuse outputs flowing down from the prefrontal cortex toward motor systems (Fuster, 1981), it is reasonable to presume that the prefrontal cortex plays an important role in the organization and control of action. That role is not yet clear; judging from the connectivity alone, it seems to be a highly complex role.

Evidence from Lesion Studies

The evidence from lesion studies in humans and monkeys appears to rule out a unitary role for the prefrontal cortex. That evidence points to the heterogeneity of functions within the prefrontal cortical region. For example, lesions in dorsolateral portions of that region are known to produce different behavioral effects than lesions in orbitofrontal portions. At least three cognitive functions have been ascribed, for good reasons, to various parts of the prefrontal cortex: short-term memory, anticipatory preparation for action, and inhibition or control of interference. On close examination, however, it becomes apparent that these seemingly diverse and heterogeneous functions subserve a supraordinate function that is essential for the organization of goal-directed behavior in the time domain. More specifically, I have characterized that function as the mediation of cross-temporal contingencies (Fuster, 1985), in other words, the structuring of behavioral actions on the basis of temporally separate but mutually contingent items of information. Obviously, such a function is supramodal and pertains to all sensory modalities, interoceptive as well as exteroceptive, whether it is spatially defined or not. Thus, the principle of the functional heterogeneity of the prefrontal cortex is not only upheld by lesion data, but is compatible with the supraordinate function that I have postulated. Below, I provide a brief review of the evidence indicating that the neurons of the prefrontal cortex participate in that supraordinate function of temporal integration or its subordinate functions; as noted above, among these functions we have to consider a temporally retrospective one of short-term memory, a temporally prospective one of preparatory set, and a third one of interference control. All are suggested by lesion data.

Evidence from Neuroelectrical Studies

The first neuroelectrical evidence for a temporally integrative function of the prefrontal cortex was provided by Walter and his colleagues in the early 1960s, when they described what they called the "contingent negative variation" (CNV). This is a slow surface negative potential that appears in frontal regions of human subjects immediately after a stimulus that has been associated by conditioning with the need to perform a given behavioral act in the very near future (i.e., one or a few seconds later). Because of that particular set of conditions, the potential has also been called the "expectancy wave." From the results of investigations on animals, especially monkeys (Sasaki & Gemba, 1982), we may conclude that the CNV or "expectancy wave" is generated in the prefrontal cortex.

Delay Tasks

It is apparent that the behavioral paradigm used by Walter and his associates to demonstrate the CNV is very similar to those that have been used with monkeys and other animals, and which can be categorized under the general heading of delay tasks: delayed response, delayed alternation, and delayed matching to sample (Figure 1). All these tasks include the basic need to bridge the time between interdependent events. All incorporate the basic logic that can be expressed by statements such as, "If now this, then later that" or "If earlier that, then now this." In all of them, an action, a motor response, a choice, or a

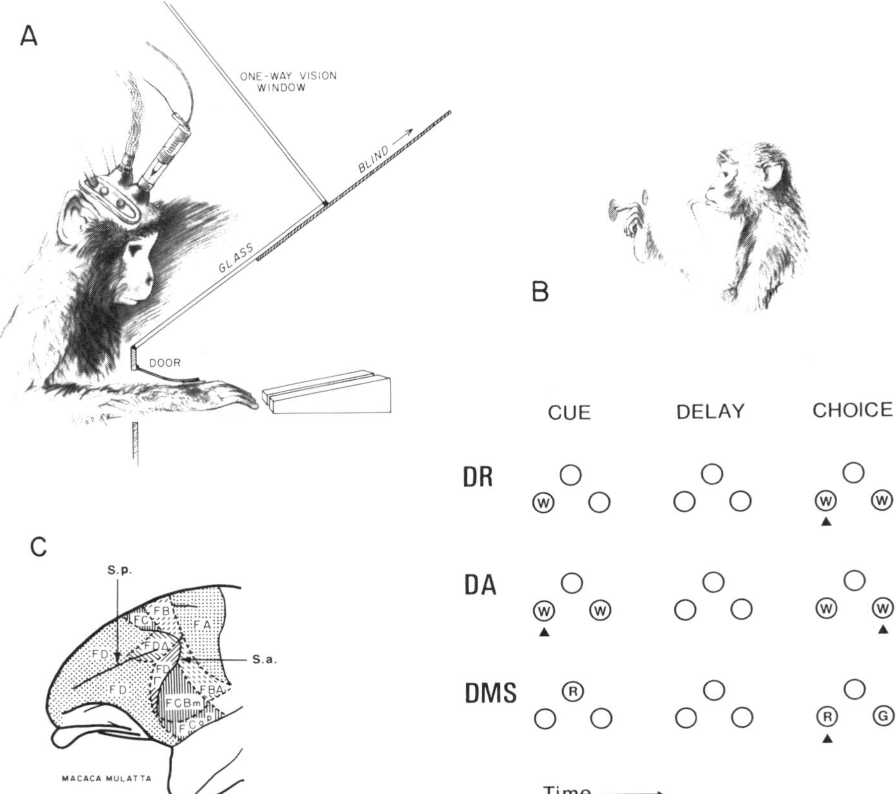

FIGURE 1 (A) Monkey performing the classic delayed-response task. A trial begins with the raising of the opaque screen ("blind"); in full view of the animal, a morsel of food is placed under one of the two blocks. The screen is then lowered for the duration of a delay period (a few seconds or minutes). Following the delay, the screen is again raised and the animal allowed to choose one object. If the monkey chooses the object concealing the food, he is allowed to retrieve the food. Incorrect choices terminate the trial without record. The position of the bait is changed at random from one trial to the next. (B) Monkey facing a panel with three stimulus–response buttons for performance of memory tasks. Below, schematic representation of the event sequence in three such tasks: delayed response (DR), delayed alternation (DA), and delayed matching to sample (DMS). In DR, the cue to remember is the brief white-light (W) illumination of one of the two lower buttons, randomly varying between right and left; after the delay, the two lower buttons are illuminated simultaneously and the animal must then press the button that had the cue. In DA, the animal must press alternately the right or left button of a pair that are simultaneously illuminated between delays: The "cue" to remember is the last response. In DMS, the cue or sample is a colored light, red (R) or green (G), presented on the top button; after the delay, the two colors appear in the lower buttons and the animal presses the one displaying the sample color. The sample color and its position in the lower buttons are changed randomly between trials; in this "nonspatial" task, color is the memorandum. The site of correct response is marked with black triangles; each correct choice is rewarded with fruit juice delivered through a spigot to the mouth of the animal. (C) Cytoarchitectonic map of the frontal cortex of the monkey, according to von Bonin and Bailey (1947). The prefrontal cortex is area FD. Abbreviations: S.p., principal sulcus; S.a., arcuate sulcus.

decision is contingent upon two items of information that are temporally separate. The trivializing of such behavioral tasks as contrived or unnatural reflects an ignorance of the universality of the essential principle that they test and manifest. That principle—that is, the principle of the temporal integration of behavior—is common to all forms of deliberate, temporally extended behavior. It applies to the formation of any behavioral structure that is deliberate, nonautomatic, and requires such operations as anticipation, short-term memory, and control of interference.

Lesions of the prefrontal cortex (cortical area FD of von Bonin & Bailey, 1947) induce marked deficits in learning and performance of delay tasks (Fuster, 1980; Jacobsen, 1935). The deficit is reversible if the lesion is reversible, as it is by use of localized cortical cooling (Bauer & Fuster, 1976; Fuster & Bauer, 1974). Spatial as well as nonspatial delay tasks (i.e., even when the cue to be retained across a delay is not spatially defined) are impaired by lesions of the dorsolateral prefrontal convexity.

The behavioral deficit from dorsolateral cortical cooling increases as a function of the length of the delay interposed between cue and response. This characteristic of the deficit suggests that the function impaired is one with a temporal decay, such as short-term or working memory.

THE CONTRIBUTION OF SINGLE-UNIT STUDIES

The above-mentioned evidence derived from slow-potential and lesion studies constituted much of the rationale for our single-unit studies of the prefrontal cortex (Fuster, 1973; Fuster & Alexander, 1971; Fuster et al., 1981; Goldberg, Fuster, & Alvarez-Pelaez, 1980; Rosenkilde, Bauer, & Fuster, 1981). Our first unit investigations of the prefrontal cortex made use of animals trained to perform the classic delayed-response task (Figure 1A). That task is similar to the one originally utilized by Jacobsen, Wolfe, and Jackson (1935) for his ablation studies. The task has certain drawbacks for neurophysiological study because it only allows limited control of sensory stimulation and motor responses; on the other hand, it lends itself to a number of interesting variations that can be used as control procedures for some of the neuropsychological functions that intervene in performance of the task.

Figure 2 illustrates the types of units that can be observed in the prefrontal cortex in the course of delayed-response performance. Some units react to the alerting signals that precede presentation of the cue; others are activated during the cue, the period of delay, or the choice; still others are activated in temporal relationship to the subsequent reward. One important finding is that substantial numbers of cells are attuned to two or more events in the task—cue, delay, choice, and reward—in practically all possible combinations. Thus, one and the same cell might react to attributes of different events that are part of the trial. The

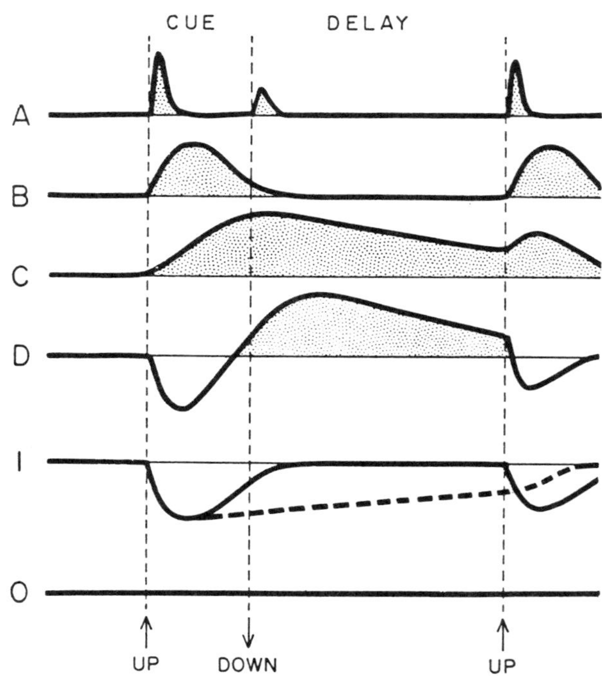

FIGURE 2 Six types of units observed in the prefrontal cortex of monkeys performing the classic delayed-response task (Figure 1A). Elevations of firing above intertrial baseline are emphasized by shading. Arrows indicate the movements of the opaque screen.

cellular reactivity to various constituents of the behavioral structure of the trial is in itself an indication of the temporal integrative functions of prefrontal neurons. Another indication is the coexistence, within narrow confines of prefrontal cortex, of cells with different reactive properties with regard to the events of the trial; in other words, cells with widely different properties may be seen in close proximity to each other, although there is a certain tendency for cells of the same type to cluster (Figure 3).

Cellular Activation during Delay

One of the most remarkable observations of single-unit studies is that there are cells which show sustained activation during the delay period (Figure 2, Types C and D). Such cells seem to bridge the temporal gap between the events preceding and succeeding the delay. To some degree, that activation can be shortened or lengthened by experimentally changing the duration of that short-term retention period—in our experiments usually between 0 and 30 sec. During that period, some cells undergo inhibition instead of activation. Generally speak-

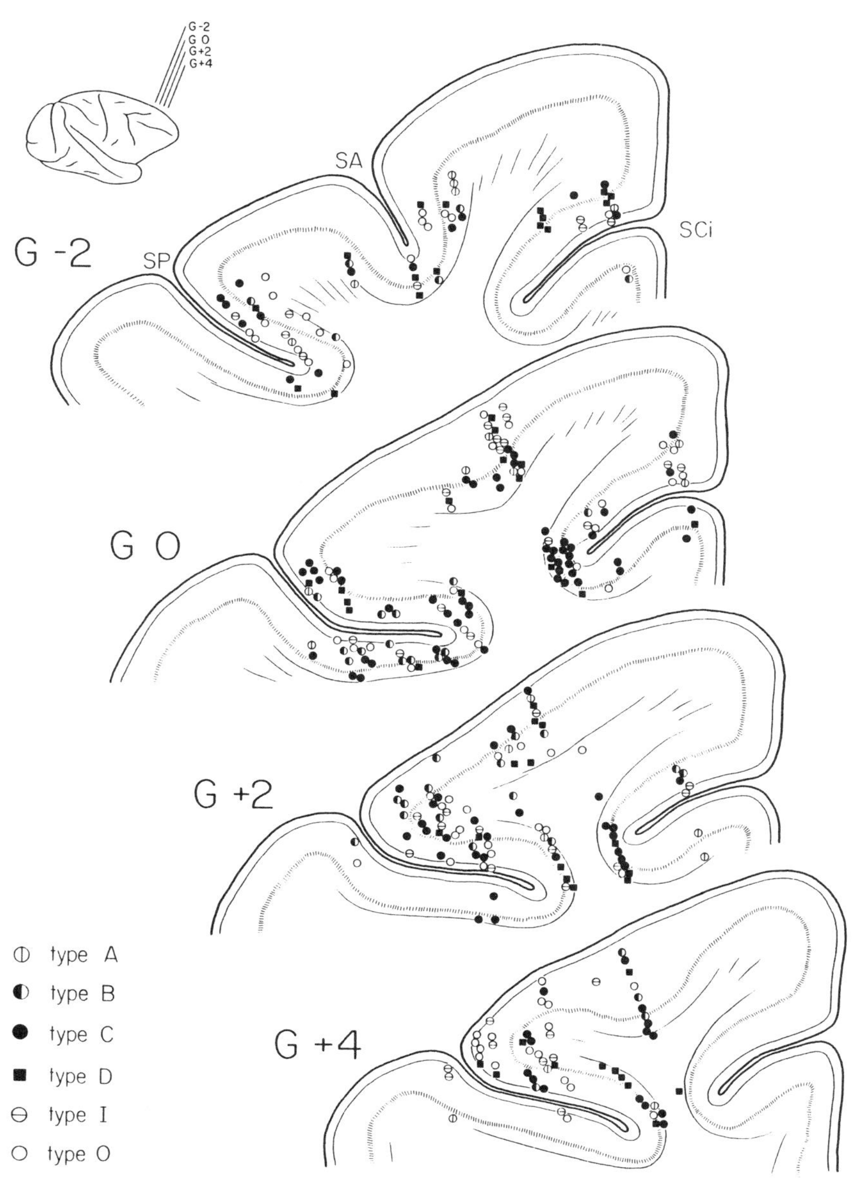

FIGURE 3 Distribution of units of the six different types (Figure 2) in four sections of the monkey's prefrontal cortex. Abbreviations: SP, principal sulcus; SA, arcuate sulcus; SCi, cingulate sulcus.

ing, cells that manifest altered delay discharge, whether it be activation or inhibition, are more common in dorsolateral than in orbital or medial prefrontal cortex (Figure 4).

Cellular activation during the delay is conditional: It depends on the presence of an item of information to be retained in short-term memory or on the requirement to perform a decision or motor choice in the near future. Another property of delay activation is its relationship to the correctness of that motor choice. Still another is its susceptibility to distraction: When the animal's attention is attracted by significant stimuli that are unrelated to the task, delay activation may be attenuated or aborted.

These properties of the delay activation of prefrontal cells cannot be readily tested or observed in every cell. It appears, however, that delay activation is strictly dependent on the conditioned link that, as a result of previous training,

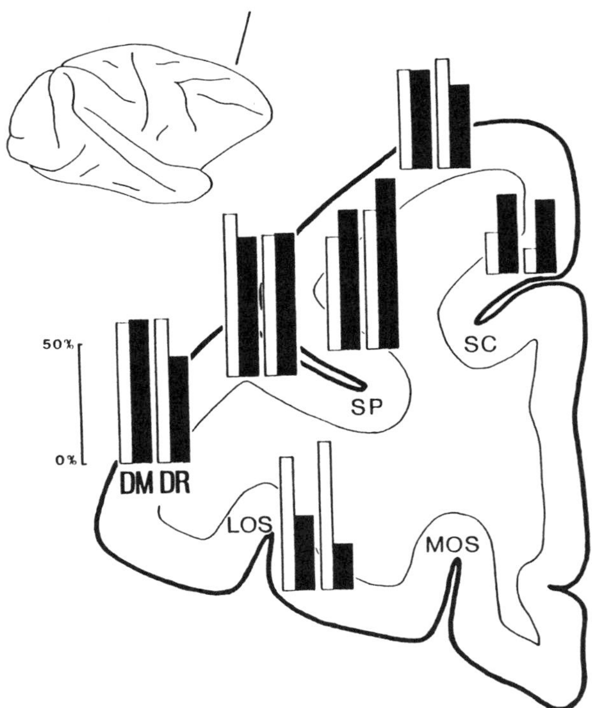

FIGURE 4 Section of one hemisphere indicating the proportions of units that showed changes related to sample/cue presentation (white bars) or delay/activity changes (black bars) during delayed matching (DM) and delayed response (DR). SC, cingulate sulcus; SP, principal sulcus; LOS, lateral orbital sulcus; MOS, medial orbital sulcus. Note the greater incidence of units exhibiting altered delay/activity in the region of the principal sulcus.

has been established between the events that are temporally separated by the delay (Fuster, 1973).

Cellular delay activation of the prefrontal cortex is present not only in performance of spatial delay tasks, such as delayed response and delayed alternation, but in that of nonspatial tasks, that is, those tasks, such as delayed matching to sample (Figure 1B), in which the cue (usually a colored light) cannot be defined by spatial properties alone. In delayed matching one can observe the same general types of cell discharge as in delayed response (Fuster, Bauer, & Jervey, 1982). By using color as the sample (cue), it becomes possible to ascertain that some prefrontal units are differentially activated during the delay depending on sample color, thus indicating that they are engaged in short-term retention of sensory information. In either task, delayed matching or delayed response, some cells show decreasing activation during the delay, while others show increasing activation (Fuster et al., 1982). It appears that the former are related to short-term memory, while the latter are related to preparatory set for motor response. Both kinds of cells have been found intermingled along microelectrode tracts (Figure 5). The existence of two general types of neurons in the prefrontal cortex, that is, some apparently "looking back" to the cue and some "looking forward" to the response, is further demonstrated by the presence of units that are differentially attuned to the position or color of the cue (Fuster et al., 1982; Niki, 1974; Niki & Watanabe, 1976; Rosenkilde et al., 1981) and units that, instead, are attuned to the direction of the response (Batuev, Orlov, & Pirogov, 1981; Fuster et al., 1982; Kojima & Goldman-Rakic, 1984; Kubota & Funahashi, 1982; Kubota, Tonoike, & Mikami, Niki, 1974; Niki & Watanabe, 1976; Rosenkilde et al., 1981; Sakai, 1974).

Cells related to sensory cues and cells related to motor responses are widely distributed throughout the dorsolateral prefrontal cortex, including the banks of the sulcus principalis (Fuster, 1973; Fuster et al., 1982; Niki, 1974; Niki & Watanabe, 1976). However, those units that are related to the reward appear to be more common in orbital prefrontal cortex (Fuster et al., 1982; Rosenkilde et al., 1981). This finding is in accord with the evidence that the latter cortical region is profusely connected to limbic structures and thus presumably related to the motivational substrate.

In general terms, the prevalence of delay-activated units in the dorsolateral aspects of the prefrontal cortex is in agreement with the evidence that, in primates and humans, the cortex of the convexity of the frontal lobes is critically involved in the cognitive functions of short-term memory and preparatory set (Barbizet, 1970; Bauer & Fuster, 1976; Fuster, 1980; Luria, 1966; Milner & Petrides, 1984; Milner, Petrides, & Smith, 1985; Teuber, 1966). Both of these cognitive functions, one temporally retrospective and the other temporally prospective, are essentially for the integration of behavior in the time domain (Fuster, 1985).

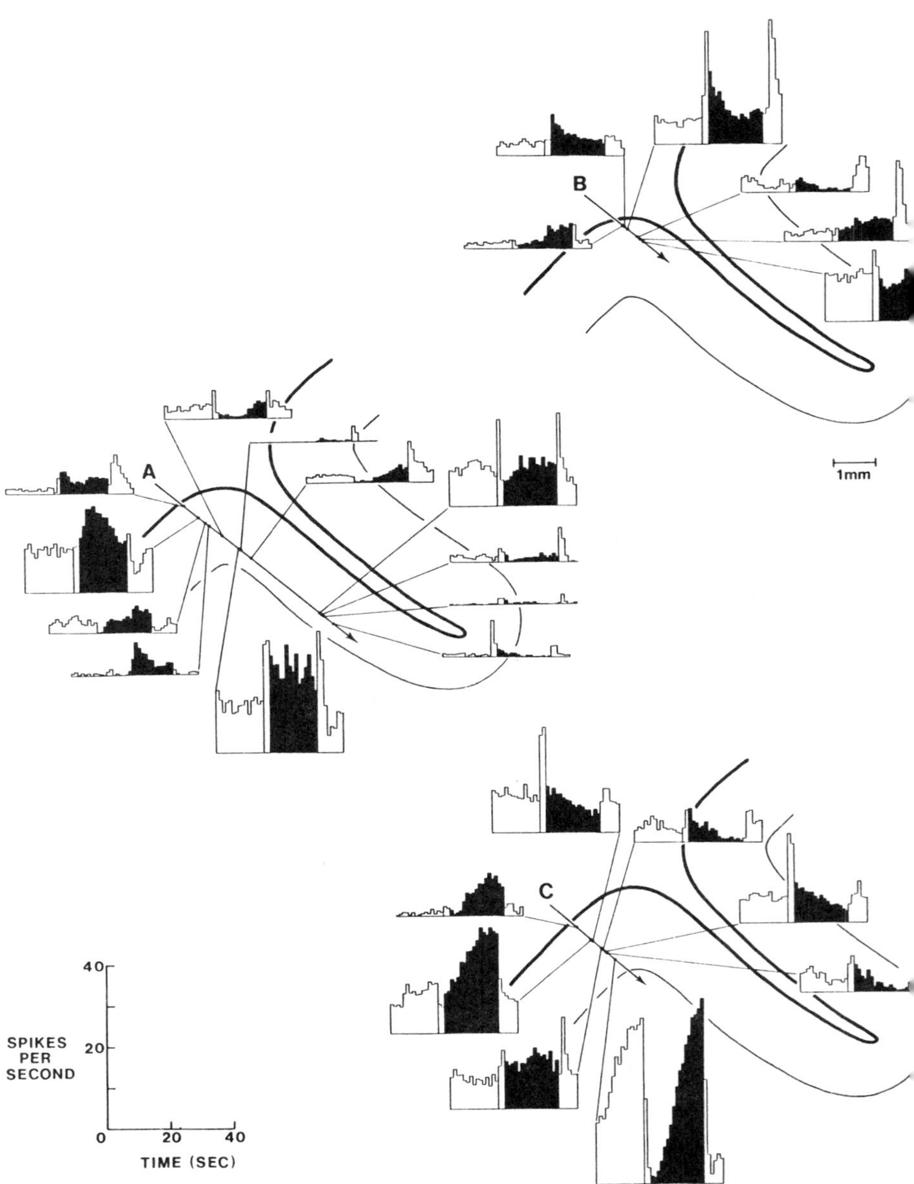

FIGURE 5 Average firing histograms of units in the lower bank of the principal sulcus during delayed-matching performance. Three microelectrode penetrations are indicated by arrows (A, B, C) and the position of each unit by a line leading from its histogram to the penetration tract. In each histogram, the activity during the delay is in black; to the left of it, pretrial and sample-period activity, and, to the right, choice-period and posttrial activity.

In conclusion, the evidence from single-unit studies for a temporally integrative function of the prefrontal cortex can be summarized as follows:

1. There is close coexistence within prefrontal cortex of units of different types, each type characterized by activation related to a given event within the temporally extended structure of the trial in a delay task.

2. Units related to multiple events in the delay-task trial are present in prefrontal cortex.

3. There is evidence showing sustained activation of prefrontal units bridging the delay between events of the trial or, more specifically, between sensory cue and the subsequent (and consequent) behavioral response to it. That sustained activation may be related either to the cue or to the response; therefore, it appears to reflect neuronal participation in the processes of short-term memory and preparatory set. Both are important for the cross-temporal mediation of behavioral contingencies. Judging from the prevalence of delay-activated units in dorsolateral prefrontal cortex, those cognitive functions appear to be mainly supported by that part of the cortex, as animal-lesion and clinical studies suggest.

REFERENCES

Arbib, M. A. (1985). Schemas for the temporal organization of behaviour. *Human Neurobiology, 4,* 63–72.

Barbizet, J. (1970). *Human memory and its pathology.* San Francisco, CA: Freeman.

Batuev, A. S., Orlov, A. A., & Pirogov, A. A. (1981). Short-term spatiotemporal memory and cortical unit reactions in the monkey. *Acta Physiologica Hungarica, 58,* 207–216.

Bauer, R. H., & Fuster, J. M. (1976). Delayed-matching and delayed-response deficit from cooling dorsolateral prefrontal cortex in monkeys. *Journal of Comparative and Physiological Psychology, 90,* 263–302.

Betz, V. (1874). Anatomischer Nachweis zweier Gehirncentra. *Centralblatt für die medizinische Wissenschaften, 12,* 578–580, 595–599.

von Bonin, G., & Bailey, P. (1947). *The Neocortex of Macaca mulatta.* Urbana: University of Illinois Press.

Brown, J. (1977). *Mind, brain, and consciousness.* New York: Academic Press.

Brown, J. W. (1983). The microstructure of perception: Physiology and patterns of breakdown. *Cognition and Brain Theory, 6,* 145–184.

Fuster, J. M. (1973). Unit activity in prefrontal cortex during delayed-response performance: Neuronal correlates of transient memory. *Journal of Neurophysiology, 36,* 61–78.

Fuster, J. M. (1980). *The prefrontal cortex.* New York: Raven Press.

Fuster, J. M. (1981). Prefrontal cortex in motor control. In V. B. Brooks (Ed.), *Handbook of physiology: Nervous system* (Vol. II: Motor Control, pp. 1149–1178). Bethesda: American Physiological Society.

Fuster, J. M. (1985). The prefrontal cortex, mediator of cross-temporal contingencies. *Human Neurobiology, 4,* 169–179.

Fuster, J. M., & Alexander, G. E. (1971). Neuron activity related to short-term memory. *Science, 173,* 652–654.

Fuster, J. M., & Bauer, R. H. (1974). Visual short-term memory deficit from hypothermia of frontal cortex. *Brain Research, 81,* 393–400.

Fuster, J. M., Bauer, R. H., & Jervey, J. P. (1981). Effects of cooling inferotemporal cortex on performance of visual memory tasks. *Experimental Neurology, 71,* 398–409.

Fuster, J. M., Bauer, R. H., & Jervey, J. P. (1982). Cellular discharge in the dorsolateral prefrontal cortex of the monkey in cognitive tasks. *Experimental Neurology, 77,* 679–694.

Goldberg, R. B., Fuster, J. M., & Alvarez-Pelaez, R. (1980). Frontal cell activity during delayed response performance in squirrel monkey (*Saimiri sciureus*). *Physiology and Behavior, 25,* 425–432.

Jacobsen, C. F. (1935). Functions of the frontal association area in primates. *Archives of Neurology and Psychiatry, 33,* 558–569.

Jacobsen, C. F., Wolfe, J. B., & Jackson, T. A. (1935). An experimental analysis of the functions of the frontal association areas in primates. *Journal of Nervous and Mental Disease, 82,* 1–14.

Kojima, S., & Goldman-Rakic, P. S. (1984). Functional analysis of spatially discriminative neurons in prefrontal cortex of rhesus monkeys. *Brain Research, 291,* 229–240.

Kubota, K., & Funahashi, S. (1982). Direction-specific activities of dorsolateral prefrontal and motor cortex pyramidal tract neurons during visual tracking. *Journal of Neurophysiology, 47,* 362–376.

Kubota, K., Tonoike, M., & Mikami, A. (1980). Neuronal activity in the monkey dorsolateral prefrontal cortex during a discrimination task with delay. *Brain Research, 183,* 29–42.

Luria, A. R. (1966). *Higher cortical functions in man.* London: Tavistock Publications.

Milner, B., & Petrides, M. (1984). Behavioural effects of frontal-lobe lesions in man. *Trends in Neurosciences, 7,* 403–407.

Milner, B., Petrides, M., & Smith, M. L. (1985). Frontal lobes and the temporal organization of memory. *Human Neurobiology, 4,* 137–142.

Neisser, U. (1976). *Cognition and reality: Principles and implications of cognitive psychology.* San Francisco, CA: Freeman.

Niki, H. (1974). Differential activity of prefrontal units during right and left delayed response trials. *Brain Research, 70,* 346–349.

Niki, H., & Watanabe, M. (1976). Prefrontal unit activity and delayed response: Relation to cue location versus direction of response. *Brain Research, 105,* 79–88.

Rosenkilde, C. E., Bauer, R. H., & Fuster, J. M. (1981). Single cell activity in ventral prefrontal cortex of behaving monkeys. *Brain Research, 209,* 375–394.

Sakai, M. (1974). Prefrontal unit activity during visually guided lever pressing reaction in the monkey. *Brain Research, 81,* 297–309.

Sasaki, K., & Gemba, H. (1982). Development and change of cortical field potentials during learning processes of visually initiated hand movements in the monkey. *Experimental Brain Research, 48,* 429–437.

Teuber, H. L. (1966). The frontal lobes and their functions: Further observations on rodents, carnivores, subhuman primates, and man. *International Journal of Neurology, 5,* 282–300.

Walter, W., Cooper, R., Aldridge, V., et al. (1964). Contingent negative variation: An electric sign of sensorimotor association and expectancy in the human brain. *Nature (London), 203,* 380–384.

von Weizsäcker, F. (1950). *Der Gestaltkreis.* Stuttgart: Thieme.

7

The Midline Frontolimbic Cortex and the Evolution of Crying and Laughter

Paul D. MacLean

What cerebral structures have subserved the evolution of crying and laughter? Why do crying and laughter so often occur in alternation as though interrelated by reciprocal innervation? Why are human beings the only creatures known to shed tears with crying? Why is it that we so often experience misting of the eyes upon witnessing an altruistic act? These are questions that direct attention to the midline frontolimbic cortex and the adjoining frontal neocortex. First, I will consider in an historical context our current research on the role of the frontolimbic cortex in crying; then I will turn to the clinical literature for evidence that there may exist in the thalamocingulate division of the limbic system a reciprocal innervation of crying and laughter.

EVOLUTIONARY BACKGROUND

Three outwardly expressed forms of behavior that characterize the evolutionary dividing line between reptiles and mammals are (1) nursing, in conjunction with maternal care; (2) audiovocal communication for maintaining maternal-offspring contact; and (3) playful behavior (for review, see MacLean, 1985a). The separation cry perhaps ranks as the earliest and most basic mammalian vocalization, serving originally to maintain maternal-offspring contact and then, later on, contact of members of an affiliated group. Contrary to, but not excluding, other interpretations I have suggested that play may have functioned originally to promote harmony in the nest and then, later on, affiliation of members of a group. It is commonly assumed that all terrestrial vertebrates vocalize. But as will be considered in a moment, it is possible that the antecedents of mammals may have been incapable of vocalization, and that, indeed, vocalization might have been prejudicial to the survival of the young.

ISBN 0-936925-00-0

Antecedents of Mammals

Paleontologists trace the ancestry of mammals back to the mammal-like reptiles—the therapsids—that, long before the dinosaurs, widely populated the world when it was but one great land mass, now known to us by Wegener's term, Pangaea (for review, see Hotton, MacLean, Roth, & Roth, 1986). There were two main types, carnivores and herbivores. The advanced carnivores that are the presumed antecedents of mammals resembled dogs and wolves (for review, see MacLean, 1986c). The jaws and teeth were acquiring mammalian characteristics. With respect to the question of hearing and vocalization, it is to be emphasized that, in several lines of therapsids, two small bones of the jaw joint—the articular and quadrate—were becoming smaller, but had not yet migrated to become the malleus and incus (the hammer and anvil) of the highly tuned mammalian ear. Hence, there is evidence that the therapsids were hard of hearing and were possibly mute like most existing lizards. It is appealing here to refer to lizards because one of the primitive mammal-like reptiles was so lizardlike in appearance as to be called *Varanosaurus,* after the monitor lizard, of which the giant varanus lizard—better known as the Komodo dragon—is perhaps the best prototype.

For many species of lizards, it would be disastrous for the hatchlings to let out a separation cry and attract the attention of their parents or other adult lizards, because they might be searched out and eaten. The young of the Komodo dragons, for example, must escape to the trees for the first year of life in order to avoid being cannibalized, while the hatchlings of the rainbow lizards must spend their first few months hiding in the deep underbrush. The first true mammals are distinguished from reptiles by the absence of the articular and quadrate bones and their presence, instead, as the malleus and incus of the middle ear (see Hotten et al., 1986). If, as now thought, the first true mammals were nocturnal and avoided predation by living within the dark floor of the forest, it is evident that the acquisition of audiovocal communication would have been a great adjunct to olfaction and vision for maintaining maternal-offspring contact. On the basis of accumulating data, it appears that separation cries (otherwise referred to as isolation or distress calls) are typical of most, if not all, infant mammals.

PHYLOGENESIS OF FOREBRAIN AND BASIC BEHAVIOR

The forebrain of advanced mammals has evolved as a triune structure comprising three neural assemblies that, anatomically and chemically, reflect an ancestral relationship to reptiles, early mammals, and late mammals (MacLean, 1970, 1975).

The counterpart of the protoreptilian forebrain consists of structures commonly referred to as the basal ganglia, including the olfactostriatum and corpus striatum. This entire constellation of structures may be referred to as the striatal complex, or, comparatively speaking, as the R-complex (MacLean, 1975). Contrary to the traditional view that the striatal complex is primarily part of the motor apparatus, recent research is beginning to show that it has a mind of its own and plays an important role in orchestrating the daily *master* routine and *subroutines,* as well as being essential for the evocation and performance of displays used in animal communication (MacLean, 1978, 1985a). The question of its adjunctive role in laughing and crying will be dealt with later.

The reptilian brain has only a rudimentary cortex. In animals representative of early mammals, there is a great expansion of the so-called archicortex and mesocortex that form a large convolution surrounding the brainstem. Broca (1878) called this convolution the great limbic lobe because it forms a border around the brainstem. Together with its connections with the brainstem, it comprises the so-called limbic system (MacLean, 1952). The part of the forebrain identified with late mammals may be defined as the neocortex and structures of the brainstem with which it is primarily connected. Parenthetically, some anatomists regard the subcortical ganglionic structures in the dorsal ventricular ridge of reptiles and birds as neocortex.

Thalamocingulate Division of the Limbic System

It is the thalamocingulate division of the limbic system that has become of special interest with respect to crying and laughter—crying in connection with separation, and laughter as the presumed evolutionary development in association with the cingulate's role in play. On the basis of anatomy and function, the limbic system can be subdivided into three main corticosubcortical subdivisions, indicated in Figure 1 by the small repeated numerals 1, 2, and 3 (MacLean, 1973). The cortical areas of the two evolutionarily older subdivisions are primarily dependent on telencephalic nuclei located, respectively, in the amygdala and septum and closely associated with the olfactory apparatus. The amygdala division has been shown to be involved in self-preservation as it pertains to feeding, the search for food, and the fighting, attack, and defense that may be required in obtaining food (MacLean, 1973, 1975). The septal division has been found to be implicated in primal sexual functions and in behavior conducive to mating and procreation.

The thalamocingulate division is called such because the afferent supply to the mesocortical areas of the cingulate gyrus derives from the thalamus. New findings on its connections will be described later. Significantly, there is no counterpart of this subdivision in the reptilian brain (Clark & Meyer, 1950). Although it had been known for many years that the rostral part of the cingulate gyrus plays a role in autonomic and somatovisceral functions, it seems likely that cingulate involvement in family-related behavior would not have been evident had it not been specifically looked for.

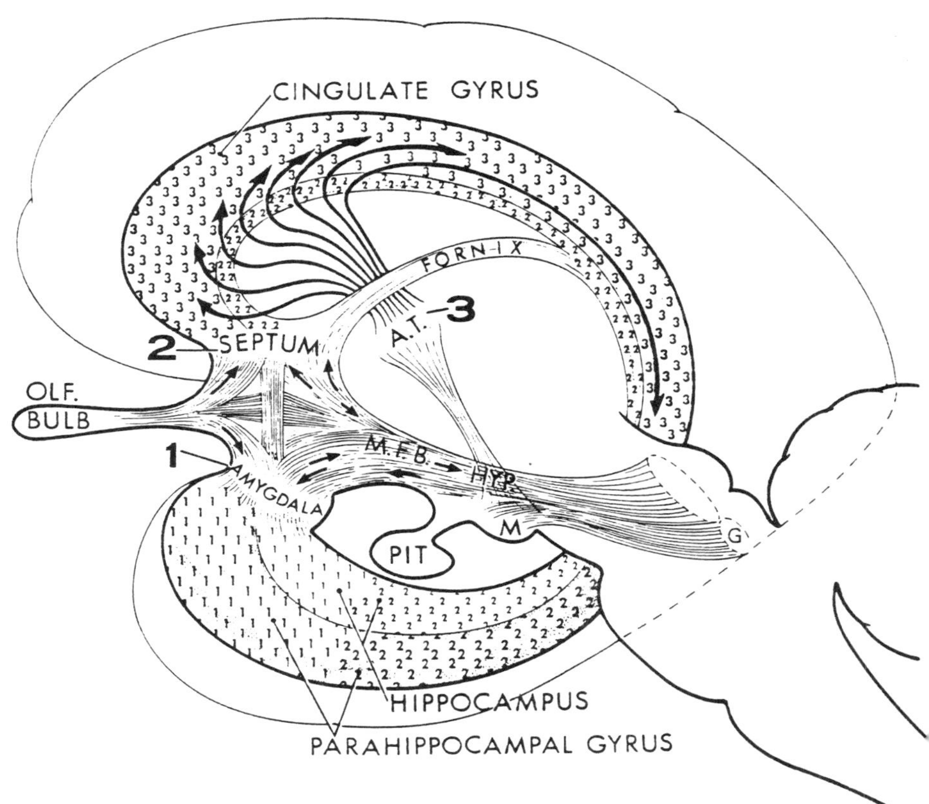

FIGURE 1 The three main corticosubcortical subdivisions of the limbic system based on assorted anatomical, electrophysiological, and behavioral findings. The small numerals 1 and 2 overlie cortical areas with a close functional relationship to telencephalic nuclei in the amygdala (1) and septum (2). Note the close relationship to the olfactory apparatus. The third subdivision is largely represented by the mesocortex (small numeral 3s) of the cingulate gyrus and its connections with several thalamic (3) nuclei (see text). It is therefore referred to as the thalamocingulate division. See text regarding significance that this subdivision appears to have no counterpart in the protoreptilian brain. Abbreviations: AT, anterior and other related thalamic nuclei (see text); G. tegmental nuclei of Gudden; HYP, hypothalamus; M, mammillary bodies; MFB, medial forebrain bundle; PIT, pituitary; OLF, olfactory. (After MacLean, 1973.)

Interested in the possible role of the limbic system in "instinctive" behavior, John Stamm undertook experimentation on the cingulate cortex and reported some quite momentous findings that, curiously, appeared to attract little attention, possibly because maternal behavior is such an expected, everyday thing. In brief, Stamm (1955) found that in adult female rats ablations of the cingulate cortex, but not of the adjacent neocortex, resulted in marked deficits in maternal behavior, including deficits in nest building, nursing, and retrieval of the young. Only 12% of the pups survived. Burton Slotnick (1967) confirmed and extended these findings.

We ourselves obtained corroborative evidence in a different kind of experiment in which we observed the behavioral development of hamsters in which a surgical ablation at the time of birth prevented the neocortex from developing (Murphy, MacLean, & Hamilton, 1981). These animals with cerebral retention of only the striatal complex and limbic system grew normally, followed their daily routines, and engaged in all hamster-typical forms of behavior. They mated, bred, and successfully reared their young. They developed play behavior at the appropriate time. If, however, in addition to the neocortex, a large part of the cingulate convolution was destroyed, there were notable deficits in maternal behavior, including the deficits in nest building, nursing, and pup retrieval described by Stamm and by Slotnick.

In addition, it was of special interest that hamsters with such lesions failed to engage in play with the control littermates. I was particularly struck by this deficit, because in observations on lizards and other reptiles, I had never observed anything resembling play. In view of the alteration of both maternal behavior and play in these animals, it was as though they had regressed toward the reptilian condition.

THE SEPARATION CRY

Given this background, we consider next the third component of the family-related behavioral triad, namely, audiovocal communication for maintaining maternal-offspring contact. All mammals that have been examined thus far have been found to produce separation cries. Possibly serving as a protection against predators such as owls, the separation cries of several small rodents are in the ultrasonic range. As illustrated by the spectrograms of the squirrel monkey, macaque, and human infant (Figure 2), the separation calls of primates are characterized by a slowly changing tone. This commonality, Newman (1985a) points out, suggests that the mechanisms controlling infant cry patterns have a conservative evolutionary history.

Findings in Squirrel Monkeys

For investigating the cerebral representation of the separation cry, Newman and I have used squirrel monkeys. By 1 year of age, the separation cry of these New World monkeys is as reproducible as a signature and can be regularly

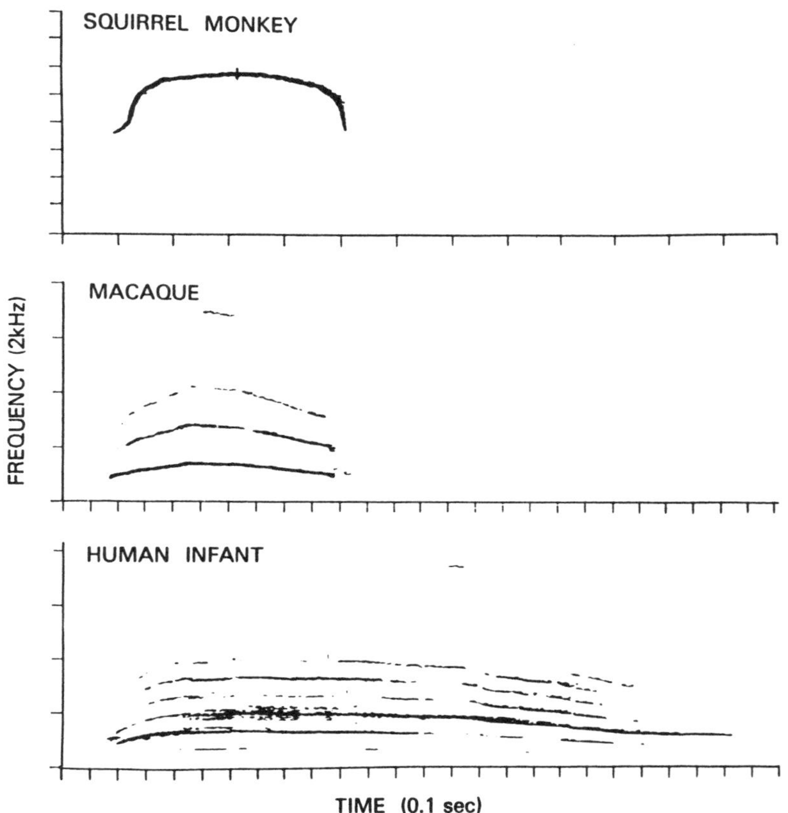

FIGURE 2 Spectrograms illustrating separation cries of a Gothic-type squirrel monkey, macaque, and human infant. In each case, the cry is characterized by a slowly changing tone. (From MacLean, 1985a, based on Newman, 1985a.)

elicited under laboratory conditions (Symmes, Newman, Talmage-Riggs, & Lieblich, 1979). The call can be reliably differentiated from more than 30 other vocalizations identified in squirrel monkeys (Winter, Ploog, & Latta, 1966).

In my comparative neurobehavioral studies on species-typical behavior, I have used two types of squirrel monkeys that are distinguished not only by their fur markings and behavior (MacLean, 1964), but also by karyotypic differences (Ma, Jones, Thorington, & Cooper, 1974). The monkey represented on the left in Figure 3 is called the Gothic type because the ocular patch comes to a peak over the eye like a Gothic arch, whereas the other type is referred to as Roman because the patch is round like a Roman arch. As shown in Figure 4, these monkeys can be just as readily distinguished by their separation cries, which respectively have a downward and upward deflection at the termination of the cry. There is evidence that these differences are inherited (Newman, 1985b). In studies on the cerebral representation of the separation cry, Newman and I test adult squirrel monkeys for their ability to produce such calls before and after ablation of different parts of the brain. Criterion performance is the production of 20 or more separation cries during a 15-minute period of isolation in a sound-reducing chamber (Newman & MacLean, 1982).

In the first series of experiments on the brainstem, we found that damage to

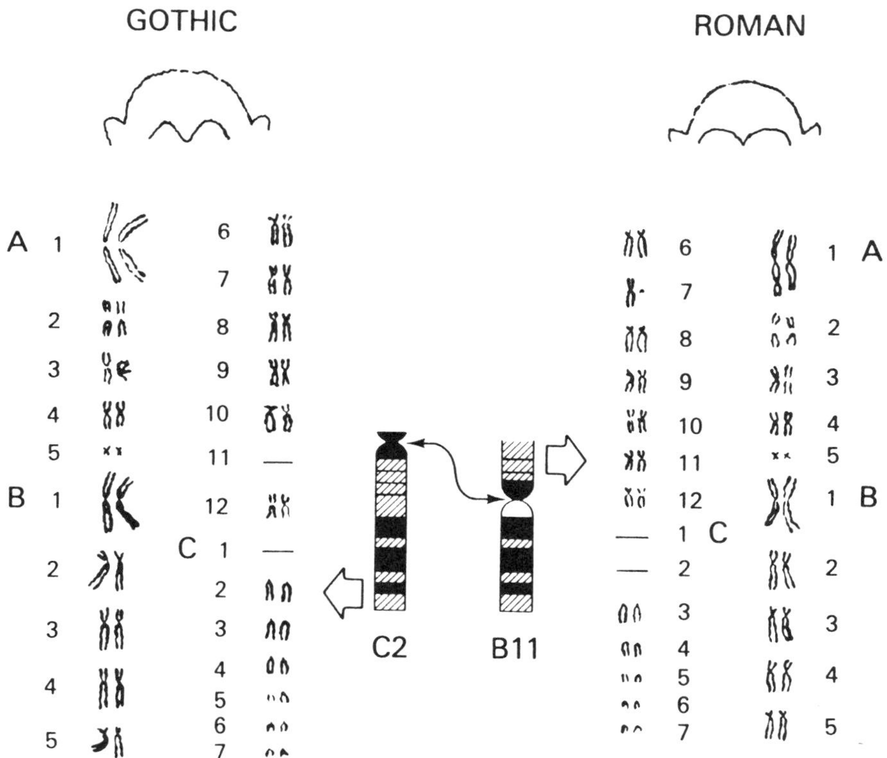

FIGURE 3 Karyotypical differences of Gothic- and Roman-type squirrel monkeys used in present studies. The 44 chromosomes of the squirrel monkey are classified into three groups (A, B, and C) on the basis of the length and position of the centromeres. Note in center enlargement the pericentric inversion postulated by Ma, Jones, Thorrington, and Cooper (1974). As indicated by the diagrams of the upper face, the two types of monkeys are physically distinguished by either a peak-shaped (Gothic) or round-shaped (Roman) arch formed by the ocular patch above the eye. Behaviorally, the two types have distinctive displays and other differentiating characteristics (MacLean, 1964). As shown in Figure 4, the two types can also be readily distinguished by the sound spectrograms of their separation cries. (From MacLean, 1985a.)

FIGURE 4 Distinctive sound spectrograms of the separation cries of the Gothic- (left) and Roman-type (right) squirrel monkeys (see Figure 3). Note the contrasting downward and upward deflections during termination of the cries. (From MacLean, 1985a.)

the core of the brainstem at the thalamo-midbrain junction affected the structure and/or the production of the separation cry (Newman & MacLean, 1982).

What structures of the telencephalon might influence the production of this vocalization? Since the initial findings of Smith in 1945, the observations by Kaada (1951) and others (e.g., Dua & MacLean, 1964; Jürgens & Ploog, 1970, Robinson, 1967) indicate that the anterior cingulate cortex is the main cortical area for eliciting vocalization in the monkey. It deserves emphasis that stimulation of the neocortex anywhere is ineffective in eliciting vocalization in the monkey.

Accordingly, in further studies on the cerebral representation of the separation call, Newman and I have centered our attention on the medial aspect of the frontal lobe. Thus far, we have conducted experiments on 12 squirrel monkeys (Newman & MacLean, 1985). The findings in three monkeys provided information about the function of gross subdivisions of the frontal lobe in the separation cry. Bilateral prefrontal lobectomy rostral to the cingulate gyrus did not significantly affect the cry during a 3-month period of testing. On the contrary, bifrontal lobectomy, or bilateral lobotomy, rostral to the knee of the corpus callosum, resulted in an immediate and enduring failure in the production of spontaneous separation cries. Other forms of vocalization continued to be expressed.

Likewise, extensive ablations confined to the medial surface of the frontal lobe resulted in a failure to produce spontaneous separation calls. In one subject, aspiration of the paragenual and subcallosal cingulate cortex (Area 24 rostral to Area 6 plus Area 25 of Figure 5), together with the greater part of the medial frontal neocortex (Area 9, Figure 5), eliminated the spontaneous production of the separation cry throughout 8 months of testing. Other vocalizations, including yaps, cackles, errs, and shrieks, were still manifest. The same outcome was subsequently obtained in another monkey in which there was aspiration of the corresponding limbic areas, but sparing of virtually all of the abutting neocortex of Areas 8, 9, and 10 (Figure 5). If, however, there was sparing of both the supragenual anterior cingulate cortex (below rostral Area 6 and Area 8, Figure 5) and the caudalmost subcallosal area (Area 25) and adjoining gyrus rectus (part of Area 12) there was recovery of the spontaneous production of the separation cry within a week's time. One monkey with destruction confined to the subcallosal cortex produced fewer calls, but continued to achieve criterion.

In contradistinction to the positive effects of limbic cortical ablation, it is notable that in a case involving aspiration of all of the midline frontal neocortex (rostral Area 6, Area 8, Area 9, Area 10, plus part of adjoining Area 12) there was no effect on the spontaneous production of the separation cry.

In human beings, it is known that the supplementary area just above the anterior cingulate cortex is involved in vocalization (Penfield & Jasper, 1954; Penfield & Rasmussen, 1952). We found that aspiration of corresponding cortex in the squirrel monkey (involving most of Area 6 and adjoining Area 8, Figure 5) resulted in a transitory elimination of the separation cry, with full recovery in 9 weeks.[1]

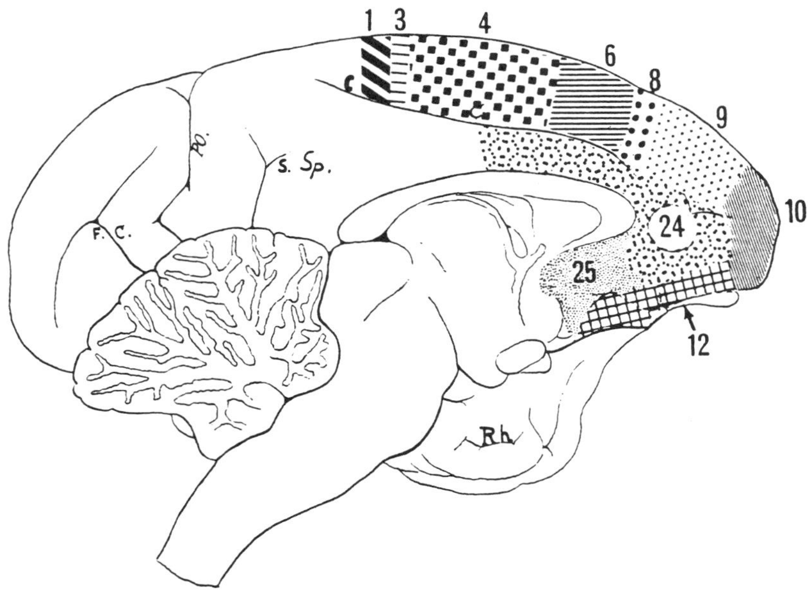

FIGURE 5 Cytoarchitectural areas of midline frontal cortex of the squirrel monkey as delineated by Rosabal. Limbic cortex is represented by Areas 24 and 25, and by the caudal part of Area 12. See text in regard to areas ablated in present study. Abbreviations for sulcate markings: C, cingulate; F. C., calcarine; P.O., parietooccipital; Rh., rhinal, S. Sp., subparietal. (From Rosabal, 1967.)

[1]Kirzinger and Jürgens (1982) reported that ablation of the anterior supplementary area in the squirrel monkey resulted in reduced vocalization primarily attributable to a decrease in production of the "isolation peep." It is our understanding that their postoperative testing did not extend beyond 4 weeks.

In summary, it appears that the spontaneous production of the separation cry depends upon the concerted action of a continuous band of limbic cortex contained in the supragenual, pregenual, and infragenual cingulate cortex together with that rostral to the septum and in the posterior part of gyrus rectus.

Thalamic Changes In macaques, it has long been recognized that cortical ablations of the medial frontal cortex fail to result in clearly discernible retrograde thalamic degeneration (e.g., Akert, 1964; Pribram, Chow, & Semmes, 1953; Walker, 1938). For example, based on an analysis of the brains of 20 macaques with various frontal cortical ablations, Pribram et al. (1953) concluded that thalamic retrograde degeneration did not occur following midline aspirations unless there was involvement of the medial polar cortex. Akert (1964) has stated that "the dorsomedial frontal granular cortex may at best receive collaterals from thalamic neurons and that it should be treated separately from the lateral and orbital cortex" that receives "heavy and essential projections from nucleus medialis dorsalis" (p. 381).

In our cases of bilateral medial lesions, including parts of the frontal neocortex, one could not be certain of retrograde changes in the thalamus. With lesions involving the frontal pole and lateral convexity, however, there was the usual evident nerve cell loss with glial infiltration in the dorsolateral quadrant of the parvocellular part of the medial dorsal nucleus extending up to the ventral margin of N. centralis superior lateralis and N. parataenialis. Subsequent to bilateral destruction of the rostral cingulate cortex it is difficult, because of the lack of an intact hemisphere for comparison, to assess the degree of thalamic degeneration. Some workers, moreover, would claim that heretofore described retrograde degeneration seen in the anterior nuclei is owing to severed fibers destined for the posterior cingulate gyrus (e.g., Vogt, Rosene, & Pandya, 1979). As I will discuss next, recent anatomical studies have helped to resolve this and other questions that arise in studying retrograde degeneration.

Medial Frontal Afferent Connections

The use of improved neuroanatomical techniques has recently thrown a whole new light on connections of the frontal cortex with the thalamus. Using autoradiographic techniques involving axoplasmic transport, Tobias (1975) appears to have been the first to show that the medial dorsal nucleus does indeed project to the dorsal medial granular cortex of the frontal lobe (see Figure 3, p. 197, of his report). Since then, studies utilizing retrograde transport of horseradish peroxidase (HRP) have demonstrated that both the medial frontal limbic cortex and the neocortex receive connections from several thalamic nuclei, including the medial dorsal nucleus (Baleydier & Mauguiere, 1980; Goldman-Rakik & Porrino, 1985; Jürgens, 1983; Vogt et al., 1979).

It is of great interest that, conforming with Leonard's (1969) observations in the rat, several of the primate studies have demonstrated a co-innervation of the anterior cingulate gyrus by N. anterior medialis and N. medialis dorsalis. In the squirrel monkey Jürgens (1983) observed labeling of numerous cells in N. anterior medialis et ventralis, N. reuniens, N. centralis densocellularis, N. centralis superior lateralis, N. parataenialis, N. parafascicularis, N. centralis lateralis, N. medialis dorsalis, N. pulvinaris medialis, and N. limitans. In an ongoing study employing wheat-germ agglutinin–horseradish peroxidase (WGA-HRP) I have observed similar labeling in the squirrel monkey and in addition have uncovered supplemental information in regard to the subcallosal cortex, which has connections with these same nuclear groups, but in somewhat different parts and different concentrations. There is, for example, heavier labeling in N. anterior medialis and N. parafascicularis.

Of special interest with respect to the expressive aspects of vocalization has been the finding that the medial frontal limbic cortex receives projections from N. ventralis anterior (VA) and N. ventralis lateralis (VL). Carmel (1970) appears to have been the first to demonstrate experimentally that VA projects widely to the cortex of the frontal lobe. In macaques, Baleydier and Mauguiere (1980) have observed labeled cells in VA subsequent to HRP injection in the anterior cingulate gyrus, and Jürgens (1983) has similarly reported such labeling in the squirrel monkey. With subcallosal application of WGA-HRP (see above), I have observed extensive labeling of the parts of magnocellular VA and of medial VL close to, and adjoining, the mammillothalamic tract.

The evidence of extensive connections of the medial frontal cortex with several of the nuclear groups that have been listed would indicate that cells of these nuclei do not undergo retrograde degeneration following frontal cortical ablations because they have sustaining collaterals. Carmel (1970) presented reasons for presuming such an explanation for the relatively small amount of retrograde degeneration seen in VA following frontal ablations. Such an explanation is particularly appealing in regard to groups of large cells that form a ring around the parvocellular sector of the medial dorsal nucleus.

A discussion of the possible significance of some of the new anatomical findings will be deferred until after the presentation of clinical findings relevant to crying and laughter.

CLINICOPATHOLOGIC FINDINGS ON CRYING AND LAUGHTER

As has been pointed out in several reviews (Davison & Kelman, 1939; Ironside, 1956; Tilney & Morrison, 1912; Wilson, 1924), pathological laughter and crying are commonly identified with pseudobulbar palsy resulting from multiple lesions of the cerebrum attributable to such conditions as cerebral arteriosclerosis and multiple sclerosis. It is emphasized that the uncontrolled episodes of laughter and/or crying are *not* in keeping with the patients' feelings and are often a great embarrassment. The part played by faciovocal mechanisms of the lower brainstem in pathological laughing and crying has been discussed by Brown (1967).

Contrary to the view that unilateral lesions are insufficient to induce pathological laughter and crying, Poeck (1969) pointed out that, of 30 cases reviewed by himself and Pilleri (1963), only one hemisphere was involved in a third of them. They noted that lesions of the anterior limb of the internal capsule was a regular finding. This observation and the frequent occurrence of lesions variously involving the corpus striatum, globus pallidus, and the associated N. ventralis anterior and N. ventral lateralis of the thalamus led them to conclude that disease of this system of structures was conducive to pathological laughing and crying. It is to be noted, however, that in over half of the cases of pseudobulbar palsy reviewed by Tilney and Morrison (1912) there was no apparent involvement of these structures. Further comment on this matter will be postponed until the Discussion.

Involvement of the Limbic System

In the rest of this section a consideration of the neuropathology relevant to crying and laughter will be limited to cases of epilepsy or of brain tumor suggesting that the symptoms may have resulted from disease of parts of the limbic system—particularly parts of the amygdalar and thalamocingulate subdivisions. Certain structures of these divisions linked by the fornix are sometimes referred to as belonging to the Papez circuit (Papez, 1937). Recent evidence indicates that it is the prosubicular and subicular parts of the hippocampal formation that project via the fornix and uncrossed tract of Gudden directly to the anterior thalamus and, via the fornix, to the medial mammillary nucleus.

The Amygdalar Division Since lacrimation may be such a prominent feature of crying and laughter, it is curious that in case reports on pathological crying and laughter the occurrence of this autonomic manifestation may not even be mentioned or, at best, may be only alluded to without details as to the duration or amount of tearing. Significantly with respect to case reports of laughing and/or crying in temporal lobe epilepsy, Pool (1954) describes that during one operative procedure entailing exposure of the hippocampus under general anesthesia "profuse lacrimation" was elicited upon stimulation of its anterior lateral extent. Penfield and Jasper (1954) cite the case of a patient with a large astrocytoma of the temporal lobe (involving the lower part of the corpus striatum) in whom tearing of the eyes occurred during a seizure. In another patient, seizures were manifest by yawning accompanied by a flow of tears.

Although feelings of depression, sorrow, or sadness are a fairly frequent experience during the aura in psychomotor epilepsy (complex, partial seizures), relatively few descriptions are given of the manifestations of crying or weeping. MacLean (1952) briefly described the case of a factory worker who experienced an epigastric aura that was associated with a feeling of sadness and wanting to cry. This feeling was followed by a welling up of tears and a sensation of hunger.

One may find crying incidentally referred to in papers featuring reports of epileptic laughter. Descriptions of this form of laughter began to appear during the last century. Since the introduction of electroencephalography, several cases have been reported in which abnormal discharges were localized either to the temporal or frontal region. Daly and Mulder (1957) introduced the expression "gelastic epilepsy" for this kind of seizure. Gelastic refers to something provoking laughter. They described two cases of ictal laughing, both with spiking or slow-wave activity localized in the left temporal region. A year later Weil, Nosik, and Demmy (1958) reported four cases in which the temporal lobe appeared to be implicated. Loiseau, Cohadon, and Cohadon (1971) described one case with a left temporal focus in which paroxysms of laughter persisted for 10 to 20 minutes.

Practically no information exists about the subjective feelings associated with laughter that might be expected during the aura. Stevens and I interviewed one patient who was able to articulate that he had a "laughing sensation" at the beginning of his seizures (MacLean, 1986b). In this respect it is of interest to note that Swash (1972) described a woman who was subject to "sustained involuntary laughter" following an infarction of the left temporal lobe. The author stated that "she was adamant that she was actually amused during the act of laughing" (p. 109).

The existence of a neural link to laughter in the limbic part of the temporal lobe has been demonstrated by Van Buren (1961), who, during a diagnostic procedure, stimulated in the region of the amygdala in a 46-year-old man and elicited on different occasions laughter as part of the automatism.

The Thalamocingulate Division A case described by Penfield and Jasper (1954) is suggestive of involvement of the thalamocingulate division in lacrimation. The patient suffered from seizures in which tearing of both eyes was a regular occurrence. At operation a small tumor, the size of a hazelnut, was found wedged in the foramina of Monro, where it exerted pressure on the anterior thalamus.

Several cases have been reported in which the mammillary bodies have been implicated in laughter and crying. Dott (1938) cites the case of a patient who had been subject to fits of laughter or screaming. At autopsy a tumor was found that involved "a limited portion of the floor of the third ventricle in the region of the mammillary bodies" (p. 107). Martin (1950) has recorded the case of a 25-year-old man who was seized by uncontrollable laughter at the graveside of his mother during her funeral. Subsequently he died of a ruptured aneurysm that was found to be compressing the mammillary bodies. List, Dowman, Bagchi, and Bebin (1958) describe two relevant cases in which a hamartoma was discretely attached to the mammillary bodies. One was that of a 15-year-old girl who was subject to attacks beginning either as laughing or crying. Microscopic examination revealed that the hamartoma was attached only to the left mammillary body and was completely free and separated from the surrounding brain. The other case was that of an 8-year-old girl who had been subject to attacks of laughter since the age of 6 months. The autopsy revealed a tumor arising from the mammillary bodies and tuber cinereum.

Finally, we consider cases in which the clinical findings either indicated or demonstrated the presence of a lesion affecting the medial frontolimbic cortex. Loiseau et al. (1971) described the case of a 20-year-old woman who had been subject to attacks in which she burst out crying or laughing. The episodes lasted for 20 to 60 seconds. One of the diagnostic procedures indicated "a left subfrontal space-occupying lesion."

Geier et al. (1977) analyzed the symptomatology of 22 patients with frontal lobe epilepsy. There were phonatory manifestations in 19 cases. The "vocalizations were brief, single, or repeated, sounding like cries, moans, or grunts" (p. 954). They give the following description of the seizure of one patient during a depth recording that revealed an epileptogenic zone on the anterior part of the cingulate gyrus and on the medial surface of the frontal pole. The patient was a 19-year-old woman who had been subject to seizures since the age of two. At the beginning of the seizure in question she "suddenly lifted herself up, turned to the left, and *moaned* for about 30 seconds." Shortly after, she said that "she had just dreamed she was playing with a friend" (p. 950). In regard to her dream of playing with a friend, it is of interest to mention an observation by Talairach et al. (1973), who report an instance when stimulation of the supracallosal cingulate elicited a playful gesture, as if the subject was giving an invitation to play.

In their review of 22 cases with frontal lobe epilepsy, Geier et al. (1977) listed two in which there were motor manifestations of laughter. Direct evidence of the involvement of the medial frontal cortex in such expression has been provided by Ludwig, Ajmone Marsan, and Van Buren (1975). They describe the case of a 13-year-old boy who was subject to seizures in which he felt himself "smile" and unable to speak. Members of his family confirmed the occurrence of a smile during his seizures and gave the additional information that the smile was followed by a "silly laugh." During a diagnostic procedure it was shown that retraction of the left side of his mouth and a smiling expression were induced upon stimulating the medial orbital area. Following such stimulation, rhythmical spike and waves were recorded by the most medial of four subdural electrodes on the orbital surface.

Loiseau et al. (1971) describe the case of a 5-year-old girl whose seizures had originally occurred at the age of 30 months by laughing "in a queer way." At operation she was found to have a cystic tumor that appeared to originate at the junction of the corpus callosum with the cingulate gyrus, and which extended rostrally to the medial cortex.

Finally, so as not to lose sight of the association between laughter and crying, reference will be made to another illustrative case. Lehtinen and Kivalo (1965) described the case of a 12-year-old girl who was subject to laughing attacks occurring as many as 20 times a day. The laughter "lasted from a few seconds to a couple of minutes," during which time she became very red in the face. Toward the end of an attack *"the laughter might change into crying"* (italics added). The electroencephalographic examination indicated a midline frontal disturbance.

The cases of ictal laughter with frontal lobe lesions that have been described recall Kramer's (1954) report of "laughing spells" in patients following bilateral, prefrontal lobotomy—laughing that was variously characterized as loud and noisy, childish laughter, laughter of the kind that neurologists associate with "witzelsucht," and incessant laughter followed by bouts of screaming.

DISCUSSION

Forebrain Mechanisms

The frontolimbic connections with N. ventralis anterior (VA) and N. ventralis lateralis (VL) that have been described recall that the striopallidum establishes connections with respective parts of these same nuclei via fibers from the medial segment of the globus pallidus (Carpenter, 1976). The rostral portion of the segment innervates the parvocellular division of VA. Fibers from the caudal part of the segment project to the oral part of VL, which in turn supplies afferents to the supplementary area (e.g., Jürgens, 1984) and other motor areas. The pars reticularis of the substantia nigra projects to the magnocellular part of VA and the medial part of VL.

When neurosurgically placed lesions were being used as a treatment for Parkinson's disease, there were reports of the effects of stimulating or destroying parts of the medial pallidum and ventral lateral thalamus. Hassler (1961) reported findings by himself and Reichert that stimulation of the pallidum or of the oral part of the ventral lateral nucleus (VL) elicited laughing with appropriate affect. Krayenbühl, Wyss, and Yasargil (1961) described a number of cases in which bilateral coagulations of VL on one side and of VL or inner pallidum on the other side resulted in compulsive crying; there was a much higher incidence of disturbances in speech, such as dysarthria or aphonic speech.

Jonas (1982) has reviewed a series of cases in which a suppression of spontaneous speech occurred after acute left thalamic lesions. Some cases were characterized as having "expressive inertia." Heppner (personal communication) recalls one case in which bilateral coagulation of VL resulted in a permanent expressive aphasia.

Penfield and Jasper (1954) found that stimulation of the anterior cingulate gyrus both interrupts speech and prevents the initiation of speech. Akinetic mutism has been reported following infarction of the anterior cingulate gyrus (see von Cramm & Jürgens, 1964, for review). Heppner (personal communication) has observed a disinclination to speech in patients with small tumors ("allocortex glioma" type) in the anterior cingulate area or following anterior cingulectomy. Jonas (1981) found that in the case reports of 21 of 32 patients with sudden injury of the supplementary motor region there was a marked suppression of speech. He noted that one patient was also mute for nonspeech sounds, weeping and laughing silently.

In summary, the new anatomical findings, together with clinical data, suggest a linkup of frontal lobe and striopallidonigral mechanisms implicated in both the mood and expression of crying and laughter.

The "Pain" of Separation

As was noted, the reptilian hatchling and newborn mammal are at opposite poles with respect to parental dependence. For mammals, any prolonged separation of the sucklings from the mother is disastrous. Because of this, nature appears to have ensured that maternal-offspring separation in mammals results in distress comparable to pain. In this regard it is particularly noteworthy that the new findings with HRP have revealed evidence of strong connections between N. parafascicularis and N. centralis lateralis and the medial frontolimbic cortex. That distress of separation continues later in life to affect socially affiliated individuals is evident by the production of separation cries by adult members of a group. In view of the pain of separation and the distressful nature of the separation cry, it is of timely interest that opiate receptors occur in high concentration in the primate cingulate cortex (Wise & Herkenham, 1982). As in the case of nonprimate mammals, experiments in our laboratory have shown that small doses of morphine sulfate suppress the separation cry of squirrel monkeys, whereas the antagonist, Naloxone, restores the cry (Newman, Murphy, & Harbaugh, 1982). In 1957, Foltz and White reported that anterior cingulate ablations alleviated the symptoms of morphine withdrawal. Such findings suggest that the thalamocingulate division may be implicated in the generation of separation feelings that are conducive to drug addiction. Hence it is possible that, "more than the fleeting effects of euphoria, those suffering from opiate addiction seek release from an ineffable feeling of isolation and alienation" (MacLean, 1986a, p. 23).

Some Evolutionary Aspects

Physiologically, both the somatic and autonomic manifestations of crying and laughter are of the kind that would rid the body of something noxious. When these manifestations occur, the affect is one of dejection with crying, and one of relief with laughing. Although chimpanzees and gorillas display elements of crying and laughter, human beings are the only creatures known to shed tears with crying (Yerkes, quoted by Collins, 1932). Human beings and their antecedents are the only creatures known to have used fire. I have suggested that, in the course of countless millennia, there may have arisen some connection between smoke and tears and activities surrounding fire, including ceremonies involved in disposing of departed loved ones (MacLean, 1985a, 1985b). Clark (1984) has discussed evidence that hominids may have had an association with fire for two and a half million years and even possibly dating back to the beginning of bipedalism.

Significantly, the prefrontal cortex, which affords us a sense of empathy, is intimately linked to the thalamocingulate division of the limbic system that has been discussed in terms of family-related behavior (MacLean, 1985a). Given mechanisms for reciprocal innervation of crying and laughter, is it possible that the tearing experienced upon seeing an altruistic act reflects a high order of generalization owing to a close association of neural mechanisms involved in crying and in parental rescue?

ACKNOWLEDGMENTS

I am grateful to C. Ronald Harbaugh for his professional care of the animals and operating-room assistance, to Robert E. Gelhard for technical and histological assistance, and to Mary Ann Bandy for typing the manuscript.

REFERENCES

Akert, K. (1964). Comparative anatomy of frontal cortex and thalamofrontal connections. In J. M. Warren & K. Akert (Eds.), *The frontal granular cortex and behavior* (pp. 372–396). New York: McGraw-Hill.

Baleydier, C., & Mauguiere, F. (1980). The duality of the cingulate gyrus in monkey. Neuroanatomical study and functional hypothesis. *Brain, 103*, 525–554.

Broca, P. (1878). Anatomie comparée des circonvolutions cérébrales. Le grand lobe limbique et la scissure limbique dans la série des mammifères. *Review of Anthropology, 1*, 385–498.

Brown, J. W. (1967). Physiology and phylogenesis of emotional expression. *Brain Research, 5,* 1–14.
Carmel, P. W. (1970). Efferent projections of the ventral anterior nucleus of the thalamus in the monkey. *American Journal of Anatomy, 128,* 159–183.
Carpenter, M. (1976). Anatomical organization of the corpus striatum and related nuclei. *Research Publications—Association for Research in Nervous and Mental Disease, 55,* 1–36.
Clark, J. D. (1984). The way we were. Speculating and accumulating: New approaches to the study of early human living. *Anthroquest, The L.S.B. Leakey Foundation News, No. 30,* Winter 1984 (1), 18–19.
Clark, W. E. LeGros, & Meyer, M. (1950). Anatomical relationships between the cerebral cortex and the hypothalamus. *British Medical Bulletin, 6,* 341–345.
Collins, E. T. (1932). The physiology of weeping. *British Journal of Ophthalmology, 16,* 1–20.
Daly, D. D., & Mulder, D. W. (1957). Gelastic epilepsy. *Neurology, 7,* 189–192.
Davison, C., & Kelman, H. (1939). Pathologic laughing and crying. *Archives of Neurology and Psychiatry, 42,* 595–643.
Dott, N. M. (1938). Surgical aspects of the hypothalamus. In W. E. L. Clark (Ed.), *The hypothalamus* (pp. 131–185). Edinburgh: Oliver & Boyd.
Dua, S., & MacLean, P. D. (1964). Localization for penile erection in medial frontal lobe. *American Journal of Physiology, 207,* 1425–1434.
Foltz, E. L., & White, L. E., Jr. (1957). Experimental cingulumotomy and modification of morphine withdrawal. *Journal of Neurosurgery, 14,* 655–673.
Geier, S., Bancaud, J., Talairach, J., Bonis, A., Szikla, G., & Enjelvin, M. (1977). The seizures of frontal lobe epilepsy. *Neurology, 27,* 951–958.
Goldman-Rakic, P. S., & Porrino, L. J. (1985). The primate mediodorsal (MD) nucleus and its projection to the frontal lobe. *Journal of Comparative Neurology, 242,* 535–560.
Hassler, R. (1961). Motorische und sensible Effekte umschriebener Reizungen und Ausschaltungen im menschlichen Zwischenhirn. *Deutsche Zeitschrift für Nervenheilkunde, 183,* 148–171.
Hotton, N., III, MacLean, P. D., Roth, J. J., & Roth, E. C. (Eds.). (1986). *The ecology and biology of mammal-like reptiles.* Washington, DC: Smithsonian University Press.
Ironside, R. (1956). Disorders of laughter due to brain lesions. *Brain, 79,* 589–609.
Jonas, S. (1981). The supplementary motor region and speech emission. *Journal of Communication Disorders, 14,* 349–373.
Jonas, S. (1982). The thalamus and aphasia, including transcortical aphasia: A review. *Journal of Communication Disorders, 15,* 31–41.
Jürgens, U. (1983). Afferent fibers to the cingular vocalization region in the squirrel monkey. *Experimental Neurology, 80,* 395–409.
Jürgens, U. (1984). The efferent and afferent connections of the supplementary motor area. *Brain Research, 300,* 63–81.
Jürgens, U. & Ploog, D. (1970). Cerebral representation of vocalization in the squirrel monkey. *Experimental Brain Research, 10,* 532–554.
Kaada, B. R. (1951). Somato-motor, autonomic and electrocorticographic responses to electrical stimulation of 'rhinencephalic' and other structures in primates, cat and dog. A study of responses from the limbic, subcallosal, orbito-insular, piriform and temporal cortex hippocampus-fornix and amygdala. *Acta Physiologica Scandinavica, 24,* 1–285.
Kirzinger, A., & Jürgens, U. (1982). Cortical lesion effects and vocalizations in the squirrel monkey. *Brain Research, 233,* 299–315.
Kramer, H. C. (1954). Laughing spells in patients, after lobotomy. *Journal of Nervous and Mental Disease, 119,* 517–522.
Krayenbühl, H., Wyss, O. A. M., & Yasargil, M. G. (1961). Bilateral thalamotomy and pallidotomy as treatment for bilateral Parkinsonism. *Journal of Neurosurgery, 18,* 429–444.
Lehtinen, L., & Kivalo, A. (1965). Laughter epilepsy. *Acta Neurologica Scandinavica, 41,* 255.

Leonard, C. M. (1969). The prefrontal cortex of the rat. I. Cortical projection of the mediodorsal nucleus. II. Efferent connections. *Brain Research, 12,* 321–343.

List, C. F., Dowman, C. E., Bagchi, B. K., & Bebin, J. (1958). Posterior hypothalamic hamartomas and gangliogliomas causing precocious puberty. *Neurology, 8,* 164–174.

Loiseau, P., Cohadon, F., & Cohadon, S. (1971). Gelastic epilepsy. A review and report of five cases. *Epilepsia,* 12, 313–323.

Ludwig, B., Ajmone Marsan, C., & Van Buren, J. (1975). Cerebral seizures of probable orbitofrontal origin. *Epilepsia, 16,* 141–158.

Ma, N. S. F., Jones, T. C., Thorington, R. W., & Cooper, R. W. (1974). Chromosome banding patterns in squirrel monkeys *(Saimiri sciureus). Journal of Medical Primatology, 3,* 120–137.

MacLean, P. D. (1952). Some psychiatric implications of physiological studies on frontotemporal portion of limbic system (visceral brain). *Electroencephalography and Clinical Neurophysiology, 4,* 407–418.

MacLean, P. D. (1964). Mirror display in the squirrel monkey, *Saimiri sciureus. Science, 146,* 950–952.

MacLean, P. D. (1970). The triune brain, emotion, and scientific bias. In F. O. Schmitt (Ed.), *The neurosciences: Second study program* (pp. 336–349). New York: Rockefeller University Press.

MacLean, P. D. (1973). A triune concept of the brain and behavior. In T. Boag & D. Campbell (Eds.), *The Hincks Memorial Lectures* (pp. 6–66). Toronto: University of Toronto Press.

MacLean, P. D. (1975). On the evolution of three mentalities. *Man-Environment Systems, 5,* 213–224.

MacLean, P. D. (1978). Effects of lesions of globus pallidus on species-typical display behavior of squirrel monkeys. *Brain Research, 149,* 175–196.

MacLean, P. D. (1985a). Brain evolution relating to family, play, and the separation call. *Archives of General Psychiatry, 42,* 405–417.

MacLean, P. D. (1985b). Editorial: Evolutionary psychiatry and the triune brain. *Psychological Medicine, 15,* 219–221.

MacLean, P. D. (1986a). Culminating developments in the evolution of the limbic system: The thalamocingulate division. In B. K. Doane & K. E. Livingston (Eds.), *The limbic system: Functional organization and clinical disorders* (pp. 1–28). New York: Raven Press.

MacLean, P. D. (1986b). Ictal symptoms relating to the nature of affects and their cerebral substrate. In R. Plutchik (Ed.), *Emotion: Theory, research and experience* (Vol. 3, pp. 61–90). Orlando, FL: Academic Press.

MacLean, P. D. (1986c). Neurobehavioral significance of the mammal-like reptiles (therapsids). In N. Hotton, III, P. D. MacLean, J. J. Roth, & E. C. Roth (Eds.), *The ecology and biology of mammal-like reptiles.* Washington, DC: Smithsonian Institution Press.

Martin, J. P. (1950). Fits of laughter (sham mirth) in organic cerebral disease. *Brain, 73,* 453–464.

Murphy, M. R., MacLean, P. D., & Hamilton, S. C. (1981). Species-typical behavior of hamsters deprived from birth of the neocortex. *Science, 213,* 459–461.

Newman, J. D. (1985a). The infant cry of primates: An evolutionary perspective. In B. M. Lester & C. F. Z. Boukydis (Eds.), *Infant crying: Theoretical and research perspectives* (pp. 307–323). New York: Plenum.

Newman, J. D. (1985b). Squirrel monkey communication. In L. A. Rosenblum & C. L. Coe (Eds.), *Handbook of squirrel monkey research* (pp. 99–126). New York: Plenum.

Newman, J. D., & MacLean, P. D. (1982). Effects of tegmental lesions on the isolation call of squirrel monkeys. *Brain Research, 232,* 317–330.

Newman, J. D., & MacLean, P. D. (1985). Importance of medial frontolimbic cortex in the production of isolation call of squirrel monkeys. *Neuroscience Abstracts 2* (Pt. 1), 495.

Newman, J. D., Murphy, M. R., & Harbaugh, C. R. (1982). Naloxone-reversible suppression of isolation call production after morphine injections in squirrel monkeys. *Society for Neuroscience Abstracts, 8,* 940.

Papez, J. W. (1937). A proposed mechanism of emotion. *Archives of Neurology and Psychiatry, 38,* 725–743.

Penfield, W., & Jasper, H. H. (1954). *Epilepsy and the functional anatomy of the human brain.* Boston, MA: Little, Brown.

Penfield, W., & Rasmussen, T. (1952). *The cerebral cortex of man.* New York: Macmillan.

Poeck, K. (1969). Pathophysiology of emotional disorders associated with brain damage. In P. J. Vinken & G. W. Bruyn (Eds.), *Handbook of clinical neurology* (Vol. 3, pp. 343–367). Amsterdam: North-Holland.

Poeck, K., & Pilleri, G. (1963). Pathologisches Lachen und Weinen. *Schweizer Archiv für Neurologie, Neurochirurgie und Psychiatrie, 92,* 323–370.

Pool, J. L. (1954). The visceral brain of man. *Journal of Neurosurgery, 11,* 45–63.

Pribram, K. H., Chow, K. L., & Semmes, J. (1953). Limit and organization of the cortical projection from the medial thalamic nucleus in monkey. *Journal of Comparative Neurology, 98,* 433–448.

Robinson, B. (1967). Vocalization evoked from forebrain in *Macaca mulatta. Physiology and Behavior, 2,* 345–354.

Rosabal, F. (1967). Cytoarchitecture of the frontal lobe of the squirrel monkey. *Journal of Comparative Neurology, 130,* 87–108.

Slotnick, B. M. (1967). Disturbances of maternal behavior in the rat following lesions of the cingulate cortex. *Behaviour, 24,* 204–236.

Smith, W. K. (1945). The functional significance of the rostral cingular cortex as revealed by its responses to electrical excitation. *Journal of Neurophysiology, 8,* 241–255.

Stamm, J. S. (1955). The function of the median cerebral cortex in maternal behavior of rats. *Journal of Comparative and Physiological Psychology, 48,* 347–356.

Swash, M. (1972). Released involuntary laughter after temporal lobe infarction. *Journal of Neurology, Neurosurgery and Psychiatry, 35,* 108–113.

Symmes, D., Newman, J. D., Talmage-Riggs, G., & Lieblich A. K. (1979). Individuality and stability of isolation peeps in squirrel monkeys. *Animal Behavior, 27,* 1142–1152.

Talairach, J., Bancaud, J., Geier, S., Bordas-Ferrer, M., Szikla, G., & Rusu, M. (1973). The cingulate gyrus and human behavior. *Electroencephalography and Clinical Neurophysiology, 34,* 45–52.

Tilney, F., & Morrison, J. F. (1912). Pseudo-bulbar palsy, clinically and pathologically considered, with the clinical report of five cases. *Journal of Nervous and Mental Disease, 39,* 500–535.

Tobias, T. J. (1975). Afferents to prefrontal cortex from the thalamic mediodorsal nucleus in the rhesus monkey. *Brain Research, 83,* 191–212.

Van Buren, J. M. (1961). Sensory, motor and autonomic effects of mesial temporal stimulation in man. *Journal of Neurosurgery, 28,* 273–288.

Vogt, B. A., Rosene, D. L., & Pandya, D. N. (1979). Thalamic and cortical afferents differentiate anterior from posterior cingulate cortex in the monkey. *Science, 204,* 205–207.

von Cramm, D., & Jürgens, U. (1983). The anterior cingulate cortex and the phonatory control in monkey and man. *Neuroscience and Biobehavioral Reviews, 7,* 423–425.

Walker, A. E. (1938). *The primate thalamus.* Chicago, IL: University of Chicago Press.

Weil, A. A., Nosik, W. A., & Demmy, N. (1958). Electroencephalographic correlation of laughing fits. *American Journal of the Medical Sciences, 235,* 301–308.

Wilson, S. A. K. (1924). Some problems in Neurology. II. Pathological laughing and crying. *Journal of Neurology and Psychopathology, 4,* 299–333.

Winter, P., Ploog, D., & Latta, J. (1966). Vocal repertoire of the squirrel monkey (Saimiri sciureus) its analysis and significance. *Experimental Brain Research, 1,* 359–384.

Wise, S. F., & Herkenham, M. (1982). Opiate receptor distribution in the cerebral cortex of the rhesus monkey. *Science, 218,* 387–389.

8

The Frontal Lobes and Control of Cognition and Memory

Donald T. Stuss and D. Frank Benson

INTRODUCTION

Understanding the role of the frontal lobes in human behavior, and in particular the influence of this brain area on human functions such as memory and cognition, is an elusive goal. To approach this problem, a basic neuroanatomical/behavioral theory of frontal lobe functioning will be presented; then research data derived from studies of cognition and memory after frontal lobe damage will be mapped onto this model.

A number of primary conclusions will be stressed. First, the human brain is an integrated unit, and division into discrete functions such as memory, cognition, and others is only at a conceptual level. Second, it is possible to differentiate the roles played in these processes by the posterior/basal areas from those of the frontal lobes. Third, as a corollary of the second, the frontal lobes play a controlling role in relation to the rest of the brain; the frontal lobes are pressed into action only when such control is demanded. Finally, there is both a continuity and diversity in frontal lobe or frontal system functioning. The unity is reflected in the general concept of executive guidance and control. The diversity may relate to focal localization of function within the frontal lobes.

A NEUROANATOMICAL/BEHAVIORAL THEORY

The theory we will present is strongly indebted to previous theories of frontal lobe function and brain organization. Investigators and theoreticians of frontal lobe functioning include early observer/experimentalists such as Bianchi (1895, 1922), Harlow (1868), Brickner (1936), Jacobsen (1935), Feuchtwanger (1923), Goldstein (1944), and Kleist (1934a, 1934b), the psychosurgery in-

ISBN 0-936925-00-0

vestigators, and a more contemporary scientific group led by Hécaen (1964), Milner (1963, 1964, 1982), Pribram (1973), Teuber (1964), Nauta (1971, 1973), Damasio (1979), Fuster (1980), Lhermitte (1983), Lhermitte, Derouesne, and Signoret (1972), Lezak (1983), Shallice (1982), Stamm (1979), and, in particular, Luria (1966/1980, 1973). Our model builds from the validity of these findings and, by incorporating our own research and conceptualizations, attempts to present a more comprehensive view. These concepts are presented in greater detail elsewhere (Stuss & Benson, 1986).

Organized Integrated Fixed Functional Systems

Understanding the role of the frontal lobes in the relationship between brain and behavior demands a concept of brain organization. Most brain function underlying overt behavior is dependent on *organized integrated fixed functional systems* working independently of frontal lobe influence; these can be localized in posterior/basal brain areas. Defining the overall characteristics of these systems facilitates, by contrast and comparison, comprehension of the role of the frontal lobes.

Functional refers to the many functional systems such as emotions, language, memory, and so on (see Figure 1), considered to be the bases of overt behavior. Many systems could be proposed and it is uncertain, with our present knowledge, whether the functions included in Figure 1 are sufficient and/or correct. There may well be an additional hierarchical organization among these functional systems. Current neuropsychology and behavioral neurology have focused on the anatomical and behavioral aspects of the specific functional systems but the influence of the frontal lobes on these systems is frequently overlooked.

Organized implies several factors. Each system consists of different components that play separate but integral parts in the successful functioning of the entire system. While each unit has a different role to play, overt behavior depends on the synthesis of these roles into the total organization of the functional system. Damage in a specific area of the organized system may produce impairment of characteristics related to the damaged area, but it also influences

POSTERIOR/BASAL FUNCTIONAL SYSTEMS

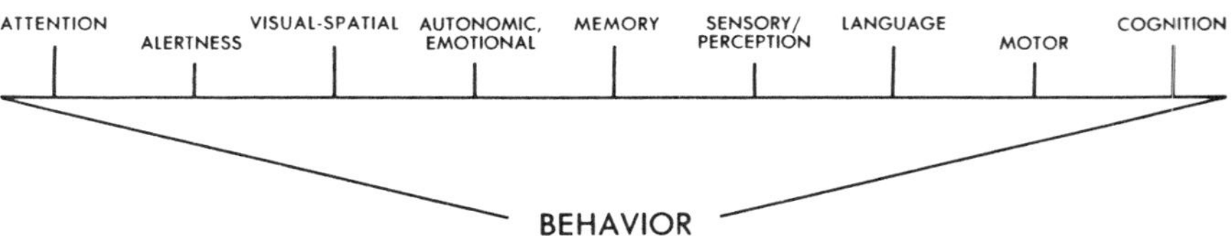

FIGURE 1 Various organized integrated fixed functional systems are hypothesized to be based, in relation to the frontal lobes, in more posterior/basal brain regions. (From Stuss & Benson, 1986.)

overall behavior. It can be said that an organized posterior/basal functional system has its own inherent control that operates at the level of well-learned and routine information.

Integrated connotes a number of activities. First, the different components of a single functional system must be interconnected to produce the function. The connections include not only cortical regions in both hemispheres but selected subcortical neurostructures and the interconnecting pathways, a neural network. Integration is both lateralized and hierarchical and cannot be viewed in a limited connectionistic sense. The pathways connect functional centers, not specific neurons. Such centers may well operate through a spreading excitation rather than a purely linear connection.

At a different level, integrated also indicates that, although each functional system is traditionally studied as an independent entity, the entire brain functions as an integrated unit. Separation of the systems is artificial; all of the functional systems operate in an interlocking fashion.

Finally, *fixed* suggests that, in the normal adult human, the function has a relatively consistent relation to neuroanatomical areas across individuals and remains relatively unchanged within individuals. The behavioral/anatomical relationship of the posterior/basal functional units represents a stable base for investigation.

Considerable evidence is accumulating that identifies such organized integrated fixed functional systems. As an example, Mesulam (1981) notes that several different cerebral regions underlie the function of attention. The reticular formation is necessary for optimal arousal, the sensory association areas provide access to the raw information to be processed, the parietal lobe gives an internal sensory map, and the limbic region provides motivational salience. This combination of posterior/basal brain areas appears to be essential for the attentional system. A fifth brain region is also active, one that explores, monitors, fixates, and shifts the direction of attention. The frontal lobes appear to play this unique role; clinical observation strongly supports this role for the frontal lobes and recent studies demonstrate that frontal areas indeed play an important role in sensory attention (Damasio, Damasio, & Chui, 1980; Heilman & Valenstein, 1972; Stein & Volpe, 1983).

A similar organized integrated fixed functional system is language. Clearly, different regions of the brain play different roles in the total language function (Benson, 1979; Geschwind, 1965) and the language functions associated with the posterior system may operate independently. The frontal lobes, particularly the prefrontal portion, appear to be related to this more posterior system in an initiating, directive role (Alexander, 1984; Luria, 1973; Stuss & Benson, 1986).

The concept of functional systems postulated above resembles the theories of Luria (1966/1980, 1973). He also views the functional systems as posterior and/or basal, each posterior/basal functional system having direct and reciprocal connections with the frontal cortex and each having its own basic role and inherent organization. This allows each posterior/basal system to function independently of frontal lobe input. This independence is normal in routine situations. When the frontal lobes are damaged, however, Luria (1973) termed this a divorce of action from the guiding control of the frontal lobes. As a corollary, it is obvious that direct assessment of frontal lobe function cannot be achieved by simply assessing functions such as language, memory, cognition, or other systems. At best such testing can provide only indirect evidence on how the frontal lobes interact with the specific function.

Frontal (Anterior) Functional Systems

Several additional brain activities appear to be organized integrated fixed functional systems but have a distinct frontal localization. We have labeled two such anterior functional systems (see Figure 2). They are functional systems in the sense that they have the same characteristics as the functional systems described above. *Anterior* indicates that the anatomical bases of these systems have at least partial localization in the frontal lobes. They can be considered independent not only because their anatomical bases lie in the more caudal regions of the frontal lobes, but, while intimately linked with other (posterior/basal) functional systems, they subserve them in a superordinate manner. Appropriate testing of appropriate subjects provides rather pure examples of their disturbance. Specifically, the posterior/basal functional systems can be demonstrated to operate adequately lacking only some higher control.

We (Stuss & Benson, 1986) postulate that at least two brain activities fit this definition for the anterior functional systems: (1) sequence, set, and integration and (2) drive, motivation, and will.

Sequence The ability to maintain and organize bits of information in meaningful sequences is an important human mental attribute that is, to a considerable

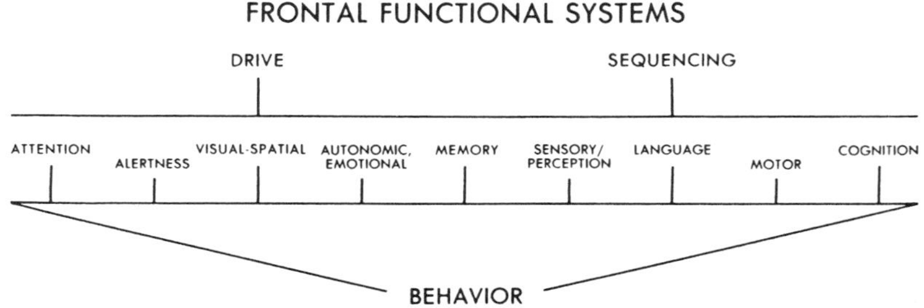

FIGURE 2 Sequencing and drive, two functions closely allied with the frontal lobes, appear to have a superordinate role in relation to the posterior/basal functional systems. (From Stuss & Benson, 1986.)

extent, dependent on the intactness of the frontal lobes. The importance of serial order was demonstrated by Albert (1972) in studies of sequencing in language functions. Milner and Petrides (1984; Petrides & Milner, 1982) and Fuster (1980) suggested that the maintenance of order of one's responses appeared most strongly dependent on intact lateral (dorsal and orbital) frontal convexity regions. When a greater degree of executive control is involved, the human brain not only handles multiple bits of information in sequence, but can extract crucial elements from the series and integrate them with data from other series of information or even from other functional systems to produce novel knowledge or comprehension. Sequencing, particularly in its higher derivations of sets and integration, is a crucial mental feat for human thought that directly affects, but is independent of, the posterior/basal functional systems and is disturbed when there is frontal lobe damage.

Drive Alterations in drive are frequent after frontal lobe damage, particularly when medial sagittal frontal and adjoining structures (including the cingulate gyrus) are involved. The most common behavior is apathy, a generalized decrease in activity. Such patients either cannot or are slow to initiate movements. Clinical observation indicates that orbital frontal abnormality is connected to the ability to inhibit drive, while medial sagittal frontal structures are important in the initiation of activity, both major aspects of the two hypothesized types of personality changes that follow frontal lobe damage (Blumer & Benson, 1975). Closely allied with drive are motivation and will, each reflecting a greater degree of intellectual control. All three are significant to posterior/basal functions but, again, in a superordinate manner that encompasses all of the functions.

In summary, two anterior fixed functional systems can be suggested. They resemble the more thoroughly investigated posterior/basal functional systems in that they have the characteristics described for these systems. They are, however, anatomically separated, located in more anterior brain structures, and they appear to play an almost exclusively superordinate role in relation to the posterior/basal functional systems.

Executive, Control Function

For most investigators and theoreticians the concept of the executive or control function of human behavior is clearly allied with the prefrontal cortex. The executive ability is conceived as providing conscious direction to the posterior/basal functional systems for the efficient processing of information in novel or nonroutine situations. In routine situations, once an activity has become routine through practice, the organization of the posterior/basal functional systems is sufficient to maintain the behavior. This concept has been demonstrated with positron emission tomography showing that thoroughly learned motor acts (writing one's signature) require only subcortical activity, whereas a newly acquired motor act demands frontal participation (Mazziotta & Phelps, 1986). Active involvement of the frontal lobes is not required once behaviors are well established, which is why some published observations and research reports have minimized the role of the frontal lobes in human behavior (Hebb, 1945; Hebb & Penfield, 1940; Meyer, 1960).

The executive, control functions dictate how and in what order the basic functions of a fixed system are to be used to achieve a specified goal. The term *executive control* is generic, reflecting the *unity* of frontal lobe function, and does not explain HOW the control is manifested in daily situations (Newell, 1977). Superordinate control is conceptually divisible (Carver & Scheier, 1982; Powers, 1973a, 1973b) (see Figure 3). First, a goal must be anticipated and established, and then planning is necessary; a series of "means-end" statements evaluates potential outcomes. Once behavior is initiated the action must be carried out in proper order and results of the behavior must be evaluated (if-then) to monitor results. Anticipation, goal selection, planning, and monitoring (including feedback)—these separate divisions of superordinate control are posited as the general control function of the frontal lobes. It would appear that these separable functions are experimentally verifiable. Animal research reported in this volume supports this proposition and even suggests specific anatomical localization for some components of the executive function. For humans, appropriate tests for examination of hypothesized subdivisions of frontal control functions are yet to be developed.

At present, frontal executive functions must be examined through the medium of posterior/basal fixed systems. To be adequate, tests must separate the basic posterior/basal functions from the superordinate frontal control functions. The executive functions, although a factor in learning new behaviors in such

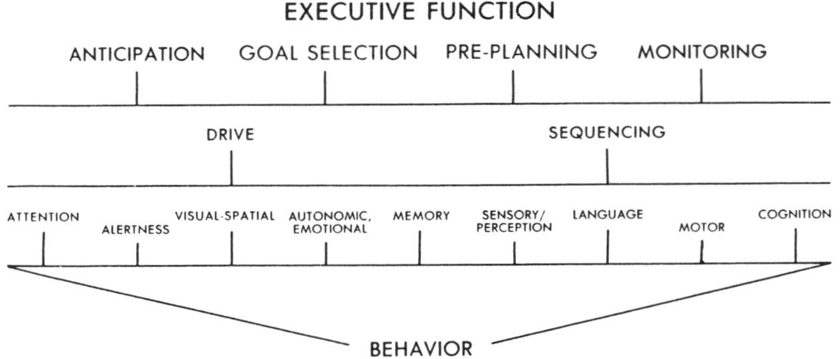

FIGURE 3 Executive control functions, called into action in nonroutine or novel situations, provide conscious direction to the functional systems for efficient processing of information. (From Stuss & Benson, 1986.)

systems as sensory perception and motor functions, are most conspicuous in functions such as "cognition" and "memory," reflecting the greater complexity of these systems. Even so, clear demonstration of frontal executive control has been difficult to achieve.

Self-Awareness and Self-Consciousness

Consciousness (self-consciousness, self-awareness, self-reflectiveness), while frequently considered the domain of philosophy, theology, or theoretical psychology, is also a behavioral function and appears to be intimately linked to the prefrontal cortex (see Figure 4). Frontally damaged patients routinely show decreased self-awareness; they are unconcerned and lack self-monitoring and self-regulation of their behavior.

A disturbance of self-consciousness does not necessarily indicate absence of self-knowledge. Frontally damaged patients may demonstrate awareness of errors but be unable to utilize this information to alter their behavior (Konow & Pribram, 1970). We have described a patient with Capgras syndrome, or reduplication, following frontal and right temporal lobe damage from a closed head injury (Alexander, Stuss, & Benson, 1979). He was convinced that his wife and children were a second family, similar yet different from the "first" wife and children. Cognitively, he recognized the impossibility of the situation and agreed he would find it "hard to believe" if someone else told him such a story. Nevertheless, he remained convinced that this was a different family. Even though he was "aware" of the correct data, was able to recite what others had told him, and was willing to accept the facts on a theoretical basis, he could not accept or act on this cognitive awareness, a defect of self-awareness.

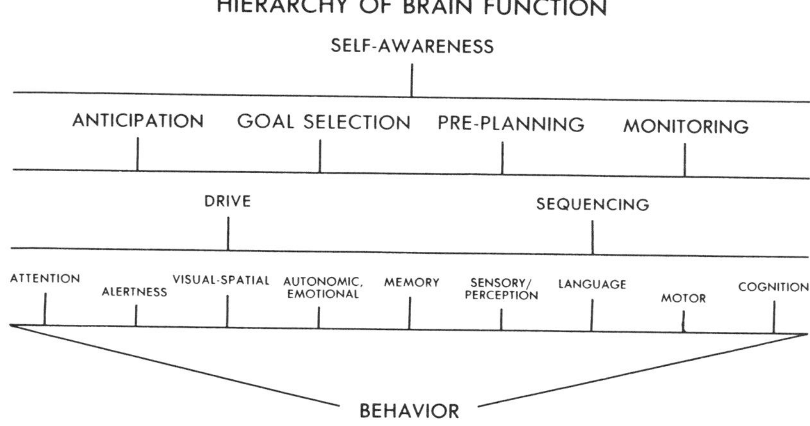

FIGURE 4 Self-awareness, or self-reflectiveness, is considered to be the highest attribute of the frontal lobes. (From Stuss & Benson, 1986.)

This prefrontal self-consciousness function appears to be similar to some of the characteristics of "metacognition" described in contemporary cognitive psychology, the "knowing about knowing" (Brown, 1978; Cavanaugh & Borkowski, 1980; Flavell, 1979). Metacognition is a general term relating to the superordinate role of reflecting on mental activity (Yussen, 1985). It is nonspecific in that self-reflectiveness may be useful for all mental activities. Thus, *metamemory* is the term used to indicate the contemplation of different strategies to assist in learning a list of words; *meta-attention* is the label for consideration of the conditions that will result in the least distractibility. Self-awareness can be considered necessary for controlling, via a feedback loop, the perceived discrepancy between a present state and a mental comparison, for contemplating various strategies to achieve a goal, and for analyzing the effects of a completed act. The frontal lobes, phylogenetically one of the newest of brain areas, appear to be essential for this function that many consider the highest and most human of mental abilities.

NEUROPSYCHOLOGICAL APPROACHES TO EXECUTIVE CONTROL

Against this theoretical background, research and clinical examples will be needed to unveil the role played by the frontal lobes in the control of cognition and memory functions. Our personal research focused on the results of a long-term follow-up of prefrontal leukotomy subjects in the Northampton Veterans Administration Medical Center Leukotomy Study. An overview of the research design and general neurological, neuroradiological, and neuropsychological results are available in previous publications (Benson et al., 1981; Naeser, Levine, Benson, Stuss, & Weir, 1981; Stuss et al., 1981). These studies compared three leukotomized schizophrenic groups to a nonleukotomized schizophrenic group and a normal control group. The most pertinent comparisons match the good recovery group to the normal control subjects. The good recovery group consisted of leukotomized schizophrenics who had been discharged from a hospital for a mean duration of 14 years and had been successful in returning to some kind of work and relatively independent living. Each had sizable bilateral prefrontal lesions demonstrated by CT scan. The normal control group was matched in age, education, socioeconomic status, and military history but had no neurologic or psychiatric history. With this population we will present the effects of prefrontal leukotomy lesions on two posterior fixed systems, memory and cognition.

Memory

"Loss of recent memory" was one of the earliest theories proposed to explain the behavioral deficits noted in animals with frontal lobe lesions (Jacobsen,

1935, 1936). This hypothesis was based on the impaired performance of frontally lesioned animals in delayed-response and delayed-alternation tasks. Although gradually rejected in the animal literature, controversy over the role of the frontal lobes in human memory functions has continued. Neurological textbooks have stated that extensive bilateral lesions of the prefrontal cortex interfere with short-term memory (Gardner, 1975) and observations on frontal tumors suggested that disturbances of memory may be observed (Hécaen, 1964; Kolodny, 1929; Stookey, Scarff, & Teitelbaum, 1941). Several formal psychological studies also suggested memory deficits following frontal lobe damage in patients. Memory problems are frequently reported (Lindqvist & Norlen, 1966; Logue, Durward, Pratt, Piercy, & Nixon, 1968) subsequent to rupture of anterior communicating artery aneurysms, suggesting frontal lobe or frontal system damage. Some evidence suggests that human patients are also impaired on delayed-response and delayed-alternation tasks (Freedman & Oscar-Berman, 1986; Lewinsohn, Zieler, Libet, Eyeberg, & Nielson, 1972; Pribram, Ahumada, Hartog, & Ross, 1964).

Although the observations may well be correct, the attribution of the demonstrated deficits to a primary memory disorder secondary to frontal lobe damage can be questioned. For instance, the memory disorder following ruptured anterior communicating artery aneurysms may result from damage of anterior communicating artery perforators that feed the anterior hypothalamus or septum (Alexander & Freedman, 1984). Many formal neuropsychological tests depend on manipulations confounded by factors such as interference, temporal ordering, and visual search. Pure memory tests rarely show problems in frontally damaged patients. Innumerable studies on patients with many different types of frontal lobe disorders have failed to reveal any deficits on basic memory tests.

Many clinical examples and some recent research have gradually refined the concept of the memory problems secondary to frontal lobe disturbance. Hécaen and Albert (1978) describe a "forgetting to remember," in which an intended act of memory is unavailable (forgotten) although it may be retrieved later. One patient who had bilateral frontal leukotomy many years earlier could not recall what the Vatican was when given the WAIS information subtest. Later in the examination, while discussing religion, the patient stated that he was a Catholic, and that the pope was the head of the Church and was situated in the Vatican in Rome. He had known the information when originally asked but had failed (forgot) to remember without the additional cue of religion.

A second clinical characteristic appears to be a loss of the controlling factor of knowledge giving the appearance of a memory disorder. A patient who had suffered bilateral frontal polar injury in a traffic accident was on a water limitation program to rule out diabetes insipidus. He was instructed by his doctor not to drink water and not to go near the water fountain. Soon, he was observed having a drink at the fountain as if he had forgotten the instructions. When asked what he had been told, he immediately and accurately stated the instructions.

These instructions, however, had not influenced his behavior. The loss appeared to be of the ability to respond to the information at the appropriate time rather than an inability to learn and retain information.

The possible role of orbital-frontal pathology on memory functioning was assessed in patients with leukotomy lesions (Stuss et al., 1982). Many, particularly those with the best psychiatric recovery, performed as well as normal subjects on standard memory tests. However, on a test requiring inhibition of interference in order to recall information (the Brown–Peterson technique), they were severely impaired regardless of the degree of recovery (see Figure 5).

Frontal lobe lesions do not cause a primary disturbance of memory but they do interfere with mnestic activity. This observation had been reported early (Goldstein, 1936a, 1936b; Malmo, 1948) and stressed by Luria (1973). Luria

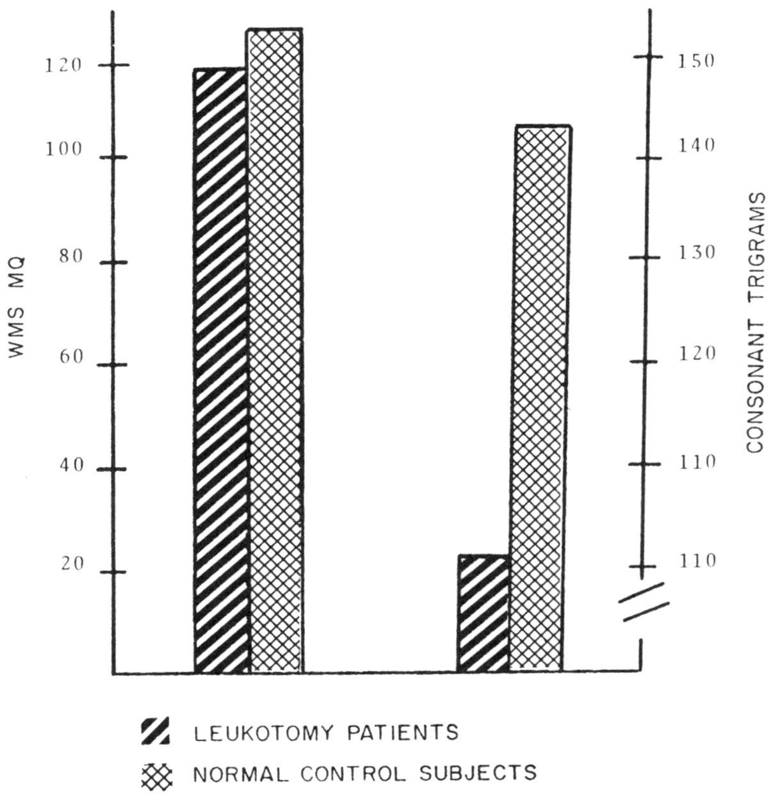

FIGURE 5 Comparison of good recovery leukotomy patients with orbital frontal lesions to matched control subjects on two memory tests: the Wechsler Memory Scale Memory Quotient, and the Brown-Peterson Consonant Trigrams test (see text). The Consonant Trigrams score is the sum of three separate versions, with a maximum score of 180. (From Stuss, in press.)

stated that the operative function of memory was intact in patients with frontal lobe damage—what was impaired was the ability to create stable motives of recall, to maintain the active effort required for voluntary recall, and then to switch from one group of traces to another; as a result the process of recall and reproduction of information is significantly impaired. Frontal lobe patients have difficulty organizing methods of memorization and retrieval, following instructions, temporally discriminating items in memory, using external cues to guide learning behavior, and comparing the results with the original intention (Corkin, 1965; Milner, 1965, 1974, 1982; Petrides, 1985; Walsh, 1978). They have a susceptibility to interference, reported in both the human and animal literature on the effects of frontal lobe pathology (Fuster & Bauer, 1974; Kimura, 1963; Malmo & Amsel, 1948; Milner & Teuber, 1968; Stuss et al., 1982).

The frontal lobe memory deficit appears to be, at least in part, an inability to maintain consistent directed attention over time based on an inability to control interfering stimuli. The prefrontal cortex has a directive, organizational controlling role in the process of memory. With proper testing, the intact ability of basic posterior memory functions can be demonstrated, as it was with the leukotomy patients. If the specific controlling aspect is assessed, however, then a memory disorder is displayed. The disorder is not one of memory per se, but one of control, the specific function of the prefrontal cortex.

Cognition

The greatest confusion concerning the function of the frontal lobes surrounds the question of its role in cognition. Past descriptions have ranged from an inability to identify any specific cognitive functions associated with prefrontal cortex to attribution of all higher mental functions to the frontal lobes. Lack of adequate definition of cognition and/or misunderstanding of the definitions provided by earlier researchers was a major impediment to the advancement of knowledge.

Early on, the possible role of the frontal lobes in cognitive functions focused primarily on issues of IQ and abstraction. In most research reported on "intellectual" functions or IQ, alteration but not loss of general cognitive abilities was described. Frequently the IQ scores were within the normal range despite rather massive frontal lobe disturbance. Such a description was presented for clinical case studies (Ackerly & Benton, 1947; Brickner, 1936; Welt, 1888) as well as group studies, including patients with frontal lobe damage secondary to surgery for epilepsy or psychiatric problems (see Stuss & Benson, 1984, for review). It is now widely accepted that frontal lobe damage, unless massive and involving other brain areas, does not result in a "dementia." Although some alterations in IQ scores may result, they are not due to loss of knowledge or ability to perform basic functions such as arithmetic or visual-spatial construction.

Clinically, disordered abstraction is often accepted as a frontal lobe sign. Frontal lobe patients may be described as concrete, having lost abstracting ability. This was assessed in patients with well-defined orbital-frontal leukotomy lesions by administering four different tests of cognitive functions to three groups of leukotomized schizophrenics and two control groups (Stuss et al., 1983). The tests were selected to isolate specific aspects of intelligence and abstraction. The first was an IQ measure, the Wechsler Adult Intelligence Scale (WAIS) (Wechsler, 1955). A second assessed the understanding of metaphor as contrasted with the verbalization of metaphor interpretation. The third contrasted simple concept formation with the ability to shift from one concept to another. Finally, an "established" frontal lobe test, the Wisconsin Card Sorting Test, was administered.

Despite the psychiatric history and leukotomy, overall WAIS IQ scores were not significantly different between the good recovery leukotomy group and the normal control group (see Figure 6). On the visual-metaphor test (Winner & Gardner, 1977) that probes dissociation of the ability to understand a pure metaphor from the ability to verbalize the meaning of the metaphor, the frontal lobe patients had little difficulty in identifying the correct metaphor. There was no deficit at this level of abstraction although they showed some difficulty in verbalizing this understanding. A third cognitive challenge, the visual-verbal test

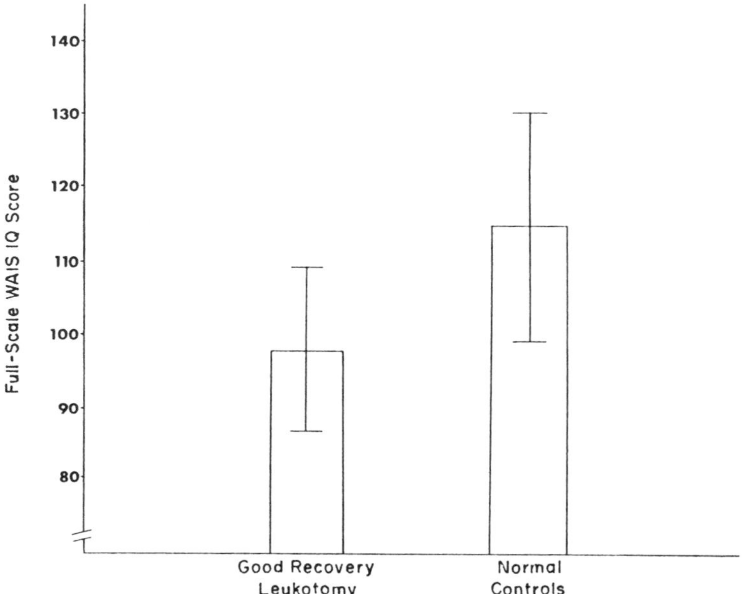

FIGURE 6 Comparison of the good recovery leukotomized schizophrenics to matched normal control subjects on the Full-Scale Wechsler Adult Intelligence Scale IQ. Standard deviation, depicted by the line extension of the bar graph, indicates the overlap of IQ scores.

(Feldman & Drasgow, 1960), also demanded a type of abstraction. The patient had to tell how three of four figures on a card were alike in some way and, in addition, how three of the same four figures were alike in some other way. Patients with frontal lobe lesions had no impairment on the first abstraction but did have difficulty making the shift.

Finally, on the Wisconsin Card Sorting Test (WCST) (Grant & Berg, 1948; Milner, 1963), our frontal lobe patients had significant difficulties, primarily an inability to maintain correct responses rather than in making perseverative responses. Frontal lobe patients may show lack of interest, respond randomly, and perseverate with incorrect responses when performing tasks requiring shifts (Drewe, 1974; Milner, 1963, 1964; Mirsky & Orzack, 1977; Robinson, Heaton, Lehman, & Stilson, 1980). Defective WCST performance is common after frontal lobe damage with the exact cause of the disorder possibly dependent on lesion location or method of test administration.

As with memory, there is little evidence of actual deficit among frontal lobe patients in intelligence (as measured by psychometric tests) or in abstraction, a fact frequently stated by previous researchers. Goldstein (1944) described it as follows: "Their *mental capacity may be sufficient for executing routine work,* but they *lack initiative, foresight, activity, and ability to handle new tasks*. They are *impaired in voluntarily shifting and choice*" (p. 192). Goldstein's "impairment of abstract attitude" in patients with frontal lobe pathology is not a simple inability to interpret proverbs or a deterioration in IQ. Rather, as demonstrated in our examples and in the research reported by others, several deficits may underlie the failed performances, such as the following:

1. An inability to translate knowledge of specific facts into appropriate action
2. A problem in shifting from one concept to another and in changing a specific behavior once started
3. A tendency to respond to a fragment with failure to grasp the totality or the key feature
4. A deficit in relating or integrating isolated details
5. A deficiency in handling simultaneous sources of information

Although this may be described as a deficit in abstraction, it may be more correctly explained as a disorder in the controlling, executive functions of the frontal lobes. If intellectual processes deal with old information, they are unaffected by frontal lobe damage, perhaps reflecting the fact that the old information is subservient to more posterior brain systems. As such, IQ results approach "normal." However, when choice, alternatives, control, goal selection, and monitoring are required (i.e., when new information must be processed or old information analyzed in new ways), involvement of the frontal lobes is required. In addition, a disorder in "higher cognition" may represent the deficit in motivation and failure in real life situations despite adequate to excellent performance on "frontal lobe" tests (Eslinger & Damasio, 1985).

SUMMARY

The arbitrary division of the role of the frontal lobes into different hierarchical functions can only be interpreted in light of an integrated model of brain functioning. Nonetheless, in an artificial conceptual way, complete understanding of human behavior requires knowledge of the controlling function of the frontal lobes. The human prefrontal cortex attends, integrates, formulates, executes, monitors, modifies, and judges all nervous system activities. From a practical viewpoint, adequate rehabilitation of brain-damaged patients demands an ability to understand and adequately assess not only the abilities of the posterior/basal functional systems but also the executive controlling role of the frontal lobes.

ACKNOWLEDGMENTS

Financial assistance for various aspects of the research reported in this chapter was received from the Medical Research Council of Canada, the National Research Council of Canada, Grant NS06209 from the National Institutes of Health to Boston University School of Medicine, the UCLA Augustus S. Rose Endowment Fund, the Ontario Mental Health Foundation, the University of Ottawa Faculty of Social Sciences, and the Research Services of the Veterans Administration. This assistance is gratefully acknowledged. M. Berry and L. Stethem are thanked for their assistance in the preparation of this manuscript.

REFERENCES

Ackerly, S. S., & Benton, A. L. (1947). Report of a case of bilateral frontal lobe defect. *Research Publications—Association for Research in Nervous and Mental Disease, 27,* 479–504.

Albert, M. L. (1972). Auditory sequencing and left cerebral dominance for language. *Neuropsychologia, 10,* 245–248.

Alexander, M. P. (1984, October). *Frontal language disorders.* Presentation to Neurobehavioral Seminar, UCLA School of Medicine.

Alexander, M. P., & Freedman, M. (1984). Amnesia after anterior communicating artery aneurysm rupture. *Neurology, 34,* 752–757.

Alexander, M. P., Stuss, D. T., & Benson, D. F. (1979). Capgras syndrome: A reduplicative phenomenon. *Neurology, 29,* 334–339.

Benson, D. F. (1979). *Aphasia, alexia, and agraphia.* Edinburgh & London: Churchill Livingstone.

Benson, D. F., Stuss, D. T., Naeser, M. A., Weir, W. S., Kaplan, E. F., & Levine, H. (1981). The long-term effects of prefrontal leukotomy. *Archives of Neurology (Chicago), 38,* 165–169.

Bianchi, L. (1895). The functions of the frontal lobes. *Brain, 18,* 497–522.

Bianchi, L. (1922). *The mechanism of the brain and the functions of the frontal lobes.* New York: W. Wood.

Blumer, D., & Benson, D. F. (1975). Personality changes with frontal and temporal lobe lesions. In D. F. Benson & D. Blumer (Eds.), *Psychiatric aspects of neurologic disease* (Vol. 1, pp. 151–170). New York: Grune & Stratton.

Brickner, R. M. (1936). *The intellectual functions of the frontal lobes*. New York: Macmillan.

Brown, A. L. (1978). Knowing when, where, and how to remember: A problem of metacognition. In R. Glasser (Ed.), *Advances in Instructional Psychology* (Vol. 1, pp. 77–165). Hillsdale, NJ: Erlbaum.

Carver, C., & Scheier, M. F. (1982). Self-awareness and the self-regulation of behavior. In G. Underwood (Ed.), *Aspects of consciousness: Vol. 3. Awareness and self-awareness* (pp. 235–266). New York: Academic Press.

Cavanaugh, J. C., & Borkowski, J. G. (1980). Searching for metamemory—memory connections: A developmental study. *Developmental Psychobiology, 16,* 441–453.

Corkin, S. (1965). Tactually guided maze learning in man: Effects of unilateral cortical excisions and bilateral hippocampal lesions. *Neuropsychologia, 3,* 339–351.

Damasio, A. R. (1979). The frontal lobes. In K. M. Heilman & E. Valenstein (Eds.), *Clinical neuropsychology* (pp. 360–412). London & New York: Oxford University Press.

Damasio, A. R., Damasio, H., & Chui, H. C. (1980). Neglect following damage to frontal lobe or basal ganglia. *Neuropsychologia, 18,* 123–132.

Drewe, E. A. (1974). The effect of type and area of brain lesion on Wisconsin Card Sorting Test performance. *Cortex, 10,* 159–170.

Eslinger, P. J., & Damasio, A. R. (1985). Severe disturbance of higher cognition following bilateral frontal lobe ablation: Patient EVR. *Neurology, 35,* 1731–1741.

Feldman, M. J., & Drasgow, J. (1960). *The visual-verbal test manual*. Beverley Hills, CA: Western Psychological Services.

Feuchtwanger, E. (1923). Die Funktionen des Stirnhirns ihre Pathologie und Psychologie. *Monographien aus dem Gesamtgebiete der Neurologie und Psychiatrie, 38,* 1–193.

Flavell, H. J. (1979). Metacognition and cognitive monitoring: A new area of psychological inquiry. *American Psychologist, 34,* 906–911.

Freedman, M., & Oscar-Berman, M. (1986). Bilateral frontal lobe disease and selective delayed response deficits in humans. *Behavioral Neuroscience, 100,* 337–342.

Fuster, J. M. (1980). *The prefrontal cortex. Anatomy, physiology, and neuropsychology of the frontal lobe*. New York: Raven Press.

Fuster, J. M., & Bauer, R. H. (1974). Visual short-term memory deficit from hypothermia of frontal cortex. *Brain Research, 81,* 393–400.

Gardner, E. (1975). *Fundamentals of neurology. A psychophysiological approach*. Philadelphia, PA: Saunders.

Geschwind, N. (1965). Disconnexion syndromes in animals and man. *Brain, 88,* 237–294, 585–644.

Goldstein, K. (1936a). Modifications of behavior consequent to cerebral lesions. *Psychiatric Quarterly, 10,* 586–610.

Goldstein, K. (1936b). The significance of the frontal lobes for mental performances. *Journal of Neurological Psychopathology, 17,* 27–40.

Goldstein, K. (1944). Mental changes due to frontal lobe damage. *Journal of Psychology, 17,* 187–208.

Grant, D. A., & Berg, E. A. (1948). A behavioral analysis of degree of reinforcement and ease of shifting to new responses in a Weigl-type card-sorting problem. *Journal of Experimental Psychology, 38,* 404–411.

Harlow, J. M. (1868). Recovery after severe injury to the head. *Publications of the Massachusetts Medical Society, 2,* 327–346.

Hebb, D. O. (1945). Man's frontal lobes: A critical review. *Archives of Neurology and Psychiatry, 54,* 10–24.

Hebb, D. O., & Penfield, W. (1940). Human behavior after extensive bilateral removal from the frontal lobes. *Archives of Neurology and Psychiatry, 44,* 421–438.

Hécaen, H. (1964). Mental symptoms associated with tumors of the frontal lobe. In J. M. Warren & K. Akert (Eds.), *The frontal granular cortex and behavior* (pp. 335–352). New York: McGraw-Hill.

Hécaen, H., & Albert, M. (1978). *Human neuropsychology*. New York: Wiley.

Heilman, K. M., & Valenstein, E. (1972). Frontal lobe neglect in man. *Neurology, 22,* 660–664.

Jacobsen, C. F. (1935). Functions of frontal association area in primates. *Archives of Neurology and Psychiatry, 33,* 558–569.

Jacobsen, C. F. (1936). Studies of cerebral function in primates: I. The functions of the frontal association areas in monkeys. *Comparative Psychological Monographs, 13,* 1–60.

Kimura, D. (1963). Right temporal-lobe damage. *Archives of Neurology (Chicago), 8,* 264–271.

Kleist, K. (1934a). *Kriegverletzungen des Gehirns in ihrer Bedeutung fur Hirnlokalisation und Hirnpathologie*. Leipzig: Barth.

Kleist, K. (1934b). *Gehirnpathologie*. Leipzig: Barth.

Kolodny, A. (1929). Symptomatology of tumor of the frontal lobe. *Archives of Neurology and Psychiatry, 21,* 1107–1127.

Konow, A., & Pribram, K. H. (1970). Error recognition and utilization produced by injury to the frontal cortex in man. *Neuropsychologia, 8,* 489–491.

Lewinsohn, P. M., Zieler, J. L., Libet, J., Eyeberg, S., & Nielson, G. (1972). Short-term memory: A comparison between frontal and nonfrontal right- and left-hemisphere brain-damaged patients. *Journal of Comparative Physiology and Psychology, 81,* 248–255.

Lezak, M. D. (1983). *Neuropsychological assessment* (2nd ed.), London & New York: Oxford University Press.

Lhermitte, F. (1983). "Utilization behaviour" and its relation to lesions of the frontal lobes. *Brain, 106,* 237–255.

Lhermitte, F., Derouesne, J., & Signoret, J-L. (1972). Analyse neuropsychologique du syndrôme frontal. *Revue Neurologique, 127,* 415–440.

Lindqvist, G., & Norlen, G. (1966). Korsakoff's syndrome after operation on ruptured aneurysm of the anterior communicating artery. *Acta Psychiatrica Scandinavica, 42,* 24–34.

Logue, V., Durward, M., Pratt, R. T. C., Piercy, M., & Nixon, W. L. B. (1968). The quality of survival after rupture of an anterior cerebral aneurysm. *British Journal of Psychiatry, 114,* 137.

Luria, A. R. (1973). *The working brain. An introduction to neuropsychology* (B. Haigh, Trans.). New York: Basic Books.

Luria, A. R. (1980). *Higher cortical functions in man* (2nd rev. ed.) (B. Haigh, Trans.) New York: Basic Books. (Original work published 1962).

Malmo, R. B. (1948). Psychological aspects of frontal gyrectomy and frontal lobotomy in mental patients. *Research Publications—Association for Research in Nervous and Mental Disease, 27,* 537–564.

Malmo, R. B., & Amsel, A. (1948). Anxiety-produced interference in serial rote learning with observations on rote learning after partial frontal lobectomy. *Journal of Experimental Psychology, 38,* 440–454.

Mazziotta, J. C., & Phelps, M. E. (1986). Positron emission tomography. Studies of the brain. In M. E. Phelps, J. C. Mazziotta, & H. R. Schelbert (Eds.), *Positron emission tomography and autoradiography: Principles and applications for the brain and heart* (pp. 493–579). New York: Raven Press.

Mesulam, M.-M. (1981). A cortical network for directed attention and unilateral neglect. *Annals of Neurology, 10,* 309–325.

Meyer, V. (1960). Psychological effects of brain damage. In H. J. Eysenck (Ed.), *Handbook of abnormal psychology: An experimental approach* (pp. 529–565). New York: Basic Books.

Milner, B. (1963). Effects of different brain lesions on card sorting: The role of the frontal lobes. *Archives of Neurology (Chicago), 9,* 90–100.

Milner, B. (1964). Some effects of frontal lobectomy in man. In J. M. Warren & K. Akert (Eds.), *The frontal granular cortex and behavior* (pp. 313–334). New York: McGraw-Hill.

Milner, B. (1965). Visually-guided maze learning in man: Effects of bilateral hippocampal, bilateral frontal and unilateral cerebral lesions. *Neuropsychologia, 3,* 317–338

Milner, B. (1974). Hemispheric specialization: Scope and limits. In F. O. Schmitt & F. G. Worden (Eds.), *The neurosciences: Third study program* (pp. 75–89). Cambridge, MA: MIT Press.

Milner, B. (1982). Some cognitive effects of frontal lobe lesions in man. In D. E. Broadbent & L. Weiskrantz (Eds.), *The neuropsychology of cognitive function* (pp. 211–226). London: The Royal Society.

Milner, B., & Petrides, M. (1984). Behavioural effects of frontal-lobe lesions in man. *Trends in Neurosciences, 7,* 403–407.

Milner, B., & Teuber, H-L. (1968). Alteration of perception and memory in man: Reflections on methods. In L. Weiskrantz (Ed.), *Analysis of behavioral changes* (pp. 268–375). New York: Harper & Row.

Mirsky, A. F., & Orzack, M. H. (1977). Final report on psychosurgery pilot study. In *Appendix—Psychosurgery. The National Commission for the Protection of Human Subjects Biomedical and Behavioral Research* (DHEW Publication No. (OS) 77-0002, pp. II-1-168). Washington, DC: U.S. Government Printing Office.

Naeser, M. A., Levine, H. L., Benson, D. F., Stuss, D. T., & Weir, W. S. (1981). Frontal leukotomy size and hemispheric asymmetries on computerized tomographic scans of schizophrenics with variable recovery. *Archives of Neurology (Chicago), 38,* 30–37.

Nauta, W. J. H. (1971). The problem of the frontal lobe: A reinterpretation. *Journal of Psychiatric Research, 8,* 167–187.

Nauta, W. J. H. (1973). Connections of the frontal lobe with the limbic system. In L. V. Laitinen & K. E. Livingstone (Eds.), *Surgical approaches in psychiatry* (pp. 303–314). Baltimore, MD: University Park Press.

Newell, A. (1977). You can't play 20 questions with nature and win: Projective comments on the papers of this symposium. In W. G. Chase (Ed.), *Visual information processing* (pp. 283–308). New York: Academic Press.

Petrides, M. (1985). Deficits on conditional associative-learning tasks after frontal- and temporal-lobe lesions in man. *Neuropsychologia, 23,* 601–614.

Petrides, M., & Milner, B. (1982). Deficits on subject-ordered tasks after frontal- and temporal-lobe lesions in man. *Neuropsychologia, 20,* 249–262.

Powers, W. T. (1973a). *Behavior: The control of perception.* Chicago, IL: Aldine.

Powers, W. T. (1973b). Feedback: Beyond behaviorism. *Science, 179,* 351–356.

Pribram, K. H. (1973). The primate frontal cortex-executive of the brain. In K. H. Pribram & A. R. Luria (Eds.), *Psychophysiology of the frontal lobes* (pp. 293–314). New York: Academic Press.

Pribram, K. H., Ahumada, A., Hartog, J., & Ross, L. (1964). A progress report on the neurological processes disturbed by frontal lesions in primates. In J. M. Warren & K. Akert (Eds.), *The frontal granular cortex and behavior* (pp. 28–55). New York: McGraw-Hill.

Robinson, A. L., Heaton, R. K., Lehman, R. A. W., & Stilson, D. W. (1980). The utility of the Wisconsin Card Sorting Test in detecting and localizing frontal lobe lesions. *Journal of Consulting and Clinical Psychology, 48,* 605–614.

Shallice, T. (1982). Specific impairments of planning. In D. E. Broadbent & L. Weiskrantz (Eds.), *The neuropsychology of cognitive function* (pp. 199–209). London: The Royal Society.

Stamm, J. S. (1979). The monkey's prefrontal cortex functions in motor programming. *Acta Neurobiologiae Experimentalis, 39,* 683–704.

Stein, S., & Volpe, B. T. (1983). Classical "parietal" neglect syndrome after subcortical right frontal lobe infarction. *Neurology, 33,* 797–799.

Stookey, B., Scarff, J., & Teitelbaum, M. (1941). Frontal lobectomy in the treatment of brain tumors. *Annals of Surgery, 113,* 161–169.

Stuss, D. T. (in press). Contribution of frontal lobe injury to cognitive impairment after closed head injury—methods of assessment and recent findings. In H. Levin, H. Eisenberg, & J. Grafman (Eds.), *Neurobehavioral recovery from head injury.* London & New York: Oxford University Press.

Stuss, D. T., & Benson, D. F. (1984). Neuropsychological studies of the frontal lobes. *Psychological Bulletin, 95,* 3–28.

Stuss, D. T., & Benson, D. F. (1986). *The frontal lobes.* New York: Raven Press.

Stuss, D. T., Benson, D. F., Kaplan, E. F., Weir, W. S., Naeser, M. A., Lieberman, I., & Ferrill, D. (1983). The involvement of orbitofrontal cerebrum in cognitive tasks. *Neuropsychologia, 21,* 235–248.

Stuss, D. T., Kaplan, E. F., Benson, D. F., Weir, W. S., Chiulli, S., & Sarazin, F. F. (1982). Evidence for the involvement of orbitofrontal cortex in memory functions: An interference effect. *Journal of Comparative and Physiological Psychology, 96,* 913–925.

Stuss, D. T., Kaplan, E. F., Benson, D. F., Weir, W. S., Naeser, M. A., & Levine, H. L. (1981). Long-term effects of prefrontal leucotomy. An overview of neuropsychologic residuals. *Journal of Clinical Neuropsychology, 3,* 13–32.

Teuber, H.-L. (1964). The riddle of frontal lobe function in man. In J. M. Warren & K. Akert (Eds.), *The frontal granular cortex and behavior* (pp. 410–444). New York: McGraw-Hill.

Walsh, K. W. (1978). *Neuropsychology. A clinical approach.* Edinburgh & London: Churchill-Livingstone.

Wechsler, D. (1955). *Manual for the Wechsler Adult Intelligence Scale.* New York: Psychological Corporation.

Welt, L. (1888). Ueber Charakterveranderungen des Menschen infolge von Lasionen des Stirnhirns. *Deutshes Archives des Klinischen Medizin, 42,* 339–390.

Winner, E., & Gardner, H. (1977). The comprehension of metaphor in brain-damaged patients. *Brain, 100,* 717–729.

Yussen, S. R. (1985). The role of metacognition in contemporary theories of cognitive development. In D. L. Forrest-Pressley, G. E. MacKinnon, & T. G. Waller (Eds.), *Metacognition, cognition, and human performance: Vol. 1. Theoretical perspectives* (pp. 253–283). Orlando, FL: Academic Press.

9

The Frontal Lobes and Hierarchical Organization of Cognitive Control

Elkhonon Goldberg and Robert M. Bilder, Jr.

THE FRONTAL LOBES AND MULTIPLE LEVELS OF COGNITIVE REPRESENTATION

The role of hierarchical organization in the central nervous system and the idea that the frontal lobes are positioned at the peak of the neuraxial hierarchy were well articulated over a century ago with specific reference to the motor system. Hughlings Jackson was able to state in 1884 that "the hierarchy of nervous centres . . . accords with the doctrine of evolution. . . . I now arrange them on an anatomico-physiological basis, that is especially as to degree of indirectness with which each represents the body, or part of it" (Taylor, 1932, p. 53). He saw the lowest nervous system centers (e.g., the anterior horns of the spinal cord and the cranial nerve nuclei) as the simplest and most organized, representing parts of the body in the most direct form. He called this type of control "representative." The next highest level of control he considered to be inherent in the pre-Rolandic cortical "motor" region; here the nature of control was considered more complex and less organized, representing wider regions of the body in a "doubly indirect" fashion. He called this type of control "re-representative." Finally, the highest motor centers, identified with the premotor and prefrontal cortical zones, he considered to be the most complex and least organized, and to represent the broadest regions of the body. He termed this highest form of "triply indirect" control to be "re-re-representative."

Critical to this formulation of a progression from lowest to highest centers is the concept that, at each superordinate level, the lower or subordinate representations are represented over again, but in more complex and elaborated forms. Also implicit in this Jacksonian model is the idea that the "units" of representation (in the case of motor centers, the regions of the body that are subject to control) become "larger" or more general, and lose specificity at superordinate levels of the neuraxial hierarchy.

ISBN 0-936925-00-0

The Jacksonian theory of hierarchical control has had a clear impact on the development of modern neuroscience. Today, the concept of hierarchical organization has become so popular in theories of neural control that it is considered virtually a truism. Jackson's concepts of hierarchical control pertained to the structural organization of the central nervous system rather than to cognitive constructs. The hierarchical model, however, has served as a prototype for more recent formulations directly bearing on cognitive processes. Among these, two scientific contributions are most responsible for introducing the concept of hierarchical organization into the conceptual arsenal of contemporary cognitive psychology and neuropsychology. One is the work of the Russian physiologist Nicholas A. Bernstein, which is summarized in the English language translation of his collected articles written between the 1930s and 1960s—*The Co-ordination and Regulation of Movements* (1967). Second is the book by G. Miller, E. Galanter, and K. Pribram—*Plans and the Structure of Behavior* (1960).

Although developed independently, these two treatises offer remarkably similar approaches in their general outlines of the structure of cognitive control. In both models, a given cognitive activity is presumed to rely on multiple levels of representation of the desired objective or cognitive "product." These different levels of representation differ in terms of their molarity; that is, each level manifests a distinct degree of generality in its representation of the ultimate cognitive product. The relationship between these different representations of the cognitive product at different levels of the neurocognitive hierarchy may best be described as homomorphic (i.e., many to one, as opposed to isomorphic, or one to one). This homomorphism provides a mechanism for distributing a great amount of information across several levels of the hierarchy, thereby ensuring that the representation at any single level remains "observable" and "manageable" in terms of its complexity.

This view of hierarchical organization is particularly appealing to the student of cognition and resembles the Jacksonian concept of re-representation at different levels of the hierarchy of nervous centers. Unlike the hierarchical model of Hughlings Jackson, however, it is cognitive representations rather than nervous centers that constitute the levels of the neurocognitive hierarchy.

Neurocognitive hierarchies are viewed not only as repositories of specific "static" knowledge, but also as active cognitive operations involved in the process of categorization. This active role is implicit in the mapping of representations derived at one level of neurocognitive hierarchies onto representations derived at another level.

The intellectual appeal of these notions of hierarchical organization of cognitive control proved to be enormous, and precipitated a shift from the "linear," "Markovian," and "stochastic" views of cognition widely held in the 1940s and 1950s to the more recent concepts of "vertical" and "hierarchical" forms of cognitive control. Nevertheless, the appeal of hierarchical concepts in cognitive psychology is due more to their elegance and heuristic power than to their empirically demonstrated validity and psychological reality.

We believe in the challenge of understanding the fine operational composition of complex normal cognitive processes through observing the disintegration of these processes in brain pathology. This belief rests on the assumption that cognitive pathology can be understood best as an alteration or distortion of the normal hierarchical organization of cognitive control, rather than as a radically different or unique organization . Moreover, it is implied that cognitive operations that are normally fused so as to make their elementary components indiscriminable may be decomposed or uncoupled in certain kinds of pathology in a way that enables isolation of cognitive subprocesses.

We have attempted to validate the psychological reality of the hierarchical model of cognitive control by studying cognitive pathology. Among the diverse sets of brain diseases affecting cognitive control, we decided to study pathological conditions involving the frontal lobes. It is commonly accepted that the frontal lobes are invested with the executive aspects of cognitive control: planning, sequential organization, and the selectivity of behavior. Based on what is known about the functions of prefrontal brain, it would appear that, of all cerebral structures, it must be most critically involved in the hierarchical organization of cognitive control, and that it is specifically the disruption of processes controlled by prefrontal brain that should leave the hierarchical organization of cognition most disrupted.

The assumption underlying this reasoning is that the contribution of prefrontal cortex is critical primarily for the application of preexisting cognitive representations in ongoing cognitive activities. It is not necessarily assumed that prefrontal cortex is important for the initial formation of those representations, but that it is essential for the executive operations of selection among the long-term representations once these are generated, for the application of these representations in specific cognitive contexts, and for control over the interaction among different levels of representation within the hierarchy.

Perseverations occupy a special place within the rich phenomenologic domain of cognitive pathology associated with frontal lobe damage. Perseveration is usually defined descriptively as any situation in which elements of previous tasks or behavior(s) fuse with an ongoing task or behavior, or when a behavior or operation cannot be terminated (Goldberg, in press; Luria, 1966/1980).

Perseveration is a particularly common and conspicuous consequence of prefrontal pathology (Goldberg & Costa, 1985; Halstead, 1947; Luria, 1966/1980; Stuss & Benson, 1984), though it is not always pathognomonic of prefrontal pathology, and examples of perseverative behavior may be found in a variety of conditions not affecting the frontal lobes (Critchley, 1964; Hécaen, Penfield, Bertrand, & Malmo, 1956; Stuss & Benson, 1984). In these focal nonfrontal syndromes, however, perseveration is most frequently limited to a specific sensory modality or type of behavior that is directly related to the site of the lesion (Goldberg & Tucker, 1979). Quite a contrast is seen in prefrontal pathology, where perseveration may be ubiquitous, affecting virtually every domain of cognition and behavior, regardless of the sensory modalities or the modes of output involved (Goldberg, in press; Goldberg, & Tucker, 1979; Luria, 1966/1980). Examples of perseveration associated with prefrontal lesions are well documented in a broad range of systems: motor (Goldberg & Tucker, 1979; Luria, 1966/1980); oculomotor (Goldberg, in press; Luria, 1966/1980); verbal (Kleist, 1934); and mnestic (Goldberg & Bilder, in press; Goldberg & Costa, 1985). We refer to this broad impact of prefrontal pathology across multiple cognitive/behavioral domains as the "horizontal pervasiveness" of perseveration.

We will attempt to demonstrate in this chapter that another equally fundamental property is found in prefrontal pathology, which can be called the "vertical pervasiveness" of perseveration. By vertical pervasiveness we mean the fact that perseveration can be observed at multiple levels of the neurocognitive hierarchy (Goldberg, in press; Goldberg & Tucker, 1979; Sandson & Albert, 1984). We hope to show, in other words, not only that different *types* of behavior can be affected by perseveration, but also that perseveration may affect multiple *levels* of cognitive control that are implicit in any single behavior. Our goal is to provide evidence that prefrontal pathology may lead to the disintegration of hierarchical relations among different representational levels, and that different types of perseveration may serve as markers of disintegration at specific levels of representation within the neurocognitive hierarchy. We will argue that the following levels may all be affected by perseveration: selection of the general cognitive mode or semantic set; retrieval from semantic store; execution of individual task items; and elementary cognitive or motor operations (Goldberg, in press; Goldberg & Tucker, 1979; Luria, 1966/1980).

We will then ask the question that every neuropsychologist interested in normal cognition inevitably asks: What properties must normal organization possess, in order to account for the observed phenomena of cognitive pathology? We shall argue, based on a survey of the phenomenology of perseveration, that a picture of normal cognitive organization is revealed that adheres closely to the theories of Bernstein and of Miller, Galanter, and Pribram, and that strongly supports the hierarchical model of cognitive control.

Among the different manifestations of perseveration, perseverations of motor behaviors are most easily elicited and documented in patients with prefrontal pathology. Analysis of patients' graphomotor performance (drawing) is a particularly valuable and practical technique. Few other activities leave behind a permanent, detailed record of performance at such small expense. Techniques for eliciting motor perseverations in graphomotor tasks were introduced and used extensively by Luria (1966/1980). In these tasks, subjects must draw sequences of graphical elements (e.g., geometric forms, letters, numbers) in response to a rapid series of specific commands.

The sequential arrangement of these commands may be manipulated to increase the probability of perseveration. In general, repetitive and overlearned sequences that lead to motor or semantic stereotypes tend to produce perseveration most reliably. Further demands for speeded performance exacerbate perseverative tendencies. In cases with massive frontal lobe lesions, however, task demands may be minimal and still precipitate perseveration and perseverative responses may be observed even in the execution of simple motor tasks.

Luria (1965) differentiated motor perseverations seen in the drawing of graphical sequences into two classes, and proposed their neuroanatomical substrates. The first type he termed "efferent" motor perseveration. These efferent perseverations have been characterized by Luria as manifestations of a pathological "inertia" in the execution of elementary motor acts. Luria attributed this type of perseveration to frontal lesions that include the basal ganglia. The second type identified by Luria (1965) may be referred to as higher order, "cortical" perseveration (Goldberg & Costa, 1985). In this type of perseveration, individual motor acts may be executed without errors, and the patient may be fully able to terminate the elementary components of a motor task. Difficulties arise when the patient must "switch" to perform a new motor task. Perseveration is demonstrated in these patients as a failure to shift completely to the new task. The patient may stereotypically reenact the previous instructions, or the new task may be "contaminated" by qualities of the prior task. This may lead to the observation of "fragments of several motor sequences combined in a single behavior" (Goldberg & Costa, 1985). Luria (1966/1980) suggested that this type of perseveration is due to a pathological inertia of the "action program" or "whole systems of action" (pp. 300–302). Luria (1966/1980) and Lebedinsky (1966) felt that these higher order perseverations were due to bilateral prefrontal lesions with no involvement of the basal ganglia.

Goldberg and Tucker (1979) used the techniques developed by Luria to illustrate how disintegration may occur at different levels of the neurocognitive hierarchy. Their investigation involved 19 postoperative patients with prefrontal lesions of various etiologies, originally studied at the Burdenko Institute in Moscow. A further sample description is available elsewhere (Goldberg & Tucker, 1979).

In their analysis of patients' drawings, Goldberg and Tucker found support for the distinction between efferent and higher order perseveration that had been made by Luria (1966/1980) and Lebedinsky (1966). Representing the efferent motor perseverations were what Goldberg and Tucker referred to as hyperkinesia-like motor perseverations, in which single motor acts, or single graphical elements, could not be terminated. This interminable repetition of an elementary motor act, such as the continuous overdrawing of a circle in response to a single command, along with other examples of this type, may be seen in Luria (1966/1980) on pages 298 (Figure 83) and 303 (Figure 88).

Goldberg and Tucker also identified higher order perseverations such as those described by Luria, in which no defects in the execution of elementary acts were present, but in which difficulties appeared when patients were asked to shift from one task to another. Close scrutiny of the patients' drawings revealed distinct subtypes of perseveration within this higher order class, some of which could not easily be described as simply "motor." Goldberg and Tucker (1979) identified, in addition to the hyperkinesia-like motor perseverations, the following distinct types of higher order perseveration: *perseveration of elements*—involving a whole motor sequence corresponding to a set of graphical components that collectively constitute a geometric form or a fragment thereof; *perseveration of features*—perseveration of abstract, generic properties of a geometric form (e.g., the property of being a closed figure, a convex figure, or a curvilinear figure); and *perseveration of activities*—perseveration of a whole type of activity or semantic class rather than of a specific task item. Such perseveration may occur when the patient is required to make rapid transitions between various behavioral modes (e.g., writing vs. drawing) or semantic categories (e.g., drawing geometric forms vs. drawing mathematical symbols).

Examples of these higher order perseverations are presented in Figure 1.

Perseveration of Elements Perseveration of elements is represented in Figures 1a and 1b. No hyperkinetic effect can be observed. The patient accurately drew the first figure (a cross), but subsequent instructions to draw a circle and then a square revealed perseveration: He continued to draw a cross within each figure. Many of the patients merged fragments of figures or whole figures in this way.

Perseveration of Features These phenomena are represented in Figures 1c and 1d. Here, no complete graphical elements or fragments were confused. Rather, the perseverations seem to involve more general confusions between certain features, including the "closedness" versus "openness" of the figures or the number of their elementary graphical components, independent of the specific graphical configuration of these components. This type of perseveration appears to involve general spatial characteristics describing prototypical concepts of different classes of figures (the class of crosses vs. the class of circles, etc.) rather than the actual motor or graphomotor sequences involved in execution of the figures.

Perseveration of Activities or Semantic Categories Perseveration between different types of activities is illustrated in Figure 1e. The patient was instructed to draw a circle, a square, and a triangle, and then to write a sentence (which did not include the names of any geometric figures). None of these tasks elicited

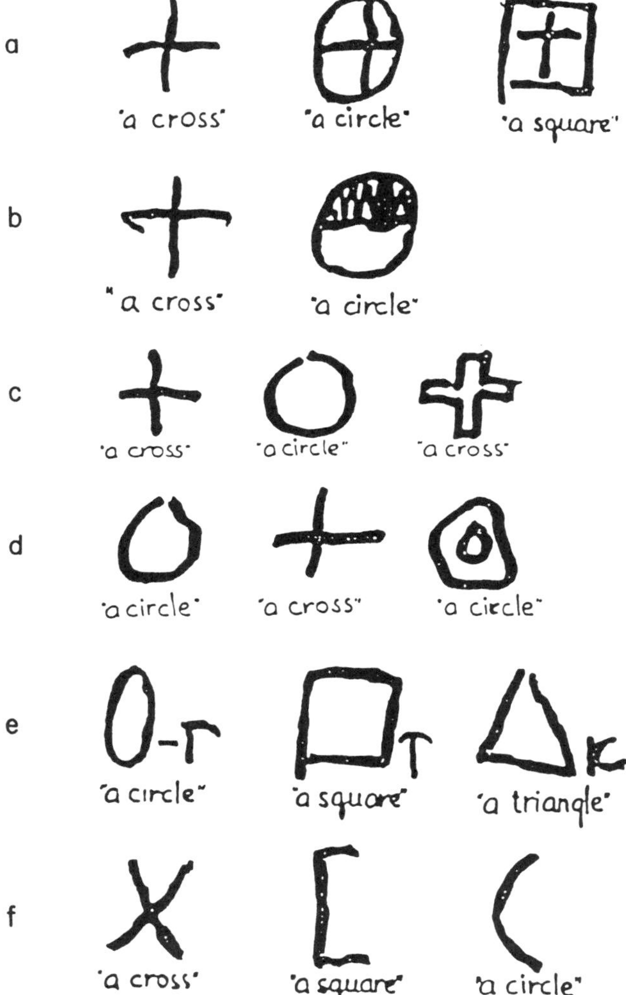

FIGURE 1 Types of perseveration. (a, b) Perseveration of elements; (c, d) perseveration of features; (e) perseveration of activities; (f) perseveration of semantic categories. a, b, e, and f are from Patient K., who suffered head trauma with prefrontal site of impact and fracture of the frontal bone. The operation consisted of removal of the fractured bone and resection of the frontal poles. Pronounced symptoms of convexital and mediobasal frontal dysfunction were observed. The experimental data were obtained 2 weeks to 3 1/2 months after the operation. In f, the patient's choice of items in a wrong semantic category was facilitated by the similarity of verbal labels (see text for explanation). Figures c and d are from Patient S., who had a cystic tumor of the third ventricle. The operation consisted of the removal of the cyst, with the approach through the premotor zone and the body of the third ventricle. Postoperative edema was observed, with the prevailing dysfunction of deep and medial areas of the premotor zone and ventral areas of the brainstem. The data were obtained 8 to 12 days after the operation. (From Goldberg and Tucker, 1979, pp. 276–277. Reprinted by permission.)

perseveration. Subsequently, however, when instructed to draw a series of geometric figures, the correct forms were accompanied by letters (Figure 1e). These are the terminal letters of the Russian words corresponding to each shape. The Russian word for circle is КРУГ, for square it is КВАДРАТ, and for triangle it is ТРЕУГОЛЬНИК. Thus, the activity of writing words was perseverated into the subsequent activity of drawing geometric forms.

Perseverations between different semantic categories of stimuli can be identified in Figure 1f. The patient had previously drawn a series of geometric forms and then performed simple arithmetical computations, without any evidence of perseveration. When subsequently instructed to draw geometric figures, however, the patient replaced these with mathematical symbols. Similar to the perseveration of writing into drawing described above, this introduction of mathematical symbols into drawing was not random. A multiplication sign "×" replaced a cross, showing an obvious perceptual similarity. In the same way, the two subsequent replacements (bracket for square, parenthesis for circle) show a natural semantic/perceptual resemblance to the requested figures. This natural semantic resemblance is fully appreciated when one considers that the Russian term for bracket translates as "square bracket" and that parenthesis translates as "circle bracket."

Unlike the other types of perseveration, these perseverations cannot be explained readily as confusions between simple graphical elements, or distortions of forms based on the features of individual items. Instead, these manifestations appear to illustrate confusions between distinct types of activities or semantic categories.

It is clear that not all of the perseverations described in these examples are "motor." Only the hyperkinesia-like perseverations and the perseverations of elements appear to reflect deficits restricted to the domain of motor activity and execution. We may ask, then, what aspects of processing are reflected in these other types of perseveration. We shall discuss these different classes of phenomena and attempt to place them within a hierarchical model integrating different processing stages required for the execution of a cognitive task.

For any set of cognitive operations, two requirements should be satisfied to allow the hypothesis of hierarchical interaction among operations. First, the cognitive operations should be organized sequentially, such that the content of any operation ($i + 1$) is dependent on the output of the prior operation (i). Second, earlier stages of the process should involve more generalized representations of the desired output of the task than later ones.[1]

[1]Here we are speaking specifically of operations applicable to executive motor output functions, and the organization of responses in general. A parallel series of operations could be considered as prerequisites for the hierarchical "assembly" of cognitive perceptual representations in sensory, receptive, or "input" modalities, but in reverse order. In such systems, one might hypothesize that earlier stages involve less generalized representations, which become more generalized at subsequent stages of processing.

While the output of one level of a cognitive hierarchy contains all the information about the output of the antecedent level, the opposite is not true. In other words, there must be a homomorphic (many-to-one, as opposed to isomorphic, or one-to-one) relation between the contents of two sequential cognitive operations for those operations to be considered hierarchically organized.

The different types of perseveration illustrated above appear to reflect deficits at different levels of a cognitive hierarchy that satisfies these requirements. Perseveration of activities or semantic categories, Figures 1e and 1f, involves confusion between whole semantic categories, such as the category of mathematical symbols and that of geometric forms, or pictorial and linguistic representations. In these instances, the errors may be seen as involving retrieval of the most appropriate item from an inappropriate category of mnestic representations. Perseveration of features, Figures 1c and 1d, seems to reflect confusions of generic spatial characteristics of individual items within a given semantic category, in this case the domain of geometric forms. Perseveration of elements, Figures 1a and 1b, appears to involve unification of individual components of specific graphical sequences, each of which corresponds to a different individual item. Finally, the hyperkinesia-like perseverations involve loss of motor control over the execution of individual graphical components, specifically the inability to terminate elementary movements.

If we reconstruct the presumed normal cognitive operations whose impairment leads to these perseverations, a sequential relation among them is evident. First, the most general category of information, or mnestic representation, must be addressed. Interference with this process would lead to perseveration of activities or semantic categories. Second, a more specific representation describing the appropriate type of form within that category must be accessed. Interference at this level of processing would lead to perseveration of features. Third, specific "metrics" must be imposed on this representation, leading to the formulation of a motor-execution sequence. Interference at this stage would lead to perseveration of elements. Finally, specific muscle groups must be innervated for the execution of each of the specific motor components of this sequence. Disruptions at this level would lead to hyperkinesia-like perseverations. Thus, the four types of cognitive operations involved in these tasks appear to meet the requirements of sequential organization and to constitute distinct stages of processing.

The second requirement, that there should exist a descending generality of representation at successive levels, also appears to be satisfied. Comparing the final motor output stage (hypothetically disrupted in hyperkinesia-like perseveration) to its antecedent level (disrupted in perseveration of elements), there is a loss of information about specific muscle innervation required for task execution. This penultimate level of representation could as easily maintain programs for actions involving other motor systems as those involving the hands. Moving from this level (associated with perseveration of elements) to its antecedent level (associated with perseveration of features), there is a loss of specific "metric" information. This level of representation could therefore generate a variety of unique instances of a given form. Moving from this level (associated with perseveration of features) to the earliest or highest level (associated with perseverations of activities or semantic categories), there is a loss of information regarding the specific item to be retrieved or generated from long-term memory. The only information retained at this level is the specification of the general semantic class to which the target item belongs.

Although these cognitive operations (whose impairment presumably underlies the presented types of motor perseveration) can be arranged hierarchically, it is not yet established that this hierarchy in fact describes normal processing. Should this be the case, then the different types of motor perseverations would appear to correspond to breakdowns at specific levels in this hierarchy. Although this interpretation is hypothetical, it is supported by the following considerations.

First, these phenomena cannot be explained as being due to memory impairments affecting recall for the items used in the experiment. In control procedures each of the patients was able to draw, name, and identify each of the individual stimuli. Perseverations only emerged in the context of rapid stimulus presentation and alternation between tasks. It is likely, therefore, that the observed deficits are specific to the domain of executive functions.

Second, one might wonder whether these executive deficits reflect general features of normal organization revealed through pathological change or unique instances of deranged organization that are specific to the individual cases of pathology studied. Several observations suggest that these perseverations reveal general features of cognitive control. In those cases where more than one type of perseveration was present during the early postoperative stages, the process of recovery was invariably the one predicted by the hierarchical model. Regardless of the combination of perseveration types present, it was found that higher order perseverations recovered later than did lower order perseverations. Furthermore, the fact that the same types of perseverations occur across a wide variety of pathological conditions supports the hierarchical model as a reconstruction of normal organization (Goldberg & Tucker, 1979, pp. 278–279).

These illustrations support our assertion that patients with anterior lesions show perseverations that can be interpreted in the context of a hierarchical model of executive functions that incorporates motor, cognitive, and executive features. Insofar as these types of perseverations may be used as markers, revealing disruptions at different levels of a normal neurocognitive hierarchy, they serve to identify distinct levels, each characterized by its own molarity, or "size," of representational units. The first or highest involves the selection of a general type of activity, or class of mnestic representations (perseveration of activities reflects a breakdown at this level). The second level involves the selection of the specific representation that corresponds to a given task within the more general category of tasks that were selected at the preceding level (perseveration of features reflects a breakdown at this level). The third level involves a conversion of the "simultaneous" representation or "gestalt" representation of the task, selected at the previous level, into a sequential set of motor procedures required for task execution (perseveration of elements reflects a breakdown at this level). Finally, the fourth level involves the implementation of the detailed, individual components of the motor sequence that were specified at the previous level (hyperkinesia-like perseverations reflect a breakdown at this level).

FRONTAL LOBES AND "TOPOLOGICAL" REPRESENTATION OF THE VISUAL FORM

As long ago as the 1930s, Bernstein noted that higher order motor behaviors are not controlled by the specific circumstances of the physical and psychological environment alone, but rather by a generic, invariant representation of the objective, or the desired cognitive "product" (see Bernstein, 1967). In a somewhat metaphorical fashion, Bernstein drew a distinction between "topological" and "metric" levels in the representation of a desired motor product. By topological, he meant the invariant aspects of representation that could be seen to apply across a given class of motor products; the metric aspects of representation were seen, on the other hand, as variable and situation dependent within a given class of motor products.

Identifying the specific nature of the topological, generic, invariant cognitive representations became one of the central themes of cognitive psychology as it developed in later years. In their pioneering attempts to arrive at a "psychophysics" of shape or pattern perception, Attneave and Arnoult recognized that, although shape involves many dimensions, "presumably some (descriptive) terms have more psychological meaningfulness than others," and that "unless some meaningful units of variation are specifiable, functional relationships cannot be obtained" (Attneave & Arnoult, 1956, p. 452).

Given the critical role attributed to prefrontal cortex in executive operations over these invariant cognitive representations, it was felt that closer examination of cognitive deficits seen in prefrontal pathology could enhance understanding of the nature of normal cognitive representations.

In the previous section of this chapter, it was proposed that perseveration of features reflects disruption of that level within the neurocognitive hierarchy at which selection from the long-term memory representations occurs, involving the generic aspects of a desired task item. Perseveration of features was therefore viewed as confusion between two or more such generic representations.

It was further felt that if the above-specified assumptions are true, a more detailed examination of these perseverations of features could be used to elucidate the nature of the cognitive code, and specifically to identify the ways in which some simple visual concepts may be represented in semantic memory. The method involved determining whether there might be some selectivity among the generic properties of the visual form that tend to perseverate. To the extent that such selectivity exists (in other words, that some properties perseverate but not others), it could be argued that these properties represent the "psychologically meaningful (descriptive) terms" and reflect the units of encoding implicit in normal cognitive representations of visual forms.

A description of the procedures and the patient sample involved in this study was provided briefly in the previous section; more details are available elsewhere (Goldberg & Tucker, 1979). The following dimensions or "parameters" of visual form were identified as being consistently subject to perseveration, and are illustrated in Figure 2.

Parameter of Closedness/Openness Figure 2a illustrates that an open figure (e.g., a cross) may become "closed" when drawn after closed figures. When a whole sequence consisted of open figures only, this phenomenon was never observed.

Parameter of Number of Elementary Components This parameter appeared to be perseverated in the following ways. In Figure 2b, a circle, which was preceded by a two-component cross, was drawn as two concentric circles. Parallel to this example, but not shown here, a dot was drawn as a colon when the instruction to draw the dot was preceded by a task in which the patient drew an equal sign. In another related example, a patient was instructed to print a series of letters. Each letter was repeated by the patient more than once, despite instructions requesting the patient to draw only single letters. This repetition, by itself, was not unexpected, but the number of repetitions was not random. Each letter was written as many times as the number of its elementary graphical components: MMMM for M; HHH for H.

Parameter of Straightness/Curvedness The feature of curvilinearity can affect a straight-lined figure, as in Figure $2c_1$. A cross, following a "moon" crescent, was not only drawn as closed (following the same pattern as seen in Figure 2a), but also had curved lines. In Figure $2c_2$, the reverse effect was seen: the substitution of a curvilinear shape by a linear one. The patient was asked to draw "the numeral 2" followed by a few straight-lined figures (a cross, stairs, and an angle). He was subsequently instructed to write "1 + 2 = 3." He executed the instruction as shown in Figure $2c_2$ replacing the conventional Arabic notation with a rectilinear Roman numeral. The same phenomenon can be demonstrated in the printing of letters. A patient wrote the numeral "0" as a vertically oriented parallelogram

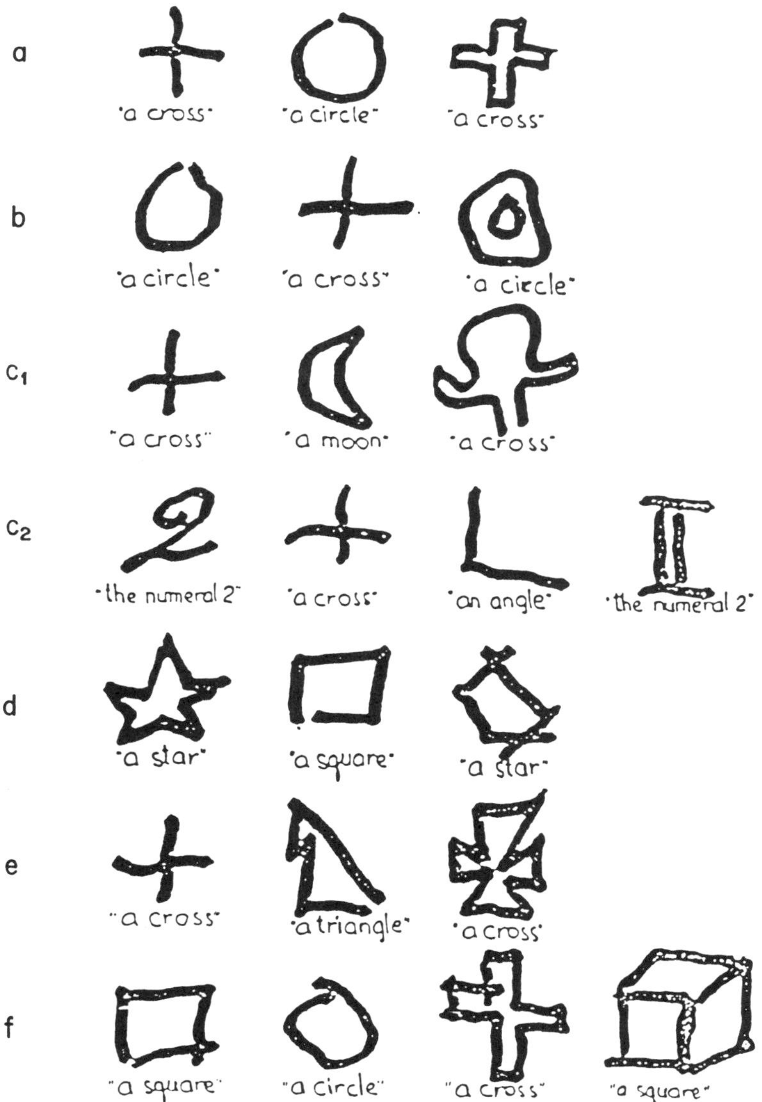

FIGURE 2 Perseveration of features. (a) Perseveration of "closedness/openness"; (b) perseveration of the number of elementary components; (c_1, c_2) perseveration of "straightness/curvedness"; (d) perseveration of "convexity/concavity"; (e) perseveration of "orthogonality/nonorthogonality"; (f) shift of the figure's position on the "subjective dimensional scale." (From Goldberg and Tucker, 1979, pp. 282–283. Reprinted by permission.)

when it was preceded by п (the Russian equivalent of P). Conversely, when п was written after 0, it took the form of a curvilinear P (the Latin equivalent of п).

Parameter of Convexity/Concavity An example of this type of feature perseveration can be observed in the transitions from concave to convex, illustrated in Figure 2d.

Parameter of Orthogonality/Nonorthogonality When drawn after a sequence of trapezoids and triangles, a cross not only was drawn as closed, but also contained many diagonal lines, as shown in Figure 2e.

Parameter of the Type of Symmetry Along with perseveration of features, Goldberg and Tucker observed a "perseveration of replacement," where one figure was completely replaced by another. These replacements tended to occur separately within the class of closed figures and within the class of open figures. Only rarely did a closed figure replace an open one, or vice versa.

In analyzing the regularities of replacement within the group of closed figures, a relation to each figure's type of symmetry was evident. A circle was distorted or replaced least often (a figure with an infinite number of axes of symmetry); a square was distorted or replaced more often (a figure with four axes of symmetry); and a triangle was distorted or replaced more frequently (a figure that can have no more than three axes of symmetry). Furthermore, a circle was most often replaced by a square, but never by a triangle. A triangle was most often replaced by a square but never by a circle. Another observation relevant to these considerations is that, despite adequate ability to draw each of the three figures separately, a patient may have specific difficulties executing these figures sequentially. An instruction to draw a triangle following a circle, or vice versa, proved to be difficult for the patients. On the other hand, "square-triangle" and "circle-square" transitions were more easily performed.

Parameter of the Figure's Position on the "Subjective-Dimensional Scale" In the example of Figure 2f, a patient was instructed to draw a sequence of closed figures, then a sequence of open figures, and then a square. As shown in Figure 2f, the open figure (a cross) obtained the property of "closedness." More surprising was that the square, which was drawn subsequently, was drawn as a cube. It obtained a third dimension.

Two control sequences of instructions were presented to this patient: a series of open figures followed by a square, and then a series of closed figures with a square among them. In both instances, the square was drawn properly. It thus seems likely that the increase in the number of dimensions of the square occurred only after the open figures in the sequence had obtained closedness. What we may be observing in the joint occurrence of these phenomena is, in fact, an increase in the number of "subjective" dimensions of the figures: from essentially linear to enclosed areal representations ("one" to "two" dimensions) in the earlier figures, and from two to three dimensions for figures like a square that already have two dimensions. This combined phenomenon can be interpreted as a shift of the visual form's position on the scale of dimensions, another significant parameter of visual representation.

One has to use caution in applying data from neurological populations to the consideration of normal cognition. With this in mind, we wish to review data supporting the relevance of the hypothesized dimensions of feature-based encoding of visual forms to normal cognitive processing.

Competency in the processing of the visual forms used in this study is normally established very early in cognitive development, well before the onset of pathological conditions in these cases. It is reasonable to assume, therefore, that the patients' memories for these forms were not altered by their pathology. Moreover disregarding our interpretations of these perseverations, it is still improbable that these perseverations reflect disruption of the actual mnestic representations of visual form. If a disruption of memory had taken place, it would be difficult to understand how the patients could accurately recognize, name, and draw all the figures during previous control sessions.

There is additional evidence from studies of nonpathological samples that provides further support for the hypothesized dimensions of visual feature representation. We will briefly review some of this evidence, derived from studies of normal cognition, that relates to each of the hypothetical parameters of visual representation.

Parameter of Closedness/Openness In an investigation of reading, Gibson, Gibson, Pick, and Osser (1962) asked a group of children, 4 to 8 years old, to select from among 12 letter-like forms those that matched a standard. Among the 12 test figures were two copies of the standard, along with 10 "distractors," or variations of the standard. The error scores for each group and for each type of variation were recorded. Error scores for all variations decreased with increasing age, but the mean error scores within groups and the rates of change within variation types showed significant differences. A "closed/open" variation showed the most marked improvement. In a similar experiment, Hutko and Smothergill (1971) asked 8- and 9-year-olds to recognize standards and five variations, using the same letter-like forms that Gibson and associates (1962) had used. Mean correct scores were significantly different for figures exhibiting closedness versus openness.

Parameter of Number of Elementary Components Attneave (1954) investigated factors influencing the judged complexity of geometric forms. Subjects rated each of a series of randomly generated figures along a Likert-type scale using verbal labels, ranging from "very simple" to "very complex." The "number of elementary turns" (a measure analogous to the parameter discussed here) was the most significant factor in the judged complexity of the figures. Furthermore,

Zusne (1970) observed that the number of sides of a polygon would have the most perceptual significance when investigating simpler forms, such as triangles, squares, and circles. Such was the case in our experiment.

Parameter of Straightness/Curvedness Pritchard, Heron, and Hebb (1960) investigated the effects of stabilizing different images on the retina. Subjects reported fading and reappearance of parts of the figures in nonrandom patterns; specifically, curved shapes were preserved longer than were jagged or straight-edged shapes. Eagle and Klein (1962) reported a significant decrease in error scores for a "curved" compared to a "straight" variation, as did Hutko and Smothergill (1971) in their parallel study.

Parameter of Convexity/Concavity In a study of afterimage phenomena, Riggs (1973) presented subjects with adaptation grids composed of red or green concave-down curves. From trial to trial he varied the degree of concavity from 24° to 3°, approaching flatness. Following fixation, subjects were shown a standard test grid composed of alternating groups of concave-down and concave-up curves of 4.5° in a neutral color. The fixation time required to induce a red-green afterimage effect with the standard grid depended on the degree of concavity of the fixation grid. Grids of almost flat curvature produced no aftereffect even after more than 30 minutes of fixation. Riggs therefore proposed that there are special detectors sensitive to the degree of concavity or convexity of figures.

Parameter of Orthogonality/Nonorthogonality A number of investigations involving the perception and discrimination of lines of different orientations revealed that subjects' performances were significantly superior with vertical or horizontal lines compared to lines of other orientations (Guralnic, 1972; Wade, 1972; Houlihan & Sekular, 1972).

Parameter of Degree of Axial Symmetry Gatti (1925) asked subjects to mark the centers of different figures with a dot. Accuracy was best with circles, not as good with squares, and poorest with triangles. In developmental studies, Arnheim (1954), Piaget and Inhelder (1956), and Cratty (1970) reported that children generally learn to manipulate and to draw circles by age 3, squares by age 4, and triangles only by about age 5. These findings suggest that the degree of axial symmetry is an important feature involved in the encoding of simple figures.

The data described in this section are limited in several respects. First, the above list of parameters should not be regarded as exhaustive. Second, describing a representational structure as a simple list of features is not sufficient in itself. Special analysis would have to be devoted to revealing the composition of such representations. Moreover, one cannot be certain that a universal basic code for processing visual information exists. It is possible that there are many such codes, each of a different level of generalization, or subserving a different class of objects. In this respect the stimuli used in our research were probably too elementary and specific to make extensive generalization from the data obtained. This limitation was imposed by the methodology, which dictated that only nameable figures could be used.

We should also point out the general "linguistic" difficulty inherent in any research involving semantic labels, for example, naming the categories of significant visual features. A researcher must use his natural language to describe a nonverbal system of encoding, but must acknowledge the probable lack of isomorphism between the descriptor and that which is described. This vicious circle has been mentioned by many, but is hardly avoidable in principle.

IS SELECTIVE FRONTAL DAMAGE NEEDED TO PRODUCE SELECTIVE FRONTAL DYSFUNCTION?

In the preceding sections, specification of the neuroanatomical mechanisms underlying perseveration has been deliberately avoided. As previously mentioned, despite the regular association of perseveration with prefrontal pathology (Goldberg & Costa, 1985; Halstead, 1947; Luria, 1966/1980; Stuss & Benson, 1984), perseveration may also be seen in a variety of nonfrontal cases (Critchley, 1964; Hécaen et al., 1956; Stuss & Benson, 1984). Perseverations consequent to posterior lesions have been well documented. Hécaen et al. (1956) described perseverations of writing following parietotemporooccipital lesions of the minor hemisphere. Critchley (1964) and Lhermitte and Beauvois (1973) suggested that perseveration of naming can be part of associative visual agnosia following lesions of the occipital areas of the dominant hemisphere. Buckingham, Whitaker, and Whitaker (1979) reported linguistic perseverations consequent to left parietal and left temporoparietal lesions. Irigaray (1967) and Sjögren, Sjögren, and Lindgren (1952) have also described linguistic perseverations in diffuse conditions (dementia).

Although various focal nonfrontal syndromes may lead to perseverative behavior, perseveration in these cases is usually limited to a specific sensory modality or type of behavior. As indicated above, in cases with massive prefrontal pathology, perseveration is more ubiquitous, permeating virtually every cognitive domain, and manifest at every level of the neurocognitive hierarchy. It is, in other words, characterized by both horizontal and vertical pervasiveness.

Furthermore, whereas limited, specific types of perseverations are often components of various nonfrontal neuropsychological syndromes, perseverations pervading agnosic, aphasic, or amnestic domains are usually associated with a distinctive syndrome affecting predominantly executive control, and sparing the specific cognitive faculties that are implicated in the primary agnosias, aphasias, or amnesias. An extensive literature leads to the conclusion that massive, focal prefrontal damage almost invariably implies the presence of perseveration characterized by horizontal and vertical pervasiveness.

The following question then arises: Assuming that a massive prefrontal lesion is sufficient to produce pervasive perseveration, is such a lesion also necessary?

We propose that this question be examined in a broader context: that of the general relationship between structural and functional definitions of brain damage. Most of classical brain-behavior theory has been derived from the study of patients suffering focal lesions of abrupt onset, in which the effects of tissue destruction are superimposed on a presumably normal and completed pattern of neurocognitive development. Implicit in most neuropsychological inference is the assumption of isomorphism between destruction of certain neuroanatomical loci and certain neuropsychological syndromes. This assumption has been formulated most succinctly as the principle of double dissociation (Teuber, 1955).

It is not clear, however, that this assumption is justified in cases in which the manifest pathology is nonfocal, chronic/progressive, or early onset/static. Such conditions, encountered frequently in psychiatric, neurodevelopmental, and geriatric clinics, may violate the assumption of normal premorbid neurocognitive development and/or the assumption that inferences drawn from analysis of acute-onset focal disturbances are applicable to such cases. Recently heightened interest in the neuropsychological evaluation of patients with these conditions may precipitate a marked revision of certain concepts central to brain-behavior theory and challenge the equivalency of structural/biochemical and functional/clinical definitions of brain disease. It is possible that structurally/biochemically diffuse pathology may be associated with "focal" functional/clinical presentations; conversely, a focal clinical presentation does not necessarily imply an underlying focal structural/biochemical pathological basis.

Classic localization theory assumes that the probability of occurrence of a particular neuropsychological syndrome is determined solely by the neuroanatomic site of the lesion. Implicit in this assumed isomorphism between tissue destruction and neuropsychological deficit is the belief that all cerebral structures are characterized by identical "functional breakdown thresholds." Thus, comparable lesions in different brain regions are assumed to result in comparable disruptions of the functions mediated by those regions. But what if different parts of the brain have different functional breakdown thresholds?

There are several factors that appear quite likely to result in different functional breakdown thresholds for different cerebral structures:

1. Extensivity of connections. The richer the network of pathways in which a given structure is embedded, the more dependent is its functioning on the functioning of other cerebral regions. The functions of a "well-connected" structure are therefore more likely to be adversely affected by neuroanatomically remote dysfunction than those of a "poorly connected" structure.
2. Position within the phylogenetic and/or ontogenetic succession of development. A widely accepted postulate, articulated by Hughlings Jackson in 1884 (Taylor, 1932) in his treatise on the evolution and dissolution of nervous system function, suggests that the most recently developed cerebral structures are the most susceptible to deterioration. This means that, in the face of "equal" structural damage, it is the phylo- and ontogenetically youngest structures that may be more functionally vulnerable than older structures.
3. Degree of routinization. Generalized structural damage is known to affect the least overlearned, least routinized behaviors first and foremost: Therefore diffuse pathology is most likely to "masquerade" in its presentation as selective damage to those cerebral structures known to be involved in these behaviors.

These considerations point to a unique role of prefrontal cortex, and lead to the prediction that among cases with nonfocal pathology it is precisely the prefrontal cortex that would be implicated most frequently. First, prefrontal cortex is characterized by a uniquely rich set of afferent and efferent projection systems linking the prefrontal cortex to virtually every other functional system of the brain. These systems include posterior associative cortices; premotor cortex; limbic structures such as cingulate cortex, amygdalae, and hippocampi; higher order thalamic nuclei (dorsomedial and ventral anterior); basal ganglia; and the mesencephalic and pontine reticular nuclei. The prefrontal cortex is therefore interconnected with systems critical for perceptual integration, integrated motor control, memory, affect, and activation/arousal systems at virtually every level of the neuraxial hierarchy—at the neocortical, paleocortical, limbic, striatal, diencephalic, and mesencephalopontine levels (Nauta, 1971). In this respect prefrontal cortex is certainly unique, and it is more likely to be a functional "mirror" of disturbances affecting different loci anywhere in the brain than is any other structure.

Second, the prefrontal cortex is among the phylogenetically youngest of cerebral structures and its ontogenetic development is less rapid than that of most other parts of the brain. According to the Jacksonian concept of evolution and dissolution, the prefrontal cortex would therefore be predicted to be one of the brain regions most vulnerable to disruption. We should also consider the possibility that structures taking longer to develop over the course of ontogeny therefore have a longer duration at risk. "Critical periods" for pathogenic influences might be prolonged in these more slowly maturing systems, of which the prefrontal cortex is exemplary.

Third, the prefrontal cortex is critical for the most complex and least routinized aspects of cognitive control, planning, and decision making (Luria, 1966/1980). Its functions are presumed to be more complex than those of any other cerebral structure. We suggested earlier that generalized dysfunction affects primarily the least overlearned, least routinized behaviors, and therefore nonfocal dysfunction is likely to be manifest in the breakdown of functions controlled by prefrontal cortex more readily than in the breakdown of other functions. One may, in fact, interpret perseveration as a prime example of overly routinized, stereotypic behavior replacing more complex behaviors as a result of the failure of cognitive controls furnished by the prefrontal cortex.

Any of the above factors or combinations of these could lead to a situation in which an essentially diffuse structural/biochemical dysfunction could present as a focal disease selectively implicating prefrontal cortex. Such diffuse disturbances are more likely to masquerade as focal frontal syndromes rather than as any other focal syndrome. The principle of double dissociation, therefore, may be difficult to apply in cases with executive deficits; in contrast, this principle may be valuable in cases with other region-specific cognitive dysfunctions. It may not be necessary or even appropriate to postulate a selective frontal lobe disease to account for a behavioral pattern that is consistent with frontal lobe dysfunction. As Tilney said, "the entire period of human evolutionary existence could be considered the 'age of the frontal lobe' " (Stuss & Benson, 1984, p. 3; Tilney, 1928). In a similar light, cognitive involution due to diffuse disease in humans can be viewed as dominated by frontal lobe dysfunction.

An illustration of these principles appears to be provided by recent applications of both structural and functional brain-imaging techniques in investigations of the schizophrenic syndrome. A conspicuous discrepancy exists between those assessments of chronic schizophrenics using indices of cerebral function (such as PET, rCBF, and quantitative EEG measures) and those using indices of structural cerebral damage (such as the CT scan and pneumoencephalographic and neuropathological measures). The functional indices have often supported hypotheses that many schizophrenic patients have a predominantly prefrontal locus of dysfunction (Buchsbaum et al., 1982; Farkas et al., 1980; Franzen & Ingvar, 1975a, 1975b; Ingvar, 1976; Ingvar & Franzen, 1974a, 1974b; Morihisa & McAnulty, 1985; Krezevic, Koretic, Lazic, & Javarnik, 1982). On the other hand, in vivo measures of gross structural degeneration (e.g., CT, MRI, and pneumoencephalography) most frequently show a diffuse pattern of change without selective prefrontal preponderance (for a review, see Weinberger, Wagner, & Wyatt, 1983).

Moreover, postmortem studies have most frequently implicated pathological changes in anterior limbic, mesiotemporal, and brainstem structures; these changes include fibrillary gliosis of the septal nuclei, the nucleus accumbens, substantia innominata, globus pallidus, and bed nucleus of the stria terminalis

(Fishman, 1975; Nieto & Escobar, 1972; Stevens, 1982); disorientation of hippocampal pyramidal cells (Kovelman & Scheibel, 1984; Scheibel & Kovelman, 1980); and pathologic changes associated with decreased volume in hippocampus, entorhinal cortex, and globus pallidus (Bogerts, Meertz, & Schonfeldt-Bausch, 1985). There have been a few reports of structural abnormalities in the prefrontal cortex from the neuropathology literature (Miyakawa et al., 1972; Tatetsu, 1964), but these findings may not have been specific to prefrontal cortex, given that only prefrontal cortex was sampled. There have been some recent suggestions that atrophic changes may indeed be detected in prefrontal regions (Andreasen et al., 1986; Weinberger & Shelton, cited in Weinberger, Berman, & Zec, 1986), but as yet there is no strong evidence to support contentions that these changes are specific to prefrontal cortex.

Severe perseverations such as those described earlier in this chapter can be elicited in cases with no evidence of focal lesions, at least not in a macroscopic, "dry" structural sense. Among these are chronic schizophrenics (see Figure 3), patients with senile and presenile dementias, such as Alzheimer's disease (see Figures 4 and 5), and patients with diffuse encephalopathy secondary to viral infection (see Figure 6). Although quite extensive neuropathological and neuroradiological findings have been reported in these conditions, none reveals frontal preponderance that would be invariant across the majority of subjects in any given diagnostic category (Friedland, Brun, & Budinger, 1975; Johnstone, Crow, Frith, Carney, & Price, 1978; Katzman, 1985; Martin et al., in press; Snider et al., 1983; Weinberger, Torrey, Neophytides, & Wyatt, 1979a, 1979b).

The possibility that specific biochemical "lesions" lead to focal frontal dysfunction in these populations does not find much support either. The cholinergic system, impairment of which has been proposed as central to the pathology of Alzheimer's disease, is not known to have predominantly prefrontal terminal projections, but instead appears to maintain relatively diffuse projections which, if anything, are probably maximal in the older periallocortical regions than in associative isocortex (Lewis & Shute, 1967; Mesulam, Volicer, Marquis, Mufson, & Green, 1986; Shute & Lewis, 1966, 1967). The presence of perseveration and other manifestations of "frontal lobe" dysfunction in chronic schizophrenia may also be difficult to attribute solely to a biochemical lesion. Although cortical projections of the mesolimbic/mesocortical dopamine system(s) show a strong prefrontal preponderance (Brown, Crane, & Goldman, 1979; Lindvall, Bjorklund, Moore, & Stenevi, 1979; MacBrown & Goldman, 1977), the hypofrontality seen in functional imaging studies has been most conspicuous in negative, deficit symptom-cluster schizophrenics, and is less reliably found in positive, productive symptom-cluster schizophrenics (Bilder, 1984; Seidman, 1983). While disturbances in the dopamine system have been proposed as a mechanism underlying positive symptom-cluster, "Type I" schizophrenia, there is considerably less evidence for a specific dopaminergic

FIGURE 3 Perseverations in chronic schizophrenia. In examples a, b, and c, the task consisted of drawing geometric forms following verbal commands. Every subsequent command was delivered after the response to the previous one had been completed. (a) Interminability of activity. The sequence of commands was as follows: "Draw a cross; draw a cross; draw a circle; draw a cross." Items 3 through 8, Items 10 through 16, and Items 18 through 28 represent excessive perseverative productions. Drawn by Patient J., 47 years old, RDC diagnosis of chronic schizophrenia, disorganized type. (b) Perseveration of elements. Instructions for Items 3 through 6 were: "Draw a cross" (the notation on the figure was made by the examiner after the experiment). Drawn by Patient C., 48 years old, DSM III diagnosis of chronic schizophrenia, disorganized type. Noncontrast CT scan was normal. (c) Combined manifestation of perseveration of features and perseveration of elements/recurrent perseveration. The sequence of instructions was as follows: "Draw a cross" (executed correctly); "draw a square" (patient draws two squares, which constitutes a perseveration of features, specifically perseveration of the number of elementary graphical components); "draw a cross" (patient draws two squares, which constitutes perseveration of elements); "draw a cross" (patient draws another square, a continued perseveration of elements). Patient G., 38 years old, RDC diagnosis of chronic schizophrenia, disorganized type. Noncontrast CT scan was normal. (d) Perseveration of elements. The instruction was spoken and printed by the examiner and held in the patient's view. The patient first drew the central form, followed by the top and then the bottom forms. Patient R., 28 years old, RDC diagnosis of chronic schizophrenia, undifferentiated type. Noncontrast CT scan was normal. (From Goldberg, in press. Reprinted by permission.)

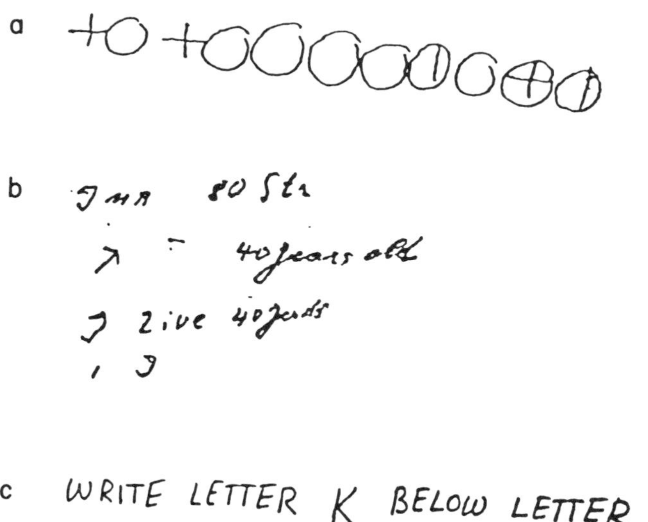

FIGURE 4 Perseverations in senile dementia. (a) Perseveration of elements in drawing. Instructions for the last four items were: "Draw a cross, draw a cross, draw a cross, draw a triangle." (b) Perseveration of elements in writing. The patient was asked to write his address (which includes the arabic numeral 4), which he did correctly. After that he was asked to write four sentences, each of which corresponds to a line in the figure: Line 1—"I am 80 years old"; Line 2—"I am 80 years old"; Line 3—"I live in New York"; Line 4—"I live in New York." (c) Perseveration of activities. The instruction was spoken and printed for the patient after he had been engaged in simple computations and the drawing of geometric forms. All were drawn by Patient M. S., 80 years old. Presumed Alzheimer's disease. CT scan revealed diffuse cerebral atrophy. (From Goldberg, in press. Reprinted by permission.)

role in the mediation of negative symptom-cluster, "Type II" schizophrenia (Angrist, Rotrosen & Gershon, 1980; Crow, 1980; Johnstone, Crow, Frith, Carney, & Price, 1978). Instead, diffuse structural damage has been hypothesized to be a pathologic feature in this subtype (Crow, 1980).

To summarize, it is proposed that the presence of massive, focal prefrontal damage, while sufficient, is not necessary to produce the so-called "executive syndrome," of which horizontally and vertically pervasive perseveration is a part. It is further proposed that the executive syndrome need not be associated

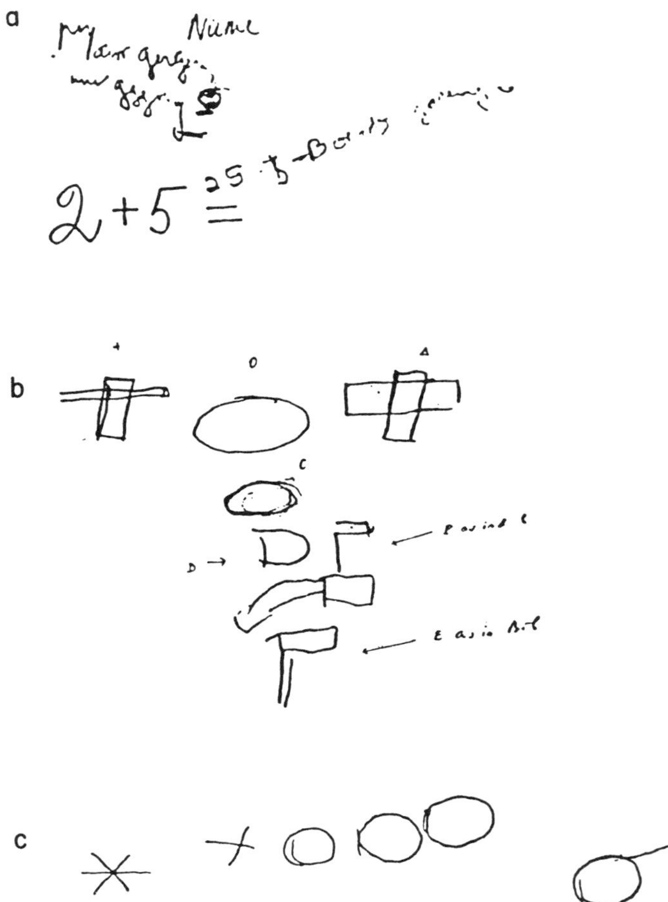

FIGURE 5 Perseverations in presenile dementia. (a) Combined presentation of hyperkinesia-like motor perseveration and perseveration of activities. The patient was instructed to write her name—the upper part of the figure exhibiting hyperkinesia-like perseveration. After that the examiner wrote "2 + 5 =" and asked the patient to write the answer. Perseveration of activities took place in that the patient continued to write words. (b) Combined presentation of perseveration of features and perseveration of elements. The sequence of instructions was as follows: "Draw a circle; draw a circle; draw a cross; draw a cross; write letter B as in Bob; write letter D." The crosses were drawn after circles became closed forms (perseveration of features). Rectangular elements of a cross appeared when the instructions were to draw letters (perseverations of elements). (c) Perseveration of features. The instruction "Draw a cross" was executed correctly (second figure from left). After drawing the cross (which has two elementary graphical components), the subsequent commands "Draw a circle; draw a circle" were each executed two times, resulting in the final four figures. All were drawn by Patient M. K., 59 years old. Normal pressure hydrocephalus (diagnosis based on cisternographic examination). MRI revealed mild to moderate ventricular dilatation and mild sulcal prominence. (From Goldberg, in press. Reprinted by permission.)

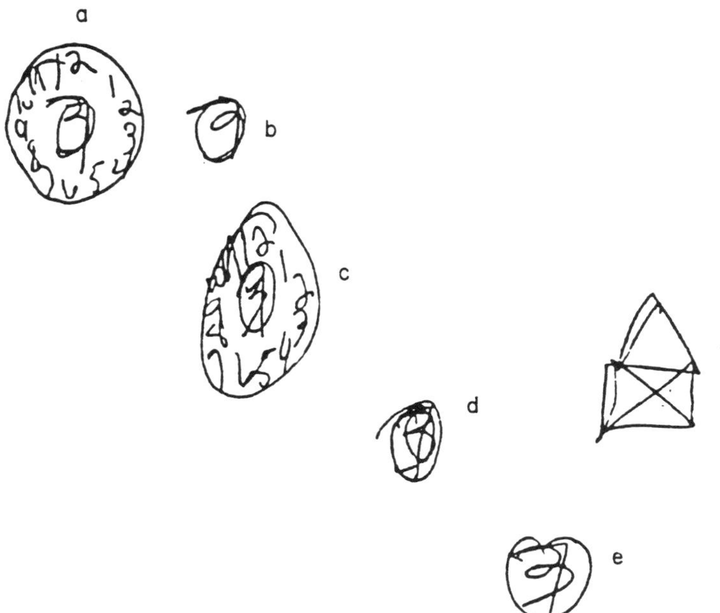

FIGURE 6 Perseveration in viral encephalopathy. Instructions for a, b, and c: "Draw a clock with hands showing 7:30." Instructions for d, e, and f: "Draw a house." Instructions were given consecutively in order of the alphabetical labels (a)–(f). Perseveration of elements from Tasks a, b, and c affects performance on Tasks d and e. Patient J. R., 27 years old. Diffuse encephalopathy secondary to viral, HTLV-III infection (AIDS) in an IV drug abuser. CT scan was normal. EEG showed mild disorganization. (From Goldberg, in press. Reprinted by permission.)

with any distinct focal lesion, but instead may be a relatively common consequence of global cerebral deterioration. We do not mean to suggest that the executive functions, including cognitive programming, planning, and the maintenance of cognitive/behavioral selectivity, are not controlled by the prefrontal brain. To the contrary, we fully subscribe to the classic point of view that they are. Instead, it is proposed that any diffuse brain dysfunction, affecting much of the brain to an equal extent from structural and/or biochemical points of view, will disrupt executive functions before it will disrupt other functions.

In a somewhat poetic vein, Miller et al. referred to the prefrontal cortex as the "organ of civilization" (1960, p. 207). Any student of history will note that this makes it by definition a rather fragile entity.

ACKNOWLEDGMENTS

The contribution of the first author was supported by a Fellowship at The Institute for Advanced Studies, The Hebrew University of Jerusalem. The authors are grateful to Kenneth Podell and Sandra Bessegato for their efforts in the preparation of the manuscript and reference list.

REFERENCES

Andreasen, N., Nasrallah, H. A., Dunn, V., Olson, S. C., Grove, W. M., Ehrhardt, J. C., Coffman, J. A., & Crossett, J. H. W. (1986). Structural abnormalities in the frontal system in schizophrenia. A magnetic resonance imaging study. *Archives of General Psychiatry, 43,* 136–144.

Angrist, B., Rotrosen, J., & Gershon, S. (1980). Differential effects of amphetamine and neuroleptics on negative vs. positive symptoms in schizophrenia. *Psychopharmacology Bulletin, 72,* 17–19.

Arnheim, R. (1954): *Art and visual perception.* Berkeley: University of California Press.

Attneave, F. (1954). Information aspects of visual perception. *Psychological Review, 6,* 183–193.

Attneave, F., & Arnoult, M. D. (1956). The quantitative study of shape and pattern perception. *Journal of Experimental Psychology, 53,* 221–227.

Bernstein, N. A. (1967). *Coordination and regulation of movements.* Oxford: Pergamon.

Bilder, R. M. (1984). *Subtyping in chronic schizophrenia: Clinical neuropsychological, and structural indices of deterioration.* Ann Arbor, MI: Ann Arbor University microfilms.

Bogerts, B., Meertz, E., & Schonfeldt-Bausch, R. (1985). Basal ganglia and limbic system pathology in schizophrenia: A morphometric study of brain volume and shrinkage. *Archives of General Psychiatry, 42,* 784–791.

Brown, R., Crane, A. M., & Goldman P. S. (1979). Regional distribution of monoamines in the cerebral cortex and subcortical structures of the rhesus monkey: Concentrations and in vivo synthesis rate. *Brain Research, 168,* 133–150.

Buchsbaum, M. S., Ingvar, D. S., Kessler, R., Waters, R. N., Cappelletti, J., van Kammen, D. P., King, A. C., Johnson, J. L., Manning, R. G., Flynn, R. W., Mann, L. S., Bunney, W. E., & Sokoloff, L. (1982). Cerebral glucography with emission tomography. Use in normal subjects and in patients with schizophrenia. *Archives of General Psychiatry, 39,* 251–259.

Buckingham, H. W., Whitaker, H., & Whitaker, H. A. (1979). On linguistic perseverations. In H., Whitaker (Ed.), *Studies in neurolinguistics* (Vol. 4.) New York: Academic Press.

Cratty, B. J. (Ed). (1970). *Perceptual and motor development in infants and children.* New York: Macmillan.

Critchley, M. M. (1964). The problem of visual agnosia. *Journal of Neurological Science, 1,* 274–290.

Crow, T. J. (1980). Molecular pathology of schizophrenia: More than one disease process? *British Medical Journal, 280,* 66–68.

Eagle, M. N., & Klein, G. S. (1962). Fragmentation phenomena with the use of the stabilized retinal image. *Perceptual and Motor Skills, 15,* 579–582.

Farkas, T., Reivich, M., Alavi, A., Greenberg, J. H., Fowler, J. S., MacGregor, R. R., Christman, D. R., & Wolf, A. P. (1980). The application of [18f]2-deoxy-2-fluoro-D-glucose and positron emission tomography in the study of psychiatric conditions. In J. V. Possonneau, R. A. Hawkins, W. E. Lust et al. (Eds.), *Cerebral metabolism and neural functions.* Baltimore, MD Williams & Wilkins.

Fishman, M. (1975). The brain stem in psychosis. *British Journal of Psychiatry, 126,* 414–422.

Franzen, G., & Ingvar, D. H. (1975a). Abnormal distribution of cerebral activity in chronic schizophrenia. *Journal of Psychiatric Research, 12,* 199–214.

Franzen, G., & Ingvar, D. H. (1975b). Absence of activation in frontal structures during psychological testing of chronic schizophrenics. *Journal of Neurology, Neurosurgery and Psychiatry, 38* 1027–1032.

Friedland, R. P., Brun, A., & Budinger, T. F. (1985). Pathological and positron emission tomographic correlations in Alzheimer's disease. *Lancet, 1,* 228.

Gatti, A. (1925). Nuove ricerche sopra l'apprezzamento del centro nelle figure piane geometriche *Publicazione dell'Universita Cattolica di Milano, Serie 1, 1* (fasc, iv), 69–112.

Gibson, E. J. Gisone, J. J., Pick, A. D., & Osser, H. A. (1962). A developmental study of the discrimination of letter-like forms. *Journal of Comparative and Physiological Psychology, 55,* 897–906.

Goldberg, E. (1986). Frontal lobe-like syndromes and schizophrenia. In C. Shagass, R. C. Josiassen, W. H. Bridger, K. J. Weiss, D. Stoff, & G. M. Simpson (Eds.), *Biological psychiatry 1985* (pp. 1127–1129). New York: Elsevier.

Goldberg, E. (in press). Varieties of perseveration: A comparison of two taxonomies. *Journal of Clinical and Experimental Neuropsychology.*

Goldberg, E., & Bilder, R. (in press). Neuropsychological perspectives: Retrograde amnesia and executive deficits. In L. Poon (Ed.), *The handbook of memory assessment of older adults.* New York: APA Press.

Goldberg, E., & Costa, L. (1985). Qualitative indices in neuropsychological assessment: Executive deficit following prefrontal lesions. In K. Adams & I. Grant (Eds.), *Neuropsychological assessment of neuropsychiatric disorders* (pp. 48–64). London & New York: Oxford University Press.

Goldberg, E., & Tucker, D. (1979). Motor perseveration and long-term memory for visual forms. *Journal of Clinical Neuropsychology, 1,* 273–288.

Guralnic, S. M. (1972). Alphabet discrimination and distinctive features—research review and educational implications. *Journal of Learning Disabilities, 5,* 427.

Halstead, W. C. (1947). *Brain and intelligence: A quantitative study of the frontal lobes.* Chicago, IL: University of Chicago Press.

Hécaen, H., Penfield, W., Bertrand, C., & Malmo, R. (1956). The syndromes of apractognosia due to lesions of the minor cerebral hemisphere. *Archives of Neurology and Psychiatry, 75,* 400–434.

Houlihan, R., & Sekular, R. W. (1972). Perception and discrimination as a function of stimulus orientation. *Psychological Bulletin, 78,* 219.

Hutko, P., & Smothergill, D. (1971). Effects of stimulus characteristics on recognition memory in elementary school children. *Perceptual and Motor Skills, 33,* 531–534.

Ingvar, D. H. (1976). Functional landscape of the dominant hemisphere. *Brain Research, 107,* 101–107.

Ingvar, D. H., & Franzen, G. (1974a). Abnormalities of cerebral blood flow distribution in patients with chronic schizophrenia. *Acta Psychiatrica Scandinavica, 50,* 425–462.

Ingvar, D. H., & Franzen, G. (1974b). Distribution of cerebral activity in chronic schizophrenia. *Lancet, 2,* 1484–1486.

Irigaray, L. (1967). Approache psycholinguisitique de language des dements. *Neuropsychologia, 5,* 25–52.

Johnstone, E. C., Crow, T. J., Frith, C. D., Carney, M. W. P., & Price, J. S. (1978). Mechanism of the antipsychotic effect in the treatment of acute schizophrenia. *Lancet, 1,* 848–851.

Johnstone, E. C., Crow, T. J., Frith, C. D, Stevens, M., Kreel, L., & Husband, J. (1978). The dementia of dementia praecox. *Acta Psychiatrica Scandinavica, 57,* 305–324.

Katzman, R. (1985, February). *The biology of Alzheimer's disease: Clinical and neuropsychological implication.* Lecture given at the annual meeting of the Thirteenth International Neuropsychological Society, San Diego, California.

Kleist, K. (1934). *Gehirnpathologie.* Leipzig: Barth.

Kovelman, J. A., & Scheibel, A. B. (1984). A neurohistological correlate of schizophrenia. *Biological Psychiatry, 19,* 1601–1624.

Lebedinsky, V. V. (1966). Execution of symmetric and asymmetric programs in frontal lobe pateints. In A. R. Luria & E. D. Homskaya (Eds.), *Frontal lobes and regulation of psychological processes.* Moscow: Moscow University Press (in Russian).

Lewis, P. R., & Shute, C. C. D. (1967). The cholinergic limbic system: Projections to hippocampal formation, medial cortex, nucleus of the ascending cholinergic reticular system, and the subfrontal organ and supra-optic crest. *Brain, 90,* 521–540.

Lhermitte, E., & Beauvois, M. F. (1973). A visual-speech disconnexion syndrome—report of a case with optic aphasia, agnostic alexia and colour agnosia. *Brain, 96,* 695–714.

Lindvall, O., Bjorklund, A., Moore, R. Y., & Stenevi, V. (1979). Mesencephalic dopamine neurons projection to neocortex. *Brain Research, 81,* 325–331.

Luria, A. R. (1965). Two kinds of motor perseveration in massive injuries of the frontal lobes. *Brain, 88,* 1–10.

Luria, A. R. (1980). *Higher cortical functions in man* (2nd rev. ed.) (B. Haigh, Trans.). New York: Basic Books. (Original work published 1966).

MacBrown, R., & Goldman, P. S. (1977). Catecholamines in neocortex of rhesus monkey: Original distribution and ontogenetic development. *Brain Research, 124,* 576–580.

Martin, A., Browers, P., Lalonde, F., Cox, C., DeLeska, P., Fedio, P., Foster, N., & Chase, T. (in press). Towards a behavioral typology of Alzheimer's patients. *Journal of Clinical and Experimental Neuropsychology.*

Mesulam, M.-M., Volicer, L., Marquis, J. K., Mufson, E. J., & Green, R. C. (1986). Systemic regional differences in the cholinergic innervation of the primate cerebral cortex: Distribution of enzyme activities and some behavioral implications. *Annals of Neurology, 19,* 144–151.

Miller, G. A., Galanter, E., & Pribram, K. H. (1960). *Plans and the structure of behavior.* New York: Holt.

Miyakawa, T., Sumiyoshi, S., Deshimaru, M., Suzuki, T., Tomonari, H., Yasuoka, F., & Tatetsu, S. (1972). Electron microscopic study on schizophrenia. *Acta Neuropathologica, 20,* 67–77.

Morihisa, J. M. & McAnulty, C. B. (1985). Structure and function: Brain electrical activity mapping and computed tomography in schizophrenia. *Biological Psychiatry, 20,* 3–19.

Mubrin, Z., Krezevic, S., Koretic, D., Lazic, L., & Javarnik, N. (1982). Regional cerebral blood flow in schizophrenic patients. *rCBF Bulletin, 3,* 43–46.

Nauta, W. J. H. (1971). The problem of the frontal lobe: A reinterpretation. *Journal of Psychiatric Research, 8,* 167–187.

Nieto, D., & Escobar, A. (1972). Major psychoses. In J. Minkler (Ed.), *Pathology of the nervous system.* New York: McGraw-Hill.

Piaget, J., & Inhelder, B. (1956). *The child's conception of space.* London: Routledge & Kegan Paul.

Pritchard, R. M., Heron, W., & Hebb, D. O. (1960). Visual perception approached using the method of stabilized images. *Canadian Journal of Psychology, 14,* 67–77.

Riggs, L. A. (1973). Curvature as a feature of pattern vision. *Science, 181,* 1070–1072.

Sandson, J., & Albert, M. L. (1984). Varieties of perseveration. *Neuropsychologia, 22,* 715–732.

Scheibel, A. B., & Kovelman, J. A. (1980). Disorientation of the hippocampal pyramidal cell and its processes in the schizophrenic patient. *Biological Psychiatry, 16,* 101–102.

Seidman, L. J. (1983). Schizophrenia and brain dysfunction: An integration of recent neurodiagnostic findings. *Psychological Bulletin, 94,* 195–238.

Shute, C. C. D., & Lewis, P. R. (1966). Cholinergic and monoaminergic systems of the brain. *Nature (London), 212,* 710–711.

Shute, C. C. D., & Lewis, P. R. (1967). The ascending cholinergic reticular system: Neocortical, olfactory and subcortical projections. *Brain, 90,* 497–520.

Sjögren, T., Sjögren, H., & Lindgren, A. G. H. (1952). Morbus Alzheimer and Morbus Pick. A genetic, clinical, and pathoanatomical study. *Acta Psychiatrica et Neurologica Scandinavica Supplementum, 28*(82).

Snider, W. D., Simpson, D. M., Nielsen, S., Gold, J. W. M., Metroka, C. E., & Posner, J. B. (1983). Neurological complications of acquired immune deficiency syndrome: Analysis of 50 patients. *Annals of Neurology, 14,* 403–17.

Stevens, J. R. (1982). Neuropathology of schizophrenia. *Archives of General Psychiatry, 39,* 1131–1139.

Stuss, D. T. & Benson, D. F. (1984). Neuropsychological studies of the frontal lobes. *Psychological Bulletin, 95*(1), 3–28.

Tatetsu, S. (1964). A contribution to the morphological background of schizophrenia. *Acta Neuropathologica, 3,* 558–571.

Taylor, J. (Ed.). (1932). *Selected writings of J. Hughlings Jackson* (Vol. 2). London: Hodder & Stoughton.

Teuber, H. L., (1955). Physiological psychology. *Annual Review of Psychology, 6,* 267–296.

Tilney, F. (1928). *The brain, from ape to man.* New York: Harper (Hoeber).

Wade, N. J. (1972). Orientation effects on like after images. *Perception and Psychophysics, 12,* 409.

Weinberger, D. R., Berman, K. F., & Zec, R. F. (1986). Physiological dysfunction of dorsolateral prefrontal cortex in schizophrenia: I. Regional cerbral blood flow (rCBF) evidence. *Archives of General Psychiatry, 43,* 114–124.

Weinberger, D. R., Torrey, E. F., Neophytides, A. N., & Wyatt R. J. (1979a). Lateral cerebral ventricular enlargement in chronic scizophrenia. *Archives of General Psychiatry, 36,* 735–739.

Weinberger, D. R., Wagner, R. L., & Wyatt, R. J. (1983). Neuropathological studies of schizophrenia: A review. *Schizophrenia Bulletin, 9,* 193–212.

Weinberger, D. R., Torrey, E. F., Neophytides, A. N., & Wyatt. R. J. (1979b). Structural abnormalities in the cerebral cortex of chronic schizophrenic patients. *Archives of General Psychiatry, 36,* 935–939.

Zusne, L. (1970). *Visual perception of form.* New York: Academic Press.

10

Concept Formation and Frontal Lobe Function

The Search for a Clinical Frontal Lobe Test

Paul L. Wang

INTRODUCTION

In his article "The Frontal Lobe Revisited," the late Professor Livingston (1969) argued for a "second look" at the frontal lobe from a psychosurgery perspective. While we are revisiting the frontal lobes during the middle of the 1980s it would be appropriate and profitable to have a second look at the neuropsychological endeavor. This endeavor, which commenced more than a half-century ago, has been searching for a concept formation test that would satisfactorily assess frontal lobe functions and diagnose alteration in those functions in brain-damaged patients.

NEUROPSYCHOLOGICAL APPROACHES TO THE PROBLEM OF CONCEPT FORMATION

The quest for a concept formation test has been going on for some time. Prior to World War II, Goldstein, Scheerer, Gelb, and Weigl (1941) devised a number of sorting tests to investigate abstract and concrete behavior (Goldstein & Scheerer, 1941). Goldstein and Scheerer (1941) concluded that "organic pathology in patients with brain disease disintegrates human behaviour in such a way that the capacity for abstract behavior is impaired to a greater or lesser degree in the patient" (p. 9). Since their publication, the impairment of abstraction has been considered a hallmark of brain injury and the literature seldom disputes this conviction. However, because of the lack of techniques

ISBN 0-936925-00-0

enabling them to reliably localize lesion sites, these early authors were not able to report information concerning the relation between different sites of cerebral lesions and impairment in abstraction. Among the early researchers, Weigl (1941) and later Grant and Berg (1948) developed a card sorting test that consisted of two decks of 64 cards with different shapes, colors, and numbers of designs. The subject had to work out the sorting principle logically and needed to be capable of switching to a different principle once a set of correct responses had been established. As a rule, the subject received no warning of the change in principle.

Early in the 1960s, Milner used the Wisconsin version of the Weigl-type test, namely, the Wisconsin Card Sorting Test (WCST), to examine epileptic patients who had quantitatively documented removal of masses in the frontal lobes and other cerebral regions. She found that frontal lobe patients performed worse than patients whose brain damage occurred outside the frontal lobes in terms of the number of perseverative errors (i.e., return to responses that were correct for the previous category). She also pointed out that the group of left dorsolateral frontal lobe lesioned patients ($N = 8$) was the worst group in terms of number of perseverative errors made and sorting categories achieved (Milner, 1964). This finding was incongruent with the earlier findings of Teuber, Battersby, and Bender (1951), which indicated that a slightly more severe deficit appeared after left parietal temporal lesions. Teuber and his associates concluded that the deficits seen in performing this task were nonspecific to frontal lesions. An investigation of the methods used in administering the WCST in these two studies disclosed a significant difference: Milner gave no warning when principles changed, whereas Teuber warned the subjects at the beginning of the test of the possible change in principles. Milner (1964) argued that her study strongly suggested that "the ability to shift from one mode of solution to another on a sorting task is more impaired by frontal than by posterior cerebral injury." In a later paper, Teuber (1964) conceded that when the warning was eliminated the frontal lobe patients did indeed do much poorer on the WCST. Thereafter, Milner's findings were generally supported by other studies that used the WCST and its modified short form (Drewe, 1974) or modified error counting procedure (Robinson, Heaton, Lehman, & Stilson, 1980; Heaton, 1981), with the exception that no differences were found between left frontal and right frontal groups. However, these latter authors also found that diffusively lesioned patients did poorly on the WCST and that the magnitude of this deficit was no different from that observed in the frontal lobe group. Thus, they concluded that the WCST was a good screening test for brain damage, but was not very helpful in distinguishing focal frontal lesions from non-frontal lobe diffusive brain damage.

In another line of study, also using the WCST, Tarter and Parsons (1971) studied 24 male chronic alcoholics who were without a history of neurological symptoms. They found that these alcoholics took more trials to reach criterion and made more errors than did normal control subjects. However, the errors they made were not of the perseverative type reported by Milner; rather, their difficulty was in lack of persistence and they tended to respond very erratically. Since the etiology of chronic alcohol consumption is more subcortical in nature, as in Korsakoff patients (Talland, 1961), erratic responses versus perseverative responses on the WCST may represent a double dissociation between frontal lobe impairment and diencephalon involvement. In our clinical examination, we have often encountered patients who have displayed both erratic behavior and perseverative responses, and who have lesions restricted to the anterior portion of the cerebrum; such an observation should not be a surprise in view of the rich reciprocal connections between the prefrontal lobes and the diencephalon, particularly the thalamic region (Pandya & Kuypers, 1969). That is to say, when a frontal lobe patient exhibits both erratic and perseverative responses on the WCST, one should suspect (1) the possibility of additional thalamic and/or basal ganglia involvement or (2) that the frontopetal pathways originating in the diencephalon may have been encroached upon by the pathological process involved.

Sharing the same zeitgeist as Goldstein, Scheerer, Gelb (Goldstein & Scheerer, 1941), and Weigl (1941), during the early 1940s Ward Halstead and Paul Settlage (1943) developed a series of 9 tests totaling 360 items to investigate the "grouping behavior" of normal subjects and brain-injured patients. Their intention was to measure abstraction ability, which they believed to be a higher form of human intelligence. Several years later, in an article entitled "Frontal Lobe Functions and Intelligence," Halstead (1950) proposed the concept of biological intelligence and stated that "the 'A' factor, or capacity for abstracting universal or rational concepts, seems to be a general property of the cerebral cortex in man that is maximized in the cortex of the prefrontal lobes." In the following decade, he devoted much work to studying this concept by using a modified version of the original nine tests, namely, the Halstead Category Test (HCT). The HCT became one of several original tests adopted by Halstead and his co-workers to be incorporated into the Halstead-Reitan Neuropsychological Battery (HRNB), which is widely used by clinical psychologists today. It is also worth noting here that, so far, the HCT has been found to be the most robust test of the HRNB in the identification of brain damage (Reitan & Davison, 1974). The adult form of HCT contains 208 stimuli that have been divided into 7 subtests. All items within each subtest are organized with respect to a single principle, such as Roman numerals, number of objects, position of oddity, quadrant, or proportion. The subject is required to learn the principle initially by way of trial-and-error methods. Throughout the testing, perceptual abstraction and logical induction are highly demanded. Once the subject formulates the artificial concept involved in any one subtest, he is able to proceed through the rest of the items in that subtest without making any more errors as long as he consistently continues to apply that concept and does not make erratic responses.

Shure and Halstead (1958) tested 72 brain-damaged patients, of whom 35 had documented frontal lobe lesions. Some of their findings were reported as follows: (1) Frontal lobe patients were more impaired than non–frontal lobe patients on the HCT; (2) the right frontal lobe groups did not differ from the left frontal group; and (3) the correlation between size of frontal lesions and HCT performance was .349. (The correlation between size of non–frontal lobe lesion and HCT performance was .201.) These authors considered the last finding to be significant in that it supported the observation reported by Rylander (1943) that performance on abstract reasoning tasks was related to the amount of frontal lobe tissue removed. In addition, they also reported that patients with left hemisphere lesions were slightly more impaired than patients with right hemisphere lesions; however, the magnitude of this difference was not statistically significant ($p =$ .07).

I have regrouped the raw data reported in Shure and Halstead's study, and these are presented in Table 1. The analysis shown in Table 1 suggests that the HCT is a test most sensitive to left frontal lobe lesions. However, the HCT also identifies 35–41% of patients whose lesions occur in regions other than the frontal lobes. Therefore, the conclusive remarks made by Robinson et al. (1980) about the WCST are also applicable to the HCT; that is, the HCT is a test sensitive to brain damage at large but is not exclusively sensitive to frontal lobe dysfunction, particularly right frontal lobe impairment.

Reitan (1959), in an attempt to look into the nature of differences observed in brain-damaged patients, administered the HCT to 52 normal controls and 52 brain-damaged patients matched for age, sex, and education. As expected, the brain-damaged group made more errors than the control group on the HCT. However, Reitan failed to notice any significant difference between patients and normal controls with respect to interrelation of performance on different subtests. Thus, he concluded that the difference in abstraction ability between those with brain damage and normal controls is a quantitative one rather than a qualitative one.

THE MODIFIED VYGOTSKY CONCEPT FORMATION TEST

In 1921, Ach devised a method, using blocks of different shapes and colors, to study the formation of artificial concepts. Vygotsky (1934) adopted a modified version of this task to study concept formation ability in schizophrenic patients and reported that the loss of such ability was a cardinal characteristic of schizophrenia. Kąsanin and Hanfmann (1937) questioned the looseness of control conditions reported in the Vygotsky study and launched their own investigation, with slight changes in administration, and gave the test to 50 hospitalized schizophrenics. They described their method of administration as follows:

The experimental material consists of 22 wooden blocks varying in color, shape, height, and size. There are five different colors, six different shapes, two heights (the tall blocks and the flat blocks) and two sizes of the upper surface (large and small). On the under side of each figure, which is not seen by the subject, is written one of the four nonsense words: lag, bik, mur, or cev. Regardless of color and shape, lag is written on all tall large figures, bik on all flat large figures, mur on the tall small ones, and cev on the flat small ones. At the beginning of the experiment all blocks, well mixed as to color and size, are scattered on the table in front of the subject. He is told that four different kinds of blocks are before him, that each kind has a name, and that his task is to find and to separate these four kinds.

By using this method, these investigators confirmed Vygotsky's conclusion

TABLE 1
Regrouping of Shure and Halstead's Data (1958)

	Left hemisphere lesions ($N = 22$) Number of errors		Right hemisphere lesions ($N = 25$) Number of errors	
	Frontal ($N = 10$)	Nonfrontal ($N = 12$)	Frontal ($N = 11$)	Nonfrontal ($N = 14$)
	47	46	48	67
	56	35	61	85
	67	52	45	46
	62	18	39	60
	55	74	26	7
	51	20	60	12
	140	38	57	47
	45	123	70	12
	81	68	84	47
	82	23	128	18
		51	47	74
		18		65
				38
				28
				36
				20
Number of patients with HCT > 50[a]	8	5	6	5
Hit rate (%)	80	41	50	35

[a]Suggested cutoff score = 50.

that abstract thinking is impaired in schizophrenic disorders. They also reported that level of education was not an important factor in the performance of this test. Neither of these researchers, however, ever examined brain-damaged patients with this task.

Wang (1984) used the 22 blocks described above but modified the administration methods and developed a new scoring system to quantify the performance. This new system is called the Modified Vygotsky Concept Formation Test (MVCFT) and the essence of the MVCFT is as follows. The 22 blocks are randomly displayed in front of the subject and the examiner chooses the small blue triangle block and sets it aside as a demonstration piece. The subject is asked to look for other pieces that would belong to the same group. If the subject makes all the correct choices, the examiner moves on to other groups in a predetermined manner. However, if the subject makes three consecutive errors the examiner will pick another piece from the same group as an additional demonstration piece and the testing continues. In such a manner, the subject should be able to learn the artificial concept by incorporating the gradually increasing amount of information. Each block is coded along its four variable characteristics, namely, shape, color, height, and width, and the choices of the subject are recorded by matching the choices with the corresponding blocks on the recording sheet in their exact sequential order. Thus, the discursive processes of the subject can be retraced without asking the subject to think aloud. Types of errors such as random guessing, perseveration on a specific physical feature of the blocks, or inability to generalize the concept can be quantified. In addition, using the same blocks, a divergent reasoning task is added to the concept formation portion of the MVCFT. This divergent thinking task provides a tool to examine the subject's creative thinking ability and "fluency of ideas." The details of the MVCFT have been published elsewhere (Wang, 1984).

Wang (1984) administered the MVCFT to 30 normal controls and 53 brain-damaged patients whose lesions were confirmed by a CT scan of the head. Tables 2 and 3 contain the major statistical results of this study. An examination of Table 2 discloses that brain-damaged patients did significantly poorer than normal controls on both concept formation and divergent thinking tasks. The right-brain-damaged group was no different from the left-brain-damaged group, but both were better than the bilaterally diffusive lesioned group. These findings suggest that concept formation and divergent thinking, as measured by the MVCFT, are not lateralized cognitive functions. The brain-damaged patients were further divided into six groups: right frontal, left frontal, right nonfrontal, left nonfrontal, bilateral frontal, bilateral nonfrontal. A close examination of Table 3 reveals that frontal patients did significantly poorer than nonfrontal patients and that diffusively lesioned patients performed worse than unilaterally lesioned patients. Moreover, the right frontal lobe patients performed somewhat poorer than the left frontal lobe patients, but the difference failed to reach the conventional level of significance ($p = .06$). These findings suggest that the

TABLE 2

General Statistics (MVCFT)

	Control group (N = 30)			Brain-damaged patients (N = 53)			
	20–40 years	41–82 years	Total	Left	Right	Bilateral	Total
Male	N = 6	N = 6	N = 12	N = 14	N = 12	N = 9	N = 35
Female	N = 9	N = 9	N = 18	N = 6	N = 8	N = 4	N = 18
Total	M = 14.0	M = 23.6	M = 14.9	M = 29.7	M = 30.5	M = 44.5	M = 33.6
error	SD = 3.7	SD = 17.4	SD = 15.3	SD = 16.0	SD = 17.8	SD = 11.6	SD = 16.7
Perseverative	M = .53	M = 8.5	M = 4.5	M = 9.3	M = 11.3	M = 19.2	M = 12.5
error	SD = .74	SD = 9.1	SD = 7.6	SD = 8.2	SD = 9.7	SD = 9.1	SD = 9.7
Cues	M = .67	M = 1.06	M = .83	M = 1.45	M = 1.9	M = 2.3	M = 1.8
	SD = .81	SD = .79	SD = .81	SD = .94	SD = 1.7	SD = 1.6	SD = 1.58
Principle	M = 5.4	M = 2.9	M = 4.1	M = 2.3	M = 2.0	M = .69	M = 1.8
	SD = 1.4	SD = 2.4	SD = 2.4	SD = 2.0	SD = 2.5	SD = 1.2	SD = 2.1

TABLE 3

Frontal versus Nonfrontal Groups (MVCFT)

	Left frontal	Right frontal	Bilateral frontal	Total	Left nonfrontal	Right nonfrontal	Bilateral nonfrontal	Total
Male	10	5	8	23	4	7	2	13
Female	4	3	2	9	2	5	1	8
Total	M = 33.4	M = 41.1	M = 43.7	M = 38.6	M = 21.0	M = 23.1	M = 47.3	M = 26.0
error	SD = 16.0	SD = 41.4	SD = 9.1	SD = 15.2	SD = 13.0	SD = 13.7	SD = 20.6	SD = 16.4
Preseverative	M = 9.7	M = 16.3	M = 19.6	M = 14.4	M = 8.3	M = 8.1	M = 18.0	M = 9.6
error	SD = 7.6	SD = 9.3	SD = 9.4	SD = 9.4	SD = 10.2	SD = 8.9	SD = 10.1	SD = 9.6
Principle	M = 2.1	M = .38	M = .30	M = 1.1	M = 3.0	M = 3.1	M = 2.0	M = 2.9
	SD = 1.8	SD = .74	SD = .67	SD = 1.6	SD = 2.5	SD = 2.7	SD = 2.0	SD = 2.5

MVCFT may be sensitive to gross frontal lobe dysfunctioning, but performance on it is also affected by the disintegration of general cerebral functioning. The aforementioned results are in total agreement with those reported in the earlier literature by other investigators who used different forms of concept formation tests.

DEVELOPMENTAL CONSIDERATIONS IN CONCEPT FORMATION

It is worth noting that older normal subjects (age 41–82) in this study, as a group, performed worse than younger normal subjects (age 20–40) on both concept formation and divergent thinking tasks. Further analysis reveals that this age-related decline in performance on the MVCFT becomes most conspicuous after age 60. That is, concept formation and fluency of ideas start to decline slowly and steadily at the age of 40 and this trend of decline becomes noticeably steeper after age 60.

It has been suggested by many investigators (Piaget, 1926; Vygotsky, 1934) that concept formation ability sets in at puberty and progressively matures throughout adulthood. Talland (1961) noted that success in solving sequential concept formation problems that he designed steadily declined with age. It has been further suggested by investigators such as Hochanadel and Kaplan (1984) that the deterioration of cognitive functions noticed in the aged population resembles that seen in patients with right-hemisphere dysfunction. This latter statement is also applicable to the ability of concept formation. For example, a close inspection of the response profiles of the older normal subjects (age 41–82) and the subjects with lesions outside the frontal lobes, particularly the right-hemisphere-lesioned group, depicted in Tables 2 and 3 of the MVCFT study, indeed reveals much similarity. In fact, these groups do not differ from each other statistically.

The notion of more apparent deterioration of right-hemisphere-related cognitive functions in the aged is by no means a novel one. Those who are familiar with the Wechsler Adult Intelligence Scale (WAIS) are well aware of the fact that ability to perform all the nonverbal subtests tends to show accelerating decline with age. Slow speed of performance may have penalized the performance of the older subjects, but psychomotor retardation alone cannot totally account for the decline in general performance. In the case of concept formation, as measured by the MVCFT, the age-related decline is a true reflection of alteration in cognitive ability and is independent of speed of performance. As mentioned before, concept formation ability progressively matures throughout adulthood, but it is also very sensitive to aging and it starts to show a decline as early as age 40. Thus, it is quite tempting to suggest that one of the developmental characteristics of this brain function is "last to appear, first to disappear." Such a statement is reminiscent of Ribot's law pertaining to human memory function; that is, recent memory is most severely affected by brain damage with less and less effect on memory that is increasingly remote in time (Ribot, 1904).

The maturation of frontal lobe functions progresses at a relatively slower pace than the rest of the brain and functional stability may not be attained until the latter part of puberty (Luria, 1973). On the other hand, frontal lobe dysfunction is readily recognizable in the aged population (Hochanadel & Kaplan, 1984), and it would not be considered presumptuous if one were to propose that disintegration of frontal lobe functions signals a more advanced stage of normal aging. Taking these developmental characteristics into consideration, it is conceivable that concept formation ability and the frontal lobe functions may share either a common course or a parallel one of rise and fall over the life span.

Thus, aging is an important factor to be considered when using concept formation tests. Indeed, Prigatano and Parsons (1976) reported that the correlation between age and HCT error score was .63 for normal subjects, but that it dropped to .36 in the brain damaged. Apparently, age and brain damage interact to affect performance on the HCT. These correlations may also suggest that individual responses to brain injury, as reflected in performance on the HCT, are less predictable and that the impact of brain injury overrides the normal aging effect.

CONTENT ANALYSIS AND CONSTRUCTION OF CONCEPT FORMATION TESTS

The studies presented to this point indicate that the MVCFT, WCST, and HCT have all been proposed as measures of a similar form of abstract behavior—in essence, concept formation, categorical behavior, and grouping behavior. Since all of these tests are affected by brain damage and aging, it is conceivable that they share some common variance with one another. Regrettably, there is no information available regarding the correlations between MVCFT and the other two tests. However, Pendleton, Heaton, Lekman, and Hulihan (1982) did report a correlation between HCT errors and WCST perseverative responses. They found that the correlation was .56 for the brain-damaged patients and .55 for normal controls, suggesting that the cognitive ability tapped by these two tests may be subserved by similar neural substrates. Furthermore, they also reported that both tests were significantly correlated with the Wechsler Adult Intelligence Scale Full Scale IQ. In other words, both tests, to some degree, were related to intellectual capacity. However, intelligence, as measured by traditional psychometric tests, is not altered to a noticeable degree by frontal lobe dysfunction (Walsh, 1978).

In comparing the discursive processes and the cognitive abilities tapped by the HCT and WCST, Bond and Buchtel (1984) pointed out that the stimuli of the

HCT are far more complex than those in the WCST, and that the perceptual abstraction requirements of the HCT are also far more demanding. It is my opinion that the HCT and WCST may require similar levels of logical induction, but the former demands a great deal more "eduction" (i.e., a process of bringing out varied and pertinent solutions based on confined but implicit information). Such ability is believed to be highly associated with intellectual ability as measured by intelligence tests such as Raven's Progressive Matrices (Ravens, 1958). When a concept formation test is highly loaded with an intelligence factor, it runs the risk of becoming an alternative form of an intelligence test rather than a concept formation test sensitive to frontal lobe dysfunction. Hence, I strongly argue that a test which is designed to ascertain frontal lobe function ideally should depend very little on eduction processes.

A detailed analysis of the discursive processes required for successful performance on the MVCFT, WCST, and HCT disclosed four common denominators:

1. Eduction of hypotheses
2. Hypotheses testing in accordance with feedback information
3. Ability to maintain a set and avoid erratic responses
4. Ability to recognize the change of conditions and flexibility in thinking in order to shift response approach

From what we know about frontal lobe functions, Numbers 2 and 4 are pertinent to frontal lobe activities, whereas Numbers 1 and 3 are considered, at best, to be indirectly related to frontal lobe function. It should be pointed out that none of these above-mentioned tests involves the measurement of "conceptual sequencing" (which differs from perceptual sequencing or spatial sequencing), a function believed to be subserved by the frontal lobes. For example, in studying calculation disorders in the brain damaged, Luria (1966) concluded that "it is [the] sequential ordering of intellectual activity that is apparently disrupted in patients with a lesion of the frontal lobes, being replaced by fragmentary operation" (p. 289). Pribram and his colleagues also found that monkeys with frontal lobe resections showed significant impairments on sequencing problems (Kimble & Pribram, 1963; Brody & Pribram, 1978). Talland (1961) studied 76 normal adults and noticed that success in solving sequential problems declined steadily with age, a trend similar to that noted on other concept formation tests. However, success in solving spatial position tasks was not affected by age. Talland's findings have special meaning in that seemingly similar sequential operations may involve different neural substrates, depending on the nature of the task. For example, conceptual sequencing involves frontal lobe processing, whereas perceptual and spatial sequencing are associated with temporal-parietal-occipital lobe functioning (Lezak, 1983). Such a distinction has received some support from a recent positron emission tomography study performed by Chase et al. (1984). In that study, the uptake of fluorodeoxyglucose F18 was most active in the frontal lobe region when the subject was performing the Digit Span subtest of the WAIS, a task requiring auditory attention and concentration to maintain sequential order of the information input without any perceptual or concrete cues. On the other hand, when the subject was performing the Picture Arrangement and Block Design subtests, tasks requiring perceptual analysis and sequential reconstruction and ordering, the most active uptake of fluorodeoxyglucose F18 occurred within the posterior cerebral regions.

Thus, it is conceivable that, by adding a conceptual sequencing demand to a test, its power in identifying frontal lobe dysfunction is enhanced. It goes without saying that an ideal frontal lobe test would be exclusively sensitive to frontal lobe impairment and as specific as a pathological reflex. Since psychometric tests are, by nature, behavioral tests, it would be impossible as well as unwarranted to expect the subject's performance to be as simplistic and clear-cut as a reflex. It would be considered a very successful attempt, therefore, if one could come up with a concept formation test that would be sensitive to alteration in frontal lobe functioning but that would share, to a much lesser degree, some common variance with brain damage at large. Figure 1 depicts such a relationship.

Figure 1A represents an effective frontal lobe test in that the performances by those individuals with frontal lobe lesions are dissociated from those with nonfrontal lesions at the same time each group shares some common symptoms of brain damage. On the other hand, Figure 1B reflects an ineffective frontal lobe test because of its lack of discriminative power. Thus, the challenge is creating a test that minimizes the measurements of behaviors common to patients with lesions either in the frontal lobes or outside them while it remains correlated with brain damage in general.

An apparent strategy in constructing such a test is to "zoom in" on the assessment of functions believed to be strongly associated with the integration of frontal lobe activities; in fact, the more such functions are included, the more robust the test. Based on the aforementioned analysis, an effective frontal lobe concept formation test ought to do the following:

1. Require simple eduction and have low intelligence demand
2. Involve conceptual sequential operation
3. Require that the individuals stick to rules but also be able to shift strategy in response to relevant external cues
4. Require that the individuals utilize information from errors made, and incorporate that information to adjust their courses of action

Following this line of reasoning, my colleagues and I have recently designed a new task aimed at identifying frontal lobe dysfunction in humans. This task is rather simple to administer in that the subject has to guess whether a small object (a coin, pencil, pen cap, etc.) is held in the examiner's left hand or right hand. The object is hidden according to a predetermined sequence in sets of three (e.g., left hand first, left hand again, then right hand, designated as the triad L-L-R). The same sequence is repeated up to a maximum of 20 sets. If the subject should

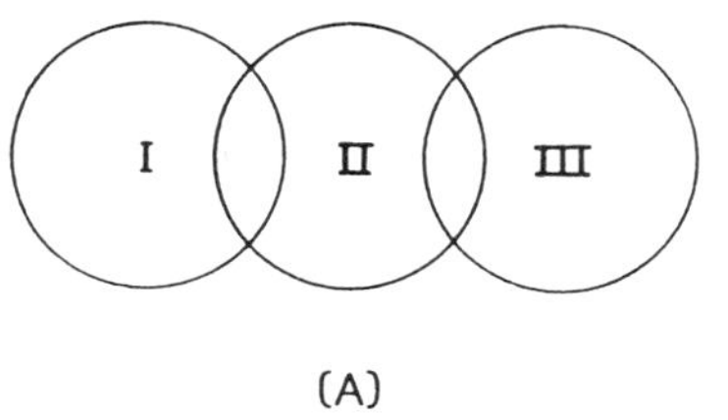

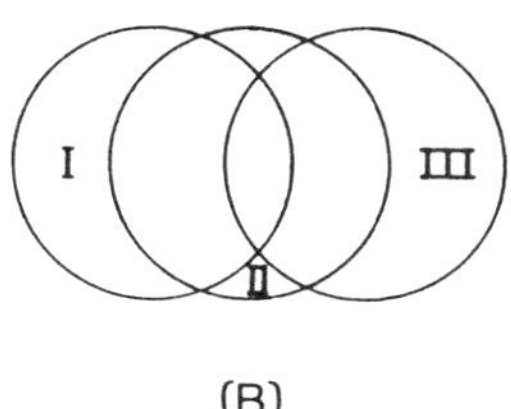

I Frontal Lobe Syndrome II-Brain Damage Symptoms III-Non-frontal Lobe Symptoms

FIGURE 1 Effective frontal lobe test (A) versus ineffective frontal lobe test (B).

grasp the sequence, it is repeated until the criterion of three successive correct triads is reached. At this time, a new sequence, which is a reversal of the previous one (e.g., R-R-L), is introduced without warning the subject. As before, this sequence is repeated for 20 sets or three successive correct triads, whichever comes first. At this point, the target sequence reverts back to that used in the first set of trials (i.e., L-L-R). The same procedure is repeated once more until completion of the fourth set, which is a replication of the second set. Figure 2 is a sample of the recording form used in this experiment.

Let us examine this new task in terms of the four frontal lobe functional characteristics discussed. Without a doubt, this is a sequential concept formation task which resembles that used by Talland (1961), but it is much simpler. Theoretically, if the subject is capable of incorporating the feedback from errors and is able to memorize the sequence, three guesses for the first block of each set and 12 guesses in total would be required. Once the sequential concept is grasped the subject should avoid erratic responses and continue for at least nine successive correct choices. At the same time, the subject should be aware of when a change in the sequence has occurred and be able to adjust his strategy accordingly. However, there is no need for sophisticated eduction or logical induction. Therefore, this new task does appear to contain the four elements believed to be sensitive to frontal lobe dysfunction.

This experimental task was given to 85 volunteer subjects (visitors to a local science center) varying in age from 18 to 82. Each subject received the following instructions:

> This test is like a game, and the idea of the game is to figure out whether this object (a pen cap) is in my left hand or my right hand. I have a set pattern that I am going to use and I can give you a hint that the pattern is in three's. For example it might be left-left-left or right-right-right or right-left-left or left-right-left or right-right-left; just remember it is some pattern of three. Since you have no idea what the pattern is you'll just have to start by guessing. Do you think it is in my right or left hand? Please point to indicate your guesses.

Our preliminary analysis of both the results and the method of administration seemed to point to problems of ambiguity in instruction, high demand on

Set A		Set B		Set C		Set D	
R	R	L	L	R	R	L	L
R	R	L	L	R	R	L	L
L	L	R	R	L	L	R	R
R	R	L	L	R	R	L	L
R	R	L	L	R	R	L	L
L	L	R	R	L	L	R	R
R	R	L	L	R	R	L	L
R	R	L	L	R	R	L	L
L	L	R	R	L	L	R	R
R	R	L	L	R	R	L	L
R	R	L	L	R	R	L	L
L	L	R	R	L	L	R	R
R	R	L	L	R	R	L	L
R	R	L	L	R	R	L	L
L	L	R	R	L	L	R	R
R	R	L	L	R	R	L	L
R	R	L	L	R	R	L	L
L	L	R	R	L	L	R	R
R	R	L	L	R	R	L	L
R	R	L	L	R	R	L	L
L	L	R	R	L	L	R	R
R	R	L	L	R	R	L	L
R	R	L	L	R	R	L	L
L	L	R	R	L	L	R	R
R	R	L	L	R	R	L	L
R	R	L	L	R	R	L	L
L	L	R	R	L	L	R	R
R	R	L	L	R	R	L	L
R	R	L	L	R	R	L	L
L	L	R	R	L	L	R	R
Error	_____	Error	_____	Error	_____	Error	_____
Principle	_____	Principle	_____	Principle	_____	Principle	_____

Total Error _____
Total Principle _____

FIGURE 2 A sample recording form for the experimental sequence concept formation test developed by Wang.

short-term memory, and possible difficulty in perceptual reversal of left and right positions. At the present time, necessary modifications are being introduced in an attempt to eliminate these technical difficulties.

Before ending this chapter, two old but pertinent points need to be reemphasized. First, a clinically useful "frontal lobe test" should be able to identify frontal lobe impairment reliably, not on a group basis, but in individual cases. A feasible method is to adopt a cutoff-point system such as that used in the HCT. Benton (1962) suggested that the lowest score obtained by the non-brain-damaged subjects be used as a cutoff point, with any scores below that point indicating brain damage. This approach would avoid the pitfall of making "false-positive" identification or overdiagnosis of brain damage, but at the same time it would increase "false-negative" diagnoses. When incidences of the latter case are too high, it tends to suggest that the test is not sensitive enough to what it proposes to measure and that necessary changes in the test's construction must be considered. Once the experimental test is given to a large and balanced sample of normal subjects as well as to truly brain-damaged patients, it would be considered appropriate to adopt Benton's approach to determine a reliable and valid cutoff point.

The second point is that a clinically oriented concept formation test should have methods by which qualitative information about the patient's problem-solving style and test-taking behavior can be obtained. Behavioral characteristics such as poor planning, stimulus-bound concrete reaction, aspontaneity, impulsivity, inability to conform to testing rules, confabulation, facetious and indifferent attitudes, and inappropriate social interactions are all important frontal lobe attributes that would be complementary to the numerical information obtained from a concept formation test that uses a cutoff-point method. In view of unsuccessful attempts to design a quantitatively oriented frontal lobe test in the past, it is conceivable that the addition of qualitative analysis may provide a necessary rectification. Most currently available concept formation tests do not permit extensive qualitative analysis because of the very limited and confined scope of responses that the patients are required to make. The new method for administering the sequential concept formation test will attempt to incorporate both of these principles (i.e., cutoff-point and qualitative analysis).

Thus, the search for a sensitive frontal lobe test continues.

ACKNOWLEDGMENTS

My thanks are due to Mrs. S. Copland and Mrs. R. Sud for their technical assistance and helpful discussions.

REFERENCES

Ach, N. (1921). *Ueber die Beigriffsbildung*. Bamberg: Buchner.

Benton, A. R. (1962). The visual retention test as a constructional praxis task. *Confinia Neurologica, 22*, 141–155.

Bond, J., & Buchtel, H. A. (1984). Comparison of the Wisconsin Card Sorting and the Halstead Category Test. *Journal of Clinical Psychology, 40*, 1251–1254.

Brody, B. A., & Pribram, K. H. (1978). The role of frontal and parietal cortex in cognitive processing. *Brain, 101*, 607–633.

Chase, T. N., Fedio, P., Foster, N., Brooks, R., DiChiro, G., & Mansi, L. (1984). Wechsler Adult Intelligence Scale Performance: Cortical localization by fluorodeoxyglucose F18-positron emission tomography. *Archives of Neurology (Chicago), 41*, 1244–1247.

Drewe, E. A. (1974). The effect of type and area of brain lesion on Wisconsin Card Sorting Test performance. *Cortex, 10,* 159–170.

Goldstein, K., & Scheerer, M. (1941). Abstract and concrete behavior: An experimental study with special test. *Psychology Monographs, 53*(2).

Grant, D. A., & Berg, E. A. (1948). A behavior analysis of degree of reinforcement and ease of shifting to new responses in a Weigl-type card sorting problem. *Journal of Experimental Psychology, 38,* 404–411.

Halstead, W. (1950). Frontal lobe function and intelligence. *Bulletin of the Los Angeles Neurological Society, 15,* 205–212.

Halstead, W. C., & Settlage, P. M. (1943). Grasping behaviour of normal persons and of persons with lesions of the brain. *Archives of Neurology and Psychiatry, 49,* 489–506.

Heaton, R. K. (1981). *A manual for the Wisconsin Card Sorting Test.* Odessa, FL: Psychological Assessment Resources.

Hochanadel, G., & Kaplan, E. (1984). Neuropsychology of normal aging. In M. L. Albert (Ed.) *Clinical neurology of aging* (pp. 231–244). London & New York: Oxford University Press.

Kasanin, J., & Hanfmann, E. (1937, May). *An experimental study of concept formation in schizophrenia.* Paper read at the 93rd annual meeting of the American Psychiatric Association, Pittsburgh.

Kimble, D. P., & Pribram, K. H. (1963). Hippocampectomy and behavior sequences. *Science, 139,* 824–825.

Lezak, M. D. (1983). *Neuropsychological assessment.* London & New York: Oxford University Press.

Livingston, K. E. (1969). The frontal lobe revisited. *Archives of Neurology (Chicago), 20,* 90–95.

Luria, A. R. (1966). *Higher cortical function in man.* New York: Basic Books.

Luria, A. R. (1973). *The working brain: An introduction for neuropsychology.* New York: Basic Books.

Milner, B. (1964). Some effects of frontal lobectomy in man. In J. M. Warren & G. Akert (Eds.), *The frontal granular cortex and behavior* (pp. 313–334). New York: McGraw-Hill.

Pandya, D. N., & Kuypers, H. G. J. M. (1969). Cortical-cortical connections in the rhesus monkey. *Brain Research, 13,* 13–32.

Pendleton, M. G., Heaton, R. K., Lekman, R., & Hulihan, D. (1982). Diagnostic utility of the Thurston Ward Fluency Test in the neuropsychological evaluation. *Journal of Clinical Neuropsychology, 4,* 307–317.

Piaget, J. (1926). *Judgment and reasoning in the child.* New York: Harcourt Brace Jovanovich.

Prigatano, G. P., & Parsons, O. A. (1976). Relationship of age and education in Halstead Test performance in different patient populations. *Journal of Consulting and Clinical Psychology, 44,* 527–533.

Ravens, J. C. (1958). *Standard progressive matrices.* London: H. K. Lewis & Co.

Reitan, R. M. (1959). Impairment in abstraction ability in brain damage: Quantitative vs. qualitative change. *Journal of Psychology, 48,* 97–102.

Reitan, R. M., & Davison, L. (1974). *Clinical neuropsychology: Current status and application.* Washington, DC: V. H. Winston & Sons.

Ribot, T. (1904). *Les maladies de la mémoire.* Paris: Alcon.

Robinson, A. L., Heaton, R. K., Lehman, R. A. W., & Stilson, D. W. (1980). The utility of the Wisconsin Card Sorting Test in detecting and localizing frontal lobe lesions. *Journal of Consulting and Clinical Psychology, 48,* 605–614.

Rylander, G. (1943). Mental changes after excision of cerebral tissue. *Acta Psychiatrica et Neurologica,* Supplement 25, 1–81.

Shure, G., & Halstead, W. (1958). Cerebral localization of intellectual processes. *Psychological Monographs, 72*(2).

Talland, G. (1961). Effect of aging on the formation of sequential and spatial concepts. *Perceptual and Motor Skills, 13,* 210.

Tarter, R., & Parsons, O. (1971). Concept shifting in chronic alcoholics. *Journal of Abnormal Psychology, 77,* 71–75.

Teuber, H. L. (1964). The riddle of frontal lobe function in man. In J. M. Warren & G. Akert (Eds.) *The frontal granular cortex and behavior* (pp. 410–444). New York: McGraw-Hill.

Teuber, H. L., Battersby, W. S., & Bender, M. B. (1951). Performance of complex visual tasks after cerebral lesions. *Journal of Nervous and Mental Diseases, 114,* 413–429.

Vygotsky, L. (1934). Thoughts in schizophrenia. *Archives of Neurology and Psychiatry, 31,* 1063–1077.

Walsh, K. W. (1978). *Neuropsychology: A clinical approach.* Edinburgh & London: Churchill-Livingstone.

Wang, P. L. (1984). *Modified Vygotsky Concept Formation Test.* Chicago, IL: Stoelting Co.

Weigl, E. (1941). On the psychology of so-called processes of abstraction. *Journal of Abnormal Psychology, 36,* 3–33.

11

Frontal Lobe Dysfunction in Obsessive-Compulsive Disorder

Paul Malloy

Obsessive-compulsive disorder (OCD) is an anxiety syndrome in which the patient is plagued by intrusive disturbing thoughts, and may engage in elaborate rituals or manuevers to avoid anxiety-provoking situations or behaviors. In severe cases these symptoms reach disabling proportions. For example, one of the patients studied in the experiments described below was unable to even rise from a chair without engaging in a series of covert rituals of several minutes' duration. OCD is sometimes amenable to behavioral or pharmacological interventions, but many cases respond minimally to treatment. This has led some researchers to seek a biological explanation for OCD, which might lead to more effective treatment.

The goal of this chapter is to present a neuropsychological model of obsessive-compulsive disorder, with emphasis on the possible role of frontolimbic connections. I describe the specialized functional zones of the human frontal lobes, review the evidence for frontal dysfunction in OCD, suggest possible mechanisms for symptoms, and present initial research on frontal functioning OCD. The research described here was conducted at Butler Hospital in collaboration with Steven Rasmussen, William Braden, and Richard Haier.

FRONTAL LOBE FUNCTIONS: DORSOLATERAL VERSUS ORBITOMEDIAL ZONES

Understanding of human frontal lobe organization has lagged behind knowledge of animal frontal functions, but at least two functional and anatomic subdivisions of the human prefrontal cortex have been suggested by recent investigations (for review, see Stuss & Benson, 1984). The *dorsolateral* (DL)

THE FRONTAL LOBES REVISITED

ISBN 0-936925-00-0

prefrontal area has been described as the "executive" of the brain. Like an executive in a corporation, the dorsolateral zone seems to be involved in evaluating ongoing behavior, determining what changes in behavior are necessary, implementing these changes effectively, and aiming efforts toward long-term goals (Luria, 1966, 1980). The *orbital* and inferior *medial* (OM) prefrontal areas have extensive connections with the limbic system (Nauta, 1972), and seem to be involved with the modulation of emotional expression and the evaluation of environmental input on the basis of internal state (Girgis, 1971).

Characteristic disturbances of these two systems have been observed in patients with frontal lobe lesions. Patients with DL lesions often overlook important details in their environment (Luria, Karpov, & Yarbuss, 1966), have trouble generating response alternatives (Jones-Gotman & Milner, 1977), and tend to perseveratively repeat the same response when it is no longer appropriate (Goldberg & Tucker, 1979; Luria, 1965). On the other hand, OM lesions result in relative preservation of intellectual functions (Walsh, 1978), but with decreased ability to inhibit responding, reduced social control, and emotional lability (Blumer & Benson, 1975; Eslinger and Damasio, 1985).

Based on observations of patients with large frontal lesions, Eslinger and Damasio (1985) have suggested that OM lesions cause deficits in "analysis and integration of stimuli pertaining to real-life situations that may be due, in part, to *ineffectual access* to previously learned strategies of action" (p. 1739, emphasis added). They noted that anatomically the OM areas not only connect directly with limbic structures, but also may provide a crucial route between dorsolateral frontal cortex and the limbic system. If these reciprocal interconnections are interrupted by lesions, the limbic system may have no way to activate frontal cortex, and frontal cortex will be unable to modulate limbic drives. Although they did not use the term, Eslinger and Damasio seem to be suggesting that a *structural disconnection* syndrome accounts for the behavioral effects of OM frontal lesions.

The actual functional relationship between frontal and limbic structures in humans is probably very complex. No fewer than five functional subdivisions of the prefrontal lobes have been identified in monkeys (Rosenkilde, 1979), and it is reasonable to suppose that human frontal organization is at least as heterogeneous. Thus a simple OM-DL functional dichotomy will likely prove to be an oversimplification. Furthermore, multiple possible routes between frontal and limbic zones have been tentatively identified in animals. Some of these would not be easily disrupted by orbital lesions, even of the size described by Eslinger and Damasio (1985). For example, there appear to be direct DL frontal-to-cingulate connections which follow a dorsomedial route, and indirect connections via the dorsomedial nuclei of the thalamus (Nauta, 1971, 1972). Despite these reservations, the notions of DL-OM functional subdivisions and frontolimbic disconnection appear to be useful heuristics at our present state of knowledge, and we will return to these concepts in our discussion of obsessive symptoms below.

FRONTAL DYSFUNCTION IN OBSESSIVE-COMPULSIVE DISORDER

Flor-Henry (1983) has noted in a recent review that a number of "soft signs" of organic disease have been found in OCD patients. For example, they have a high incidence of reported birth trauma and left-handedness, suggesting they may have atypical brain organization from a very early age (Flor-Henry, Yeudall, Koles, & Howarth, 1979). EEG abnormalities, including slow waves, spike discharges, and power spectrum lateralization differences, have been reported at rates ranging from 11% to 64% in various OCD samples (Epstein & Bailine, 1971; Flor-Henry et al., 1979; Insel, Donnelly, Lalakea, Alterman, & Murphy, 1983; Pacella, Polatin, & Nagler, 1944; Rockwell & Simons, 1947).

The frontal lobes have been specifically implicated in OCD by a few previous writers. Flor-Henry (1983), for example, has suggested that the syndrome "was a reflection of dominant frontal dysfunction, with loss of normal inhibitory processes in that zone, which accounted for the fundamental aspect of obsessions: the inability to inhibit verbal ideational mental representations and their motor consequences" (p. 305). Based on neurophysiological and psychosurgical data, Flor-Henry noted that "cingulate-orbital-frontal" inhibitory mechanisms seem to be disturbed in OCD. Gray (1982) has also hypothesized that interactions between prefrontal and limbic zones are important in obsessional and other anxiety disorders. However, the precise mechanism responsible for OCD remains obscure, with a number of possible loci of dysfunction suggested by previous writers (e.g., dominant frontotemporal lobes, cingulate gyrus, septohippocampal system).

It will be recalled that Eslinger and Damasio's (1985) observations were interpreted as indicating that OM lesions resulted in a structural disconnection between frontal and limbic zones. A possibility not previously suggested is that a *functional disconnection* may exist in obsessive-complusive disorder. OM dysfunction could have direct effects on behavior which might contribute to OCD symptoms. OM lesions in animals result in difficulty inhibiting or unlearning previous response patterns when they are no longer appropriate (Mishkin, 1964) and exaggerated emotional responses to previously nonthreatening cues (Butter, Snyder, & McDonald, 1970). OCD patients have great difficulty inhibiting rituals and obsessive thoughts, and develop progressive networks of formerly innocuous situations which are now considered "dangerous." In addition, a functional disconnection in this area could contribute to OCD symptoms in less direct ways:

1. DL hyperactivity due to lack of limbic feedback. Patients with DL lesions display marked deficits in self-monitoring, failure to maintain set, and lack of response to long-term consequences. In sharp contrast, OCD patients seem to behave as though their DL frontal zones are "hyperactive," with constant

self-monitoring, rigidly inflexible sets in thought and behavior, and excessive concern with the long-term consequences of their behavior. For example, one patient we tested became convinced that he would contaminate everything he touched. He exercised constant vigilance to avoid spreading his imagined disease, washed his hands dozens of times a day until they were raw and red, and worried obsessively about causing someone's death sometime in the future. This compulsive planning, checking, and monitoring may represent DL activity running on unchecked by limbic feedback normally provided via OM routes. Once initiated, DL routines may require such input as the adequate stimulus for termination.

2. Reduced modulation of limbic anxiety arousal due to interruption of descending DL inhibitory influences. DL frontal zones appear to be responsible for monitoring the environment, and signaling when conditions have changed as a result of the organism's responses. If this information cannot reach the limbic system, the organism may continue to react with overarousal when it is no longer appropriate. The OCD patient is thus able to verbalize that he or she is misconstruing the danger of a situation, but is unable to modulate the emotional response. In this regard, they resemble the frontal patients described by Milner (1971) and Luria (1966, 1980), who were able to repeat instructions with apparent understanding, but whose behavior nonetheless failed to conform.

This does not exhaust the possible mechanisms of frontolimbic dysfunction in OCD, and many more complex interactions are possible. The second model described above appears to fit the phenomenology of OCD best, and to provide the closest parallel to human frontal lesion data. It will be apparent to the reader that any such ideas are extremely difficult to test in humans, and inferences will eventually have to be made from studies of OCD patients using many different paradigms (e.g., behavioral, neurochemical, brain imaging). The neuropsychological and evoked potential studies that follow represent our first attempts to explore this disconnection hypothesis in OCD.

NEUROPSYCHOLOGICAL TEST DEFICITS IN OCD

Previous neuropsychological studies in OCD have yielded inconsistent results. Flor-Henry et al. (1979) administered a 28-measure battery of tests to 11 OCD patients and an equal number of normal controls matched for age, education, and intelligence. Clinical pattern analysis of OCD results were interpreted as indicating bilateral frontal dysfunction, with left hemisphere worse than right. A number of methodological questions can be raised with this study, however. Although the controls were said to be "matched" for IQ, the mean for controls was 116, while the mean for OCDs was only 106. This difference may be important in OCD, as will be noted below. It is also unclear whether raters were blind to diagnosis, and whether pattern analysis was based on strict decision rules or clinical judgment. Finally, a discriminant analysis that purported to correctly classify all subjects in terms of diagnostic group used 15 predictors with only 22 cases, casting doubt on the statistical stability of the finding (Adams, 1979).

Behar et al. (1984) also reported deficits consistent with frontal lobe dysfunction in a group of 16 adolescents with OCD, who were significantly worse than normal controls on certain frontal lobe tasks (the Money Road Map Test and the Stylus Maze Test) but not on nonfrontal control tasks. However, Insel et al. (1983) administered the Halstead-Reitan Battery (HRB) and Wechsler Adult Intelligence Scale (WAIS-R) to 18 OCD patients, and found that as a group their results were comparable to normals. Four patients produced average impairment ratings suggesting organic deficits and half were impaired on the Tactual Performance Test (TPT) subtest of the HRB, but results were interpreted as failing to show left anterior dysfunction or other specific deficit. It should be noted that, although some of these studies employed small matched control groups, none performed age or education corrections on their data using available large-scale norms. Interestingly, Insel et al. (1983) noted that their four impaired subjects were older than the other OCD patients.

In our first study, we administered a battery of neuropsychological tests to 17 adult patients meeting DSM-III criteria for OCD. The mean age of the group was 34 and average education was 13 years. Table 1 presents the tests administered and the data from the patient group. Several of the tests were selected for their demonstrated sensitivity to frontal dysfunction: Wisconsin Card Sorting Test (WCST; Heaton, 1981), Controlled Word Fluency Test (Benton, 1968), and a selection of Luria's complex motor programming tasks which we had cross-validated in previous work (Malloy, Webster, & Russell, 1985). The remainder of the tests were included as control tasks for attention (Digits Forward and Letter Vigilance), intelligence (WAIS-R), memory (revised Wechsler Memory Scale; Russell, 1975), and posterior functions (Boston Naming Test; Goodglass & Kaplan, 1983; and Line Orientation Test; Benton, Hamsher, Varney, & Spreen, 1983).

OCD scores on the tests are presented in raw score and age/education-corrected T-score form, based on published norms. T scores greater than 60 indicate performance more than one standard deviation below average. The OCD group scored abnormally on only two measures—perseverative responses and categories completed in the WCST. It should be noted that the attention and intellectual scores for the group as a whole were above average. WCST deficits were therefore not an artifact of inattention secondary to obsessional thinking or generally lowered abilities.

Inspection of the individual subject scores on the WCST revealed that there were two distinct subgroups of OCD patients, one of which failed the test badly, the other passing with ease (even anticipating when changes in correct category

TABLE 1
Neuropsychological Test Scores of Obsessive-Compulsive Subjects

Test name	Raw score *M* (*SD*)	T score *M* (*SD*)
Frontal tests		
Wisconsin Card Sorting Test		
Perseverative responses	27.4 (15.8)	61.3 (16.9)
Categories completed	4.6 (1.8)	61.8 (14.9)
Benton Controlled Word Fluency Test		
Total correct words	40.0 (14.1)	44.0 (14.5)
Luria Motor Tasks		
Total errors	2.9 (3.6)	na[a]
Control tests		
Digits Forward	7.2 (1.4)	na
Letter Vigilance (errors)	0.0 (0.0)	50.0 (0.00)
Wechsler Adult Intelligence Scale—Revised		
VIQ	105.4 (15.9)	na
PIQ	97.2 (17.6)	na
FIQ	102.2 (17.2)	na
Wechsler Memory Scale		
Semantic immediate	17.9 (5.9)	56.1 (12.5)
Semantic delayed	14.9 (7.3)	55.6 (16.5)
Figural immediate	9.3 (4.4)	52.3 (10.1)
Figural delayed	9.1 (4.4)	50.5 (13.7)
Boston Naming Test		
Total correct	54.3 (3.9)	54.0 (12.5)
Benton Line Orientation Test		
Total correct	24.2 (3.8)	49.1 (8.9)

[a]na, not available.

would occur). Subjects were divided into those with T scores above and below 60 (n = 9 and 8, respectively), and the treating clinician was asked to blindly rate their clinical status. The group that was impaired on the WCST was described as more psychotic, lower functioning, having poorer prognosis, and less intelligent than the unimpaired WCST group. The latter impression was confirmed by formal testing: The impaired group had a mean full-scale IQ of 91.9, whereas the unimpaired group had a mean IQ of 110.2. However, low IQ alone did not account for the deficits on the WCST, since significant differences were still present when IQ was controlled for in an analysis of covariance, $F(2, 14)$ =

25.91, $p < .001$ for perseverative responses, $F(2, 14) = 7.05$. $p < .001$ for categories.

EVOKED POTENTIALS AND FRONTAL LOBE BEHAVIORS

In order to gather information from multiple levels of analysis, we studied electrophysiological as well as behavioral differences in OCD. Before turning to that data, a brief review of evoked potential mapping is presented.

New techniques such as CT, PET, and MRI scanning have begun to provide us with remarkably detailed images of brain structure and metabolic activity. Similar techniques for imaging brain electrical activity have recently been developed as well. They have some advantages over other imaging techniques as research tools in that they involve no exposure to radiation, require little expensive equipment, and seem to be sensitive to both normal and abnormal cognitive processes.

The familiar electroencephalogram (EEG) remains a useful clinical tool for the detection of certain neurological abnormalities, such as seizure disorders, but is of little use in the study of complex brain activity. This is because in the EEG the brain's response to any event is buried in a welter of background electrical activity, which reflects all the other tasks in which the brain is engaged at that moment. Let us say, for example, that we are interested in studying how a person's brain processes a given word. Viewing the raw EEG at the time the word is heard will tell us little, since the EEG wave forms seen at that moment will represent a summary of the brain's monitoring of bodily functions, response to background noise, daydreaming, and so forth.

The problem has been likened to attempting to hear a single conversation in a car by using a microphone hung high above a busy city street. In order to overcome this "noise" problem, researchers have used computers to monitor brain electrical activity while the stimulus is repeated over and over. With computer averaging, background noise drops out, and the response to the particular stimulus may be seen clearly. This "event-related potential," or EP, can provide a method for measuring information processing in the brain.

The various wave forms of the EP are named for their polarity (positive or negative) and time of occurrence after the eliciting stimulus. Thus, N1 is a negative wave occurring about 100 msec after the stimulus, P3 is a positive wave at about 300 msec, and so on. The P3 component of the EP is known to vary in amplitude with the information value of the eliciting stimulus, and is thought to reflect association cortex activity (Picton & Stuss, 1980). A posterior P3 component having maximum amplitude in the centroparietal region can be evoked by a number of tasks requiring stimulus discrimination and by the presentation of unexpected stimuli to the passive subject (Ritter, Simson, & Vaughan, 1979). It is possible, however, that P3 may reflect not only posterior sensory information processing, but also more anterior association cortex activity, if a task is chosen that demands frontal lobe functions.

The frontal lobes are necessary in tasks that demand inhibition of competing responses and flexible switching to a new response when conditions change. Go/no-go tasks are an example of such tasks which animals and humans with frontal lobe lesions are known to fail (Drewe, 1975; Fuster, 1980; Malloy et al., 1985). In go/no-go paradigms the subject is required to make a response to the go signal, and to withhold or inhibit response to the no-go signal. This task appeared to offer several advantages for the present investigations because: (1) it was possible to time-lock recording of EPs to the imperative signals in the task; (2) it was simple enough to be mastered by psychiatric patients with severe psychopathology; and (3) the OM frontal zone seems to be crucial to performance on the task by primates (Rosenkilde, 1979).

Simson, Vaughan, and Ritter (1977) have reported that P3 during a go/no-go paradigm was maximum in the midparietal area during go trials (as in previous sensory discrimination studies), but was maximum in midfrontal areas during no-go trials. However, because their paradigm involved the use of a "ready" signal (to which go and no-go signals were compared), the authors noted that their P3 measurements might be confounded by the contingent negative variation (CNV), a slow potential reflecting orienting and expectancy. Because CNV is thought to originate in motor or premotor areas, this would also imply that the paradigm was not measuring prefrontal association cortex activity as intended.

EP TOPOGRAPHY IN NORMALS DURING GO/NO-GO

The second study reported here was designed to further delineate the topography of P3 topographic mapping techniques. The goal of the research was to validate a measure of prefrontal activity which could then be used to study higher cortical functions in pathological populations. Other components of the EP were also measured (to demonstrate that observed differences were not simply artifacts of other waves reflecting noncognitive activity), and a ready signal was not used (to minimize CNV expectancy and orienting effects). It was predicted that P3 would show the usual centroparietal maximum amplitudes during go trials, but that there would be a frontal shift in P3 distribution when the inhibitory requirements of the no-go trials were added.

Twenty normal volunteers were recruited from hospital staff and volunteer workers. The mean age was 28 years and the mean education was 16 years. There were 12 females and 8 males; 15 were right-handed and 5 were left-handed. None of the subjects had any history of neurological insult, psychiatric disorder, or substance abuse. None was taking any prescribed medication and none had consumed alcohol or other drugs within 48 hours of testing.

Subjects were instructed to press a telegraph key when the word "GO" appeared in block letters 2 cm high on a cathode ray tube directly in front of them. They were instructed not to press when the word "STOP" appeared. Six practice trials were followed by 45 go and 45 no-go trials presented in a pseudorandom order.

An Apple II+ computer controlled stimulus presentations and recorded correct or incorrect responses. The intertrial interval was a constant 7 sec. Evoked potentials were recorded from left-hemisphere sites based mainly on the 10-20 system of electrode placement. To ensure accurate measurement in frontal and parietal association areas of particular interest, four special electrode sites were added and designated FC, FTC, CP, and TCP (see Figure 1). Because available equipment limited the total number of recording sites to 15, this necessitated elimination of standard site 01. Electrooculogram (EOG) was recorded from two electrodes above and below the right eye, and averaged like a cortical potential.

Recording began with the onset of the go or no-go signal and continued for 500 msec. In order to ensure that subjects were engaged in the cognitive task during recordings, EPs were averaged for correct trials only (i.e., when the subject pressed to the go signal and inhibited press to the no-go signal). Cortical potentials were amplified by a Grass Model 12 polygraph and digitized every 4 msec with an 8-bit analog-to-digital converter. Peaks and valleys in the evoked potential were identified by the computer. P1 amplitude was the maximum voltage occurring between 36 and 120 msec; N1 was the minimum voltage

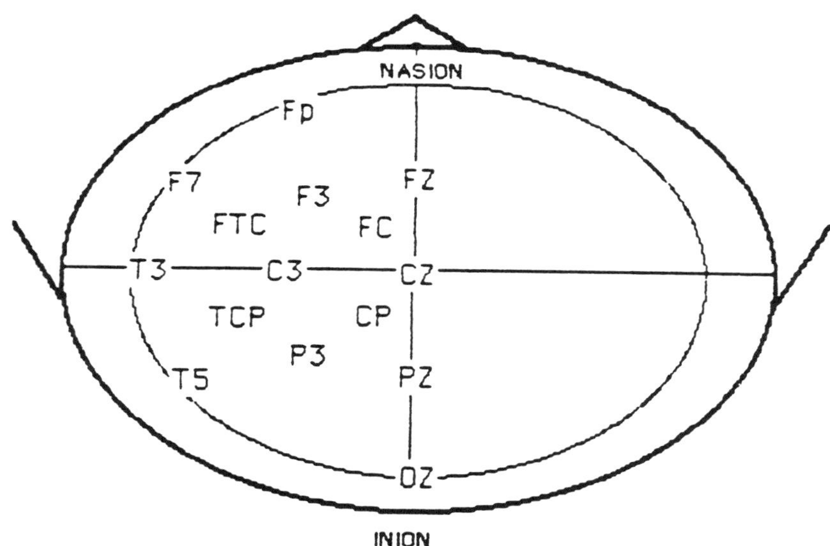

FIGURE 1 Electrode placements for P3 topographic mapping.

occurring between 100 and 160 msec; P2 was the maximum voltage occurring between 160 and 250 msec; N2 was the minimum voltage between 160 and 250 msec; and P3 was the maximum voltage between 250 and 400 msec.

Topographic mapping of mean P3 amplitude was accomplished using an adaptation of the techniques developed by Buchsbaum et al. (1982). This essentially involved interpolating P3 amplitude values for each coordinate in a 40 × 40 pixel matrix forming a lateral brain map. Interpolated pixel values were computed by weighted averaging of the values of the four nearest electrode sites. Values for the go and no-go conditions were computed and displayed as color maps, with color indicating P3 amplitude at each pixel location. Color maps were then transformed into black and white maps suitable for publication by the use of an Apple MacPaint graphics package. Finally, significance probability maps comparing the go and no-go conditions were calculated by entering paired t test values for each electrode site into the mapping program. For ease of interpretation, the resulting significance probability map values were keyed to standard significance level cutoffs (i.e., $p < .001$, $p < .01$, $p < .05$).

Analysis of each EP component revealed no significant amplitude differences for N1, P1, N2, or P2 across conditions. Subsequent analyses therefore emphasize the P3 differences that were observed. The magnitude of P3 measured at eye electrodes was small and no significant differences were found across conditions, indicating that eye-blink artifact did not affect results. There were also no significant differences between males and females or between right- or left-handers in P3 amplitude measured at any electrode site during any condition.

P3 data are displayed in Figure 2. It can be seen that, during go trials, the area of maximum activity as indexed by P3 amplitude occurred in the centroparietal area, as in previous stimulus discrimination studies. However, with the addition of inhibitory demands during no-go trials, there was an anterior shift in P3 activity. When the two task conditions were compared in the significance probability maps, a statistically significant increase in P3 magnitude was revealed. This change was maximum in prefrontal areas (sites Fp, Fz, F3, FC), less marked in sensorimotor areas (FTC, F7, CZ, C3, CP), and essentially absent in posterior areas.

The go/no-go paradigm thus appeared to evoke frontal lobe activity that could be detected by changes in P3 amplitude. This initial validation in normals laid the groundwork for application of the paradigm to psychopathological groups hypothesized to have frontal lobe dysfunction.

EP TOPOGRAPHY IN OCD PATIENTS DURING THE GO/NO-GO TASK

Brain electrical activity during this task was next investigated in the 17 OCD patients who had participated in the first study. Experimental procedures

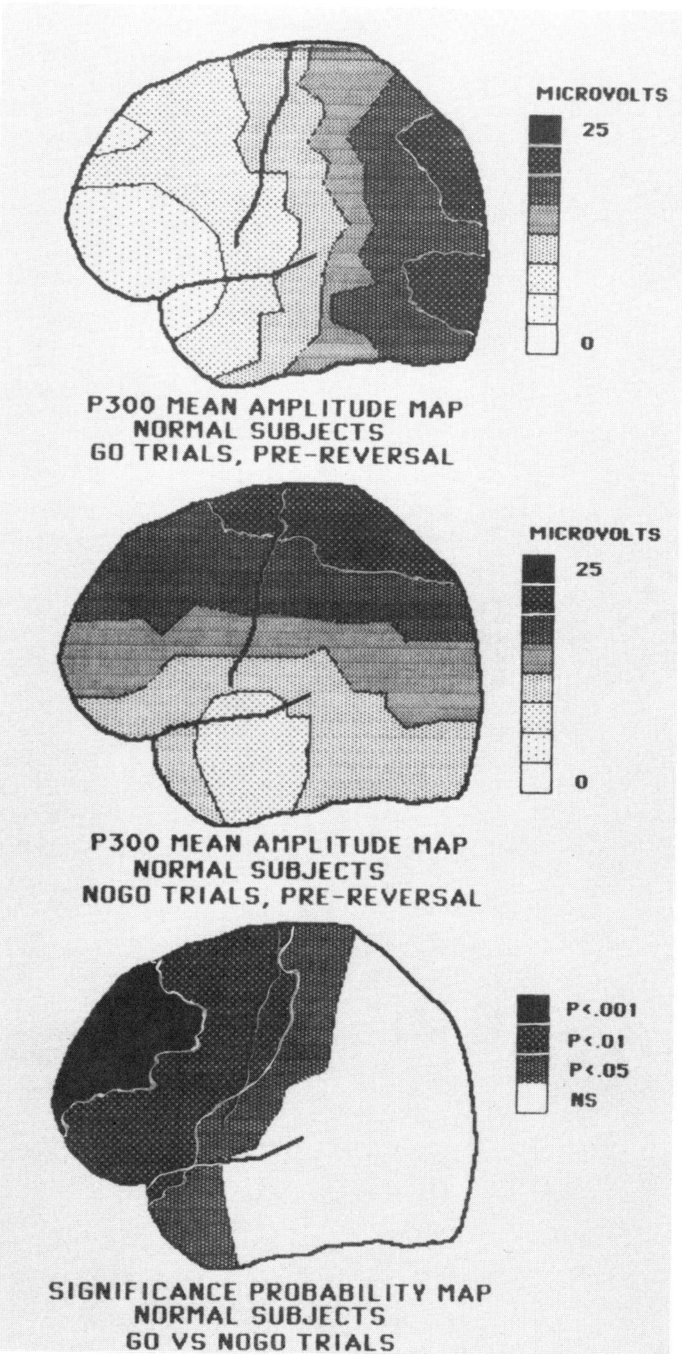

FIGURE 2 Topographic maps of left-hemisphere P3 amplitudes in normal subjects during a go/no-go task.

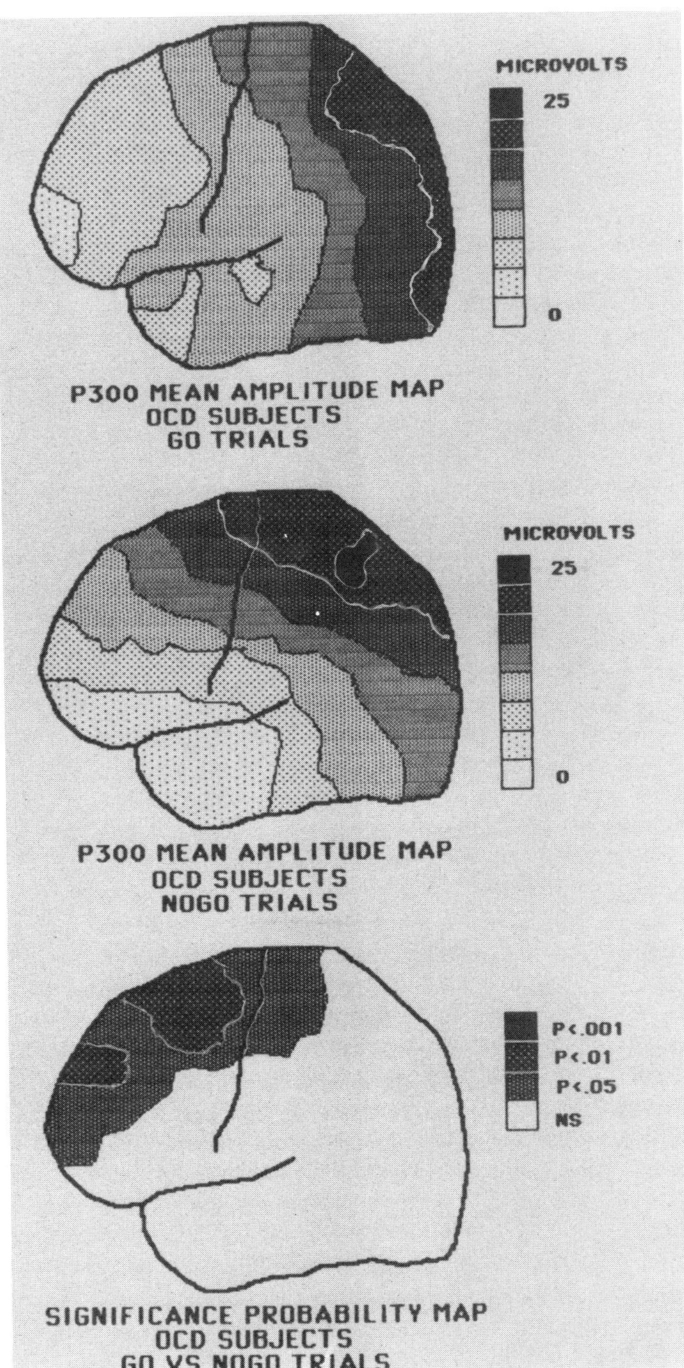

FIGURE 3 Topographic maps of left-hemisphere P3 amplitudes in OCD subjects during a go/no-go task.

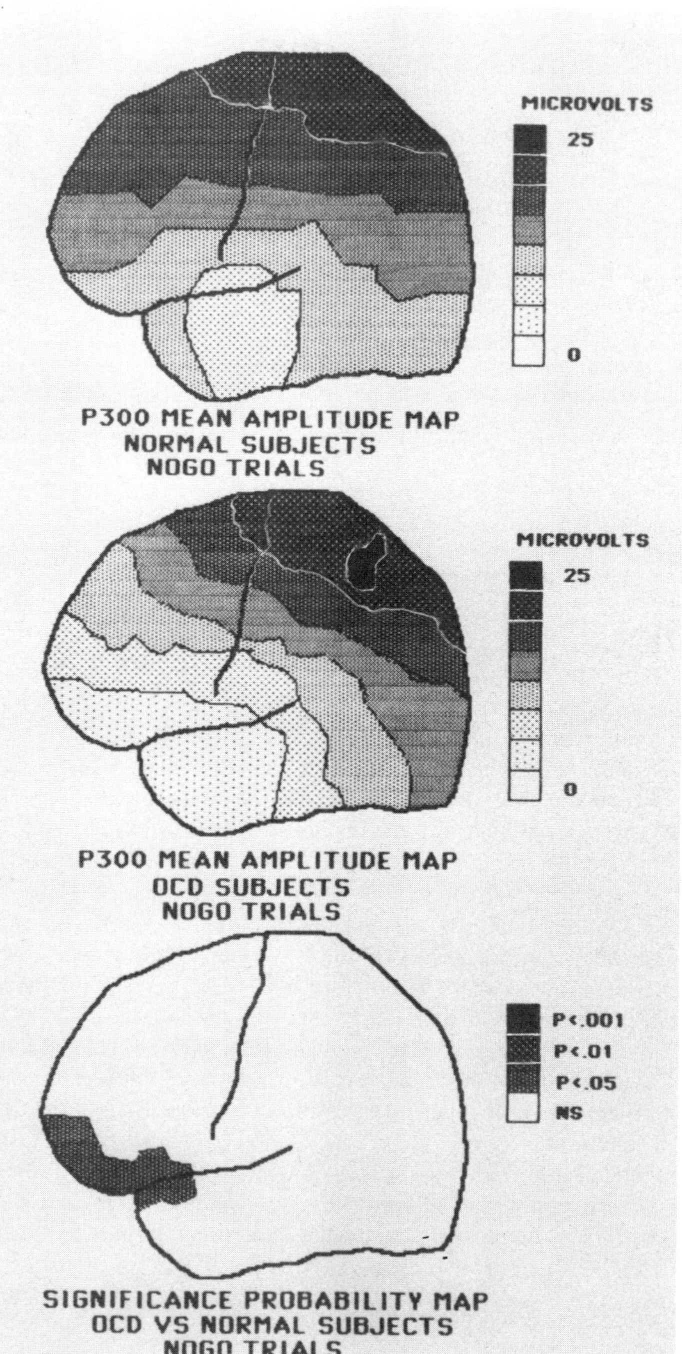

FIGURE 4 Topographic maps of left-hemisphere P3 amplitudes comparing normal and OCD subjects during no-go phases.

and analysis of evoked potential analyses were identical to those described for normal subjects above.

EP maps for the go condition, the no-go condition, and the comparison between the two conditions are presented in Figure 3. Inspection of the figure reveals that OCD patients displayed the usual posterior maximum in P3 amplitude during go trials (top map), and some anterior shift in P3 during no-go trials (middle map). Significant increases in P3 amplitude occurred at F3 and FC ($p < .01$), and at Fp, Fz, Cz, and C3 ($p < .05$). However, the significance probability map (bottom) reveals that significant increases did not occur in orbital frontal areas, as had been the case with normal subjects. Direct comparisons of normal and OCD subjects' P3 amplitudes during the no-go condition are illustrated in Figure 4. Significantly lower amplitudes were found for OCD subjects at sites Fp, $t(35)=2.66$, $p < .05$, and F7, $t(35)=2.27$, $p < .05$. As the significance probability map (bottom) illustrates, these differences indicate relative lack of activity in orbital frontal and possibly anterior temporal areas.

SUMMARY

The neuropsychological results reported here are consistent with hypotheses of frontal dysfunction in OCD. Only a subset of the OCD patients, who were rated as more disturbed, displayed these deficits; this may explain some of the discrepancies among previous studies. Despite these positive findings, neuropsychological testing may not be useful in further research on the model of OCD presented here, since existing standardized tests do not adequately differrentiate between DL and OM functions.

The EP findings with normals add to our previous understanding of P3 by demonstrating that the topography of this EP component is sensitive not only to the information value of the stimulus, but also to the response demands of the task in which the subject is engaged. This functional relationship has been suggested by Hillyard, Courchesne, Krausz, and Picton (1976), who had found different P3 topographies in various decision tasks. The present results demonstrate that P3 amplitude changes reflect prefrontal activation in tasks that require behavioral inhibition.

There are a number of reasons for concluding that the amplitude changes observed were not due to CNV recovery, as had been suggested in previous studies. The most convincing data are that maximum amplitude changes were observed in anterior prefrontal areas, rather than in central motor or premotor zones as would be expected with CNV. The omission of a warning stimulus and the use of a relatively long intertrial interval were also designed to minimize possible CNV effects. Hillyard et al. (1976) reported an anterior shift in P3 during no-go trials both with and without a ready signal. Donchin, Tueting, Ritter, Kutas, and Heffley (1975) have demonstrated that when CNV and P3 are both measured the omission of a warning signal eliminates CNV but leaves P3 unaffected. Nevertheless, the possibility that the observed changes in P3 reflect differential CNV recovery during the go versus no-go conditions cannot be ruled out entirely, since we did not measure CNV concurrently. This study was not designed to resolve this issue, but rather to demonstrate the task-dependent topography of EP late components.

Applying the EP mapping technique to OCD patients revealed patterns of P3 activity different from normals, with significantly lower amplitudes in orbital frontal areas. These findings are consistent with the suggestions of previous writers that OM frontal areas are dysfunctional in OCD. There was no evidence of "hyperactivity" of DL zones. This suggests that OCD either is directly due to OM dysfunction or is due to interruption of DL-limbic pathways which traverse this area. The latter mechanism is consistent with our functional disconnection model, but further research will be necessary to determine which of these models is correct. Measurement of EPs during behavioral tasks that are differentially sensitive to DL versus OM functions (e.g., delayed alternation vs. delayed matching to sample) may prove productive in this regard.

We are also interested in investigating possible frontal dysfunction in other psychiatric groups. Antisocial personality is a particularly interesting example, since the disorder is in many ways the antithesis of OCD. Whereas the OCD patient abhors risk, minimizes novelty, and is disabled by overinhibited behavior, the ASP patient typically engages in much dangerous behavior, is a sensation seeker, and is underinhibited by society's standards. Comparing behavioral and EP patterns in the two groups may provide the sort of "double dissociation" that has proven so useful in other neuropsychological questions.

REFERENCES

Adams, K. M. (1979). Linear discriminant analysis in clinical neuropsychology research. *Journal of Clinical Neuropsychology, 1*, 259–272.

Behar, D., Rapoport, J. L., Berg, C. J., Denckla, M. B., Mann, L., Cox, C., Fedio, P., Zahn, T., & Wolfman, M. G. (1984). Computerized tomography and neuropsychological test measures in adolescents with obsessive-compulsive disorder. *American Journal of Psychiatry, 141*, 363–369.

Benton, A. L. (1968). Differential behavioral effects of frontal lobe disease. *Neuropsychologia, 6*, 53–60.

Benton, A. L., Hamsher, K. D., Varney, N. R., & Spreen, O. (1983). *Contributions to neuropsychological assessment: A clinical manual*. London & New York: Oxford University Press.

Blumer, D., & Benson, D. F. (1975). Personality changes in frontal and temporal lobe lesions. In D. F. Benson & D. Blumer (Eds.), *Psychiatric aspects of neurological disease*. New York: Grune & Stratton.

Buchsbaum, M. S., Rigal, F., Coppola, R., Cappalletti, J., King, C., & Johnson, J. (1982). A new system for gray-level surface distribution maps of electrical activity. *Electroencephalography and Clinical Neurophysiology, 53,* 237–242.

Butter, C. M., Snyder, D. R., & McDonald, J. A. (1970). Effects of orbital lesions on aversive and aggressive behavior in rhesus monkeys. *Journal of Comparative and Physiological Psychology, 72,* 132–144.

Donchin, E., Tueting, P., Ritter, W., Kutas, M., & Heffley, E. (1975). On the independence of the CNV and the P300 components of the human averaged evoked potential. *Electroencephalography and Clinical Neurophysiology, 38,* 449–461.

Drewe, E. A. (1975). Go/no-go learning after frontal lobe lesions in humans. *Cortex, 11,* 8–16.

Epstein, A. W., & Bailine, S. H. (1971). Sleep and dream studies in obsessional neurosis with particular reference to epileptic states. *Biological Psychiatry, 3,* 149–158.

Eslinger, P. J., & Damasio, A. R. (1985). Severe disturbance of higher cognition after bilateral frontal lobe ablation: Patient EVR. *Neurology, 35,* 1731–1741.

Flor-Henry, P. (1983). *Cerebral basis of psychopathology.* Boston, MA: John Wright.

Flor-Henry, P., Yeudall, L. T., Koles, Z. J., & Howarth, B. G. (1979). Neuropsychological and power spectral EEG investigations of the obsessive-compulsive syndrome. *Biological Psychiatry, 14,* 119–130.

Fuster, J. M. (1980). *The prefrontal cortex: Anatomy, physiology, and neuropsychology of the frontal lobe.* New York: Raven Press.

Girgis, M. (1971). The orbital surface of the frontal lobe of the brain. *Acta Psychiatrica Scandinavica, 222,* 1–58.

Goldberg, E., & Tucker, D. (1979). Motor perseveration and long-term memory for visual forms. *Journal of Clinical Neuropsychology, 1,* 273–288.

Goodglass, H., & Kaplan, E. (1983). *The assessment of aphasia and related disorders* (2nd ed.). Philadelphia, PA: Lea & Febiger.

Gray, J. E. (1982). *The neuropsychology of anxiety.* London & New York: Oxford University Press.

Heaton, R. K. (1981). *Wisconsin Card Sorting Test Manual.* Odessa, FL: Psychological Assessment Resources.

Hillyard, S. A., Courchesne, E., Krausz, H. I., & Picton, T. W. (1976). Scalp topography of the P3 wave in different auditory decision tasks. In W. C. McCallum and J. R. Knott (Eds.), *The responsive brain* (pp. 81–87). Bristol; England: John Wright & Sons.

Insel, T. R., Donnelly, E. F., Lalakea, M. L., Alterman, I. S., & Murphy, D. L. (1983). Neurological and neuropsychological studies of patients with obsessive-compulsive disorder. *Biological Psychiatry, 18,* 741–751.

Jones-Gotman, M., & Milner, B. (1977). Design fluency: The invention of nonsense drawings after focal cortical lesions. *Neuropsychologia, 15,* 643–652.

Luria, A. R. (1965). Two kinds of motor perseveration in massive injuries of the frontal lobes. *Brain, 88,* 1–10.

Luria, A. R. (1966/1980). *Higher cortical functions in man* (2nd rev. ed., pp. 246–365). New York: Basic Books. (Original work published 1966)

Luria, A. R., Karpov, B. A., & Yarbuss, A. L. (1966). Disturbance of active visual perception with lesions of the frontal lobes. *Cortex, 2,* 202–212.

Malloy, P. F., Webster, J. S., & Russell, W. (1985). Tests of Luria's frontal lobe syndrome. *International Journal of Clinical Neuropsychology, 7,* 88–94.

Milner, B. (1971). Interhemispheric differences in the localization of psychological processes in man. *British Medical Bulletin, 27,* 272–277.

Mishkin, M. (1964). Perseveration of central sets after frontal lesions in monkeys. In J. M. Warren & K. Akert (Eds.), *The frontal granular cortex and behavior.* New York: McGraw-Hill.

Nauta, W. J., (1971). The problem of the frontal lobe: A reinterpretation. *Journal of Psychiatric Research, 8,* 167–187.

Nauta, W. J. (1972). Neural associations of the frontal cortex. *Acta Neurobiologiae Experimentalis, 32,* 125–140.

Pacella, B. L., Polatin, P., & Nagler, S. H. (1944). Clinical and EEG studies in obsessive-compulsive states. *American Journal of Psychiatry, 100,* 830–838.

Picton, T. W., & Stuss, D. T. (1980). The component structure of the human event-related potential. *Progress in Brain Research, 54,* 17–49.

Ritter, W., Simson, R., & Vaughan, H. G. (1979). Topographic analysis of task related cerebral potentials. In J. E. Desmedt (Ed.), *Cognitive components in cerebral event-related poetentials and selective attention* (pp. 132–139). Basel: Karger.

Rockwell, F. V., & Simons, D. J. (1947). The electroencephalogram and personality organization in the obsessive-compulsive reactions. *Archives of Neurology and Psychiatry, 57,* 71–77.

Rosenkilde, C. E. (1979). Functional heterogeneity of the prefrontal cortex in the monkey: A review. *Behavioral and Neural Biology, 25,* 301–345.

Russell, E. W. (1975). A multiple scoring method for the assessment of complex memory functions. *Journal of Consulting and Clinical Psychology, 43,* 800–809.

Simson, R., Vaughan, H. G., & Ritter, W. (1977). The scalp topography of potentials in auditory and visual go/no-go tasks. *Electroencephalography and Clinical Neurophysiology, 43;* 864–875.

Stuss, D. T., & Benson, D. F. (1984). Neuropsychological studies of the frontal lobes. *Psychological Bulletin, 95,* 3–28.

Walsh, K. W. (1978). *Neuropsychology: A clinical approach.* New York: Churchill-Livingstone.

12

Regulatory Function of the Frontal Lobes

A Neurolinguistic Perspective

B. L. J. Kaczmarek

INTRODUCTION

When we speak of the frontal syndrome, we have in mind the configuration of symptoms associated with a lesion of the prefrontal region of the brain. The prefrontal cortex has been the focus of many controversies in view of the fact that damage to it produces a variety of impairments. As a rule, basic sensory, motor, and speech functions remain intact with damage to the prefrontal cortex, while complex goal-directed behavior deteriorates. In fact, prefrontal lesions are associated with an impairment in control of all functions, both cognitive and emotional. One possible explanation for this is that there are many afferent and efferent projections between the prefrontal cortex and almost every other brain structure.

It is often stressed that the frontal lobes constitute the most recent phylogenetic region of the brain. Furthermore, while the prefrontal region in the rodent brain cannot even be distinguished as a separate structure, prefrontal cortex occupies 3.1% of the neocortex in cats, 13% in apes, and 24% in man (Batuyev, 1973). It is also one of the last cortical regions to undergo myelination. It is thus no wonder that the granular prefrontal cortex has come to be regarded as the site of intellectual functions.

While lesions of this area are not always followed by a decrease in IQ (Teuber, 1972), in subjects with frontal lobe lesions definite disturbances can be observed on tasks that demand shifting of alternative responses. Hence, the inhibitory role of the prefrontal region is emphasized by many authors in both clinical and neurophysiological studies.

THE FRONTAL LOBES REVISITED

ISBN 0-936925-00-0

ANIMAL EXPERIMENTS

It is well known that neither stimulation nor ablation of the prefrontal cortex will affect motor responses, as is the case with manipulation of the premotor and motor cortices. But removal of the prefrontal area will lead to disinhibitory prefrontal syndrome, among other behavioral disturbances. This syndrome may be observed in dogs that have undergone Pavlovian differentiation training, that is, were taught not to carry out a trained movement to the unreinforced stimulus. Konorski (1972) reports that after a lesion of the medial section of prefrontal cortex dogs again began to respond to a stimulus to which they had learned not to respond. He adds that the disinhibitory syndrome is not observed after dorsolateral ablations.

Other experiments carried out in Konorski's laboratory involved motor differentiation tasks in which the animals had to choose the correct movement (of the two trained) in response to two different stimuli. Directional cues (e.g., two sounds coming from different places) and nondirectional cues (e.g., two tones of different frequencies coming from the same place) were used in the study. Similarly, two types of responses were used: directional (e.g., go left-go right task) and nondirectional (e.g., the dog was to lift its paw or bark in response to different stimuli). The results of these studies as well as data from human pathology convinced Konorski that "verbal and gestural differentiation depend on the dominant prefrontal cortex, while locomotor differentiation depends on the nondominant one" (1972, p. 607).

These findings as well as the results of various experiments using delayed-response tasks lead to the conclusion that the main function of the prefrontal cortex is the suppression of excitatory processes arising in other parts of the brain.

The disinhibitory syndrome has been observed by Konorski's collaborators, S. Brutkowski and J. Dabrowska, after dorsolateral ablations when intervals were shortened from their usual duration of 1 minute to 15 seconds. It is also noteworthy that multiple-stage removals of prefrontal tissue fail to produce deficits characteristic of single-stage removals, and that prefrontal lesions may affect task performance differently depending on the age at which the lesion is acquired. Thus, Teuber (1972) points out that dorsolateral excisions in infant apes during the first weeks of life are not followed by impairment on delayed-response tasks, although such impairment does occur in adult apes. The possible explanation for this phenomenon is that lesions of the immature brain result in very limited destruction, while in the mature brain the focus of the lesion is surrounded "by a cloud of degenerating horizontal connections" (Teuber, 1972, p. 629).

While experiments on animals do not yield a fully satisfactory explanation of the "frontal lobe riddle," they do bring us closer to an understanding of the functions of this region.

CLINICAL OBSERVATIONS

The literature on the neuropsychology of prefrontal cortex points to its role as a regulatory mechanism. Warren and Akert (1964) present important anatomical data as well as interesting accounts of behavioral impairments following damage to the prefrontal cortex. Konorski, Teuber, and Zernicki (1972) focus mainly on physiological mechanisms of frontal lobe function. With regard to psychological processes, Teuber's stimulating hypothesis of corollary discharge is of particular interest. Teuber suggested that the prefrontal region plays an important role in preparing the posterior sensory areas to perform their functions.

Pribram (1973; Pribram & Luria, 1973) comes to a similar conclusion and calls the prefrontal region the "executive of the brain." He points to the appearance of Walter's expectancy waves as a sign of preparation to perform experimental tasks.

Luria stressed the fact that frontal lesions lead to disorders of goal-directed behavior. (For a complete presentation of the work of Luria and his collaborators in Russian, see Luria and Homskaya [1966].) Patients loose the ability to control their actions; they become passive, and are apt to respond to any impulse that might appear. They therefore reveal a tendency to enter each open door or to sit down on every chair they come across. In more extensive injuries, stereotypes occur; asked to light a candle, a patient may put the burning match into his mouth. Disturbances on visual cognitive tasks have also been observed.

It is noteworthy that the features of frontal lobe pathology are not always recognized as such by authors describing them. Thus, Ackerley (1964) gives an account of an interesting "case of paranatal bilateral frontal lobe defect" followed for 30 years and states that specific frontal symptoms were not observed. At the same time, however, he notes the patient's tendency to shift his interests, as well as an inability to plan his activities. Moreover, he did not remain at one job for very long, but rather held a number of jobs over a short period. It appears that Ackerley's patient did show a clear-cut disorder in the regulation of his behavior, which Luria believed to be characteristic of the frontal syndrome. Luria also maintained that the speech disorders associated with frontal pathology are related to disturbances of regulatory function.

LINGUISTIC REGULATION OF BEHAVIOR

Language and the Regulation of Behavior in Healthy Children

Most psychologists agree that language plays a role in organizing our behavior (see Bruner, 1973). Szuman (1985) has stressed the significance of language in formulating programmed actions. He maintains that willful actions are developed and perfected only after a child is able to put his intentions into words and thus to program the means by which to follow through the intention.

The regulatory role of verbal instruction has been subjected to detailed analysis in the work of Luria and his collaborators. They refer to Vygotsky's (1962) interpretation of Piaget's "egocentric speech" observed in children performing complex tasks. Piaget (1926) believes that the child's utterances reflect his egocentrism and his lack of socialization. Vygotsky, on the other hand, argues that "egocentric speech" is an effect of social interactions between children and adults. At first the adult gives the child the necessary instructions; next the child gives himself commands aloud; and finally the child learns to plan his actions in the form of "inner speech."

Luria (1961, 1979) argues that the 1½-year-old child is unable to stop or change the action he has been asked to complete, even though he understands the instruction given to him by an adult. The ability to respond correctly to the complex instruction "When the light appears, press the button" is established only after the end of the third year of life. Yet, if the instruction is further complicated and the child is required to condition his responses according to the color of the visual stimulus, he cannot keep from pressing the button each time the light appears, regardless of the color of the light. At the same time, he understands the instruction and can repeat it. If the adult, however, gives the commands "press" and "don't press," the child is able to perform the task correctly.

It is of interest that the regulatory role of verbal instruction is in effect at the age of 5–6 years, that is, when the frontal lobes attain the first stage of their maturity. It is also significant that "egocentric speech" disappears at about that age.

Linguistic Regulation of Behavior in Children with Developmental Disorders

It has been observed that verbal instructions do not play a regulatory role in mentally retarded children (Lubovsky, 1978). Among various Soviet works on this problem the monograph by Luria and Yudovich (1956) deserves our attention. The authors conducted a unique experiment on 5-year-old male monozygotic twins who did not communicate with anyone but each other and who furthermore communicated with each other in their own "language." When the brothers were separated by being placed in different kindergarten classes, speech developed rapidly. After 10 months, not only did they acquire normal speech, but they were able to perform complex intellectual tasks. One of the twins (the subordinate one) was given special language training. This brother became the organizer of their planned games. While the trained brother was able to repeat stories, the untrained brother could only answer questions. When classifying objects, the untrained brother grouped a picture of a carrot with a picture of a streetcar because they were both red. The trained brother, on the other hand, formed groups representing fruits, animals, vehicles, etc.

Linguistic Regulation of Behavior in Prefrontal Lesions

Most studies dealing with speech disorders after brain injury are concerned with disruptions of verbal communication. Information on the regulatory function of language can be found in the work of Luria and his collaborators. Hence, Mescheriakov (1966) reports that patients with extensive frontal lesions were unable to follow verbal commands even though they could repeat the command. Patients were incapable of following such simple instructions as "Lift your hand" or "Press the button."

Homskaya (1966) observed that patients with less extensive frontal lesions were able to follow the instruction to press or not press a button when the decision to press or not press depended on the color of a light that appeared. However, if the task was further complicated and the same patients were asked to press *hard* in response to a red light and *lightly* in response to a blue one, none of the patients performed the task correctly, and all tended to press the button with the same force each time. No improvements were seen in these patients when they were asked to say to themselves the word "hard" when the red light appeared and "lightly" when the blue light appeared. In patients with posterior lesions such self-instruction did improve performance.

Maruszewski (1970) tested subjects with less severe prefrontal injuries on this task and found that they performed well. He introduced so-called conflicting tasks, in which patients were asked to press a button for a long duration in response to a brief visual signal, and to press it for a short time in response to a long visual signal. Frontal patients tended to press the button for a brief duration in response to brief stimuli, and for a longer duration in response to lengthy stimuli, even though they evidently understood the instructions and were aware that their responses were incorrect.

A similar dissociation between language and motor behavior was observed by Teuber (1972), whose patients failed to inhibit motor responses that were inconsistent with the verbal instructions, while recognizing that their responses were incorrect.

Despite qualitative differences, there are similarities between these patterns of performance and the behavior of young children. It is much easier to initiate a child's activity than to terminate that activity. In other words, verbal commands do not control the child's motor behavior.

EEG studies (see Luria & Homaskaya, 1966; Pribram & Luria, 1973) also point to impairments in arousal both in a case of evoked and in one of spontaneous bioelectric activity. Verbal regulation of this activity is particularly subject to disturbance. The authors believe it reflects impairment of the physiological basis of attention.

The studies reviewed above indicate that language plays an important role in the regulation of human behavior, particularly in self-regulation. It would therefore seem plausible to assume that impairment of regulatory function might be related to disturbances in language production.

NEUROLINGUISTIC ANALYSIS OF THE FRONTAL SYNDROME

The problem of characterizing the frontal syndrome is a serious one. The diversity of symptoms observed in prefrontal lesions makes it difficult to specify an identifying symptom or set of symptoms. Moreover, methodological differences among experimental studies often make it impossible to compare results. We have overcome this difficulty by using the technique of neurolinguistic analysis of narrative structure to compare the properties of language samples elicited from different patients with prefrontal pathology.

Subjects

The study included patients with lesions of the prefrontal region in whom neither classic aphasic symptoms nor any other neurological disturbances were found. Three groups were distinguished among them: (1) patients with left dorsolateral lesions ($n = 15$), (2) patients with left orbitofrontal lesions ($n = 15$), and (3) patients with right frontal lobe lesions ($n = 15$). There were also three control groups: (1) posterior aphasics ($n = 15$), (2) posterior brain-damaged patients without aphasia ($n = 15$), and (3) a non-brain-damaged group ($n = 30$).

All brain-damaged patients were evaluated with the Luria battery for neuropsychological and psychological dysfunction. Patients with brain tumors localized at surgery and/or using radiologic techniques were selected for the study. The mean age of the 45 frontal subjects was 46.6 years; for controls, 45.9 years. Subjects ranged in age from 20 to 66, and were matched for sex and level of education.

Procedure

Patients suffering from lesions of the prefrontal cortex show a considerable reduction in their level of activity, including their language production. It was therefore necessary to construct tasks that would induce subjects to speak. With that goal in mind, patients were asked to (1) repeat a story (a) that was told to them, (b) that they had read themselves; (2) describe a situation presented in (a) a single picture, (b) a sequence of pictures; and (3) talk about a given topic (a) relating to the patient's personal life (e.g., his work, his hometown), (b) of a more impersonal nature (e.g., the sea, mountains, school).

Subtests a and b were used to try to gain insight into the nature of the difficulties encountered by each group of patients. Although each task was administered several times to each frontal subject in order to observe the dynamics of the disturbance, only narratives collected during a single session with a given subject were chosen for the purpose of quantitative analysis. Mean phrase length and fluency scores achieved by each group were also calculated. The validity of results was tested with *t* tests.

An extensive discussion of the results of this study is found elsewhere (Kaczmarek, 1984, in press). Only those results bearing on the topic of this chapter will be presented here.

SEMANTIC STRUCTURE OF THE NARRATIVES

Reproducing the Story

The way in which a subject organizes information can be revealed when he is asked to reproduce a story. Since both semantic and syntactic information are given, we can isolate the subject's ability to organize the information he is given, that is, the extent to which he is able to reproduce a number of propositions in sequential order.

The following propositions were identified in the tale "The Fox and the Goat":

A fox was running after a hen
The fox fell into the barrel
The fox could not get out of it
The fox saw a goat
The fox pretended to drink water
The goat jumped into the barrel
The fox climbed onto the goat
The fox ran away
The goat stayed in the barrel

Each of these elemental propositions is joined one to another according to the rules of grammar to form a story. Note that the additional information (e.g., that the event took place in a garden or that the barrel was dug into the ground) is not necessary to understand the story. The number and sequence of propositions in each story were identified by at least 21 healthy normal subjects who had been asked to list only those propositions they felt were essential to the story. A total of 324 subjects evaluated the stories.

Patients with prefrontal lesions tend to displace individual propositions, and exhibit difficulties in making the transition from one point to another (see Table 1). As a rule they omit propositions from the middle of the story and consequently are unable to reproduce the story. The following example illustrates this:

> [A. O., a 34-year-old female farmer, ablation of the left prefrontal region] The goat (laughs) . . . No, how shall I start? The goat . . . was running across a meadow . . . and it fell into the well . . . What was next? . . . Well, the goat was running again[1]

---

[1] Since there are neither phonological nor gross syntactic errors in the sample utterances, direct English translations are given in this chapter.

However, if we ask detailed questions, patients are able to reproduce the story. Moreover, they are much better at reproducing stories they have heard than stories they have read. The symptoms described cannot, therefore, be explained in terms of a memory disorder. Perseveration of propositions is also quite common, and as a rule patients cannot initiate a story without the help of an examiner.

Difficulties encountered by posterior aphasics are of a different character and they appear to reflect word-finding as well as phonemic difficulties. Hence, verbal (46.4%) and phonemic (21.4%) paraphasias are common, although, on the whole, patients are able to reproduce the stories despite their language difficulties. Indeed, 40% of the patients with posterior brain lesions performed the task well. The difficulties illustrated in Table 1 are associated with very extensive lesions, and are therefore nonspecific in character.

Though non-brain-damaged subjects are apt to confuse some unimportant details, they are, at the same time, able to correct themselves. It is also releveant that, while repetition of information was noted in these subjects, this would not be classified as perseveration since the same information was being conveyed in different forms (e.g., "The bear was cooking, preparing meals" or "fell into the barrel, jumped into the barrel").

TABLE 1
Distribution of Semantic Errors in Reproducing a Narrative

	Subject group			
Error type	Frontal lobe lesion	Posterior lesion with aphasia	Posterior lesion without aphasia	Controls
Perseveration of propositions	42.2[a]	—	—	—
Perseveration of words	—	14.3	19.0	—
Digression	11.1	14.3	9.5	—
Displacement of propositions	40.0	3.6	19.0	—
Misnaming	—	46.4	—	—
Misarticulation	—	21.4	—	—
Failure to respond	—	—	9.5	—
No errors	6.7	—	43.0	100.0

[a]Data presented are percentages.

Describing Pictures

Most patients with prefrontal lesions are not capable of describing a situation presented in a picture and they limit themselves to naming single elements within the picture (see Table 2). These subjects treat each element in the larger picture as a separate unit, and as a result cannot follow the thread of the story presented in the picture. Misnamings of elements within the picture can also lead to the wrong interpretation of the picture as a whole. But these misnamings do not seem to be attributable to a deficit in visual perception since the patients are able to name objects correctly when they are presented in separate drawings. The more likely explanation is that the difficulties reflect a disturbance of the ability to organize incoming information.

The performance of posterior aphasics on this task is similar to their performance on the first task. Yet, 41% of the errors on this task were word-finding errors (see Table 2).

Describing pictures proves to be an easy task for the brain-damaged patients without aphasia, and nearly 50% of their narratives are correct. Despite deficits in visual perception, they are able to describe complex pictures. They are much worse, however, at describing picture stories, where each picture provides less information.

TABLE 2
Distribution of Semantic Errors in Describing a Picture

	Subject group			
Error type	Frontal lobe lesion	Posterior lesion with aphasia	Posterior lesion without aphasia	Controls
Perseveration of propositons	28.4[a]	—	—	—
Perseveration of words	—	24.1	11.7	—
Digression	5.5	—	—	—
Naming single objects	33.8	—	—	—
False interpretation	13.5	6.9	11.7	6.6
Misnaming	14.8	41.4	29.4	—
Phonemic paraphasias	—	27.6	—	—
No errors	4.0	—	47.2	93.4

[a]Data presented are percentages.

As can be seen in Table 2, non-brain-damaged subjects attained almost 100% success.

Spontaneous Narratives

Discussing a given topic turns out to be a very difficult task for patients with prefrontal injuries. In 60% of cases these patients are unable to convey any information. Sometimes they cannot produce even one full statement. Table 3 shows a prevalence of perseveration of propositions as well as a tendency toward stereotyped phrases. These stereotyped phrases are more likely to appear when patients speak about topics of general interest, for example, mountains. We may then learn that "Mountains are very high" or that "Mountains are beautiful."

Posterior aphasics encounter the same difficulties with the present task as with the preceding two. Yet, in spite of word-finding impairments and frequent phonemic paraphasias, they are able to convey the necessary information.

Discussing a topic is an even easier task for the posterior brain-damaged group. The only disruptions are repetitions, which occur in 26.7% of the narratives. Non-brain-damaged subjects have no problem completing this task.

If we compare scores across groups on the three tasks, we see that errors occur only in narratives elicited from patients with prefrontal lesions, and that the most common error is perseveration of propositions. In other brain-damaged groups, only words are perseverated. Another form of disturbance typical of the

TABLE 3
Distribution of Semantic Errors in Spontaneous Narratives

	Subject group			
Error type	Frontal lobe lesion	Posterior lesion with aphasia	Posterior lesion without aphasia	Controls
Perseveration of propositions	32.2[a]	—	—	—
Perseveration of words	—	29.6	26.7	—
Digression	25.5	3.7	—	—
Stereotyped phrases	25.5	—	—	—
Misnamings	14.8	40.7	—	—
Phonemic paraphasias	—	26.0	—	—
No errors	2.0	—	73.3	100.0

[a]Data presented are percentages.

frontal group is digression, which often leads to confabulation. Digression appears to a lesser degree in other populations, especially during the reproduction of stories.

When comparing Tables 1, 2, and 3, notice that the pattern of errors produced by frontal subjects is less stable than that of other groups and that the error pattern depends on the type of task. Hence, the displacement of proposition can be observed during story repetition, while telling a story from a picture provokes a tendency to name single objects, and discussing a given topic leads to the use of stereotyped phrases.

It has also been observed that the third task (discussing a given topic) is most difficult for the experimental group, in contradistinction to the control group. It may therefore be concluded that prefrontal lesions are followed by considerable difficulties in organizing information for both comprehension and production.

SYNTACTIC STRUCTURE OF NARRATIVES

Reproducing Narratives

Injuries to the prefrontal cortex cause distinct changes in the syntactic complexity of utterances produced. Thus, simple sentences constitute nearly 40% of all statements, and the number of nonfinite clauses (i.e., clauses lacking a predicate) is also high (24.2%). At the same time, utterances produced by aphasics are more complex than those of prefrontal patients without aphasia, revealing 10% fewer simple sentences and nonfinite clauses. The syntactic structure of the remaining two groups is also more complex than in the frontal group.

Describing Pictures

In all groups there is a significant increase in the percentage of sentence fragments and nonfinite clauses on picture description. However, overall proportions of utterance types remain the same as in reproductions of model stories.

Spontaneous Narratives

The simplification of syntactic structure is most pronounced in spontaneous narratives of frontal subjects. Consequently, the disturbances described above are manifested to a greater degree in this case. On the whole, however, the distribution of utterance types is analogous to that observed in the previous tasks. Therefore, the distribution of utterance types elicited from subjects will be presented across all three tasks (see Table 4).

As Table 4 indicates, there are some similarities between patients with prefrontal lesions and posterior aphasics. Thus, only in these two groups do we observe sentence fragments and "phatic phrases." Phatic phrases were first

TABLE 4
Distribution of Utterance Types in All Narratives

	Subject group			
Error type	Frontal lobe lesion	Posterior lesion with aphasia	Posterior lesion without aphasia	Controls
Simple sentence	36.6[a]	27.4	27.6	27.6
Compound sentence	7.2	8.4	11.1	14.7
Complex sentence	13.3	18.1	29.0	37.2
Sentence fragment	5.1	8.1	2.7	1.6
Interjected phrase	2.5	2.8	4.8	2.9
Nonfinite clause	34.2	30.8	24.8	16.0
Phatic phrase	1.1	4.4	—	—

[a]Data presented are percentages.

defined by Malinowski (1946), who described them as statements that do not play any communicative function but rather help people maintain contact with their interlocutors. Malinowski pointed to ritual phrases and greetings as the best examples of the "phatic communion."

In the narratives analyzed in the present study, the following phrases appeared: "Wait a moment"; "Well, let me think"; "That'll be . . ., " etc. The phrases give patients time to overcome their production difficulties.

DIVERSITY WITHIN THE FRONTAL SYNDROME

Symptoms Associated with Dorsolateral Prefrontal Lesions

The most evident deficit in dorsolateral prefrontal lesions is a difficulty developing narratives. Above all, patients show a tendency to perseverate on the first proposition; 70% of patients demonstrate perseveration on repetition and story telling. The difficulty in formulating verbal messages is reflected in the grammatical structure of their utterances. Simple sentences are three times as frequent as complex sentences (i.e., those involving subordination). Moreover, compound (i.e., coordinate) sentences predominate among the few complex structures, while in the remaining frontal groups (left orbitofrontal and right frontal) the ratio of compound (coordinate) to complex (subordinate) sentences is reversed. Also, the percentage of nonfinite clauses and sentence fragments is highest in the dorsolateral prefrontal group (see Table 5), reflecting the poverty of their language.

TABLE 5
Distribution of Utterance Types in All Narratives of Frontal Subjects

Utterance type	Subject group[a]		
	L1	L2	P
Simple sentence	39.7[b]	34.1	36.3
Compound sentence	5.7	5.7	10.2
Complex sentence	5.1	14.8	19.6
Sentence fragment	7.4	5.9	2.1
Interjected phrase	2.5	2.5	2.4
Nonfinite clause	37.9	35.3	29.4
Phatic phrase	1.7	1.7	—

[a]L1, Left dorsolateral frontal lesion; L2, left orbitofrontal lesion; P, right Frontal lobe lesion.
[b]Data presented are percentages.

As reported elsewhere (Kaczmarek, 1984), patients with damage to the lateral aspects of the prefrontal cortex scored similarly to aphasics on other tasks as well. Thus, no statistically significant differences were found between this group and aphasics both in phrase length and in word fluency scores. All these findings suggest impairment of language production as the underlying dimension of the observed disorder.

Symptoms of Left Orbitofrontal Lesions

Orbitofrontal lesions cause a different form of disturbance in the production of narratives. Most typical of this group is digression, which often leads to confabulation. The quality of these errors seems to indicate a disturbance in word selection.

The grammatical structure of narratives in the left orbitofrontal group is more complex than in the dorsolateral prefrontal group (see Table 5). Furthermore, patients in the left orbitofrontal group are apt to talk more and their word fluency scores are higher than those of other frontal groups (see Kaczmarek, 1984). In fact, they are equal to the fluency scores of nonaphasic patients with posterior lesions. These data suggest that the difficulties encountered by patients with orbitofrontal injuries are not caused by disorders of language production, but rather by an inability to control their verbal behavior. Such patients might therefore produce quite contradictory statements, as did B. S., a 52-year-old male engineer with an orbitofrontal glioma, who, when asked to repeat a story, answered: "I shall do it . . . with great pleasure . . . since I haven't any great pleasure in it." Automatic verbal behavior is preserved in this patient, but he has trouble regulating the content of his utterances.

Symptoms of Right Frontal Lobe Lesions

Difficulties characteristic of the frontal groups described above can be observed with right frontal lesions as well. At the same time, there are some differences. Thus, in story repetition, patients with right frontal lobe lesions tend to displace propositions in over 60% of narratives. Furthermore, they give incorrect interpretations of whole pictures (27.4% of all disruptions), while in the other frontal groups misinterpretation of individual elements of a picture is most common.

The requirement to produce stories based on a specified topic causes the right frontal subjects to depend on stereotyped phrases. The phrases appear in half of all utterances of these subjects, while in the other groups they do not reach 15%.

The grammatical complexity of narratives is also greater in the right frontal group than in the other two frontal groups. We observe here a significant increase in the number of embedded structures (i.e., compound and complex sentences) and a decrease in the percentage of sentence fragments. Still across frontal subjects, narratives remain structurally simplified.

CONCLUSIONS

The findings presented above show that all patients with prefrontal lesions have difficulty processing verbal messages. It should be stressed, however, that language is only one of the modalities of behavior impaired in frontal lobe pathology.

Patients with left dorsolateral injuries demonstrate considerable difficulty in carrying out any behavioral act. Moreover, general verbal instructions do not facilitate their actions. These patients are able to complete the required task only after the instruction is given in the form of a simple command. It appears then that this part of the prefrontal cortex is involved in the formulation of plans in particular.

On the other hand, left orbitofrontal lesions are followed by disturbances in controlling ongoing activity, and patients are apt to change the course of action in response to any external or internal impulse. As a rule, they do not correct their mistakes in spite of hints given by the examiner. It is therefore plausible to assume that the orbitofrontal cortex is responsible for monitoring the course of action.

Most characteristic of right frontal damage is an inability to evaluate one's present condition. Hence, patients often deny that they are ill and sometimes attribute their difficulties to an effect of drugs given to them by doctors. Disorientation in place and time can also be noted. It is probable, therefore, that the right frontal lobe is important for the holistic, spatial organization of information. Speculations offered by Konorski (1972) seem to support these observations (see above, p. 226).

In sum, I have presented a linguistic analysis of narratives produced by patients with frontal lesions in order to demonstrate that the regulatory function of the prefrontal region is bound up to a great extent with language. Indeed, Pontius and Yudowitz (1980) depend on the diagnostic value of narratives to identify frontal lobe dysfunction.

Language helps us organize incoming stimuli and formulate our knowledge, experience, and emotions into a message. In other words, language plays a role in information processing, and consequently in thinking and other forms of human behavior. Of particular interest in this context is the role of the frontal lobes in thought disorders, that is, schizophrenia. Morice (in press) discusses the relation between the frontal lobes and "changes in the structural complexity of the spoken language of schizophrenic patients." The work of Morice suggests that, in future research, a focus on analysis of language samples may yield insight into the nature of the problems patients encounter.

REFERENCES

Ackerley, S. S. (1964). A case of paranatal bilateral frontal lobe defect observed for thirty years. In J. M. Warren & K. Akert (Eds.), *The frontal granular cortex and behavior* (pp. 192–216). New York: McGraw-Hill.

Batuyev, A. S. (1973). [*Evolution of the frontal lobes and an integrative function of the brain*]. Leningrad: Medicina (in Russian).

Bruner, J. S. (1973). *Beyond the information given. Studies in psychology of knowing*. New York: Norton.

Homskaya, E. D. (1966). [Regulation of intensity of voluntary motor reactions in lesions of the frontal lobes.] In A. R. Luria & E. D. Homskaya (Eds.) [*Frontal lobes and regulation of psychological processes*] (pp. 463–499). Moscow: Moscow University Press (in Russian).

Kaczmarek, B. L. J. (1984). Neurolinguistic analysis of verbal utterances in patients with focal lesions of frontal lobes. *Brain and Language, 21*, 52–58.

Kaczmarek, B. L. J. (1986). [*Frontal lobes, language, and human behavior*]. Wroclaw: Ossolineum (in Polish).

Konorski, J. (1972). Some hypotheses concerning the functional organization of prefrontal cortex. *Acta Neurobiologiae Experimentalis, 32*, 595–613.

Konorski, J., Teuber, H. L., & Zernicki, B. (Eds.). (1972). The frontal granular cortex and behavior [Special issue]. *Acta Neurobiologiae Experimentalis, 32*.

Lubovsky, V. I. (1978). [*Development of verbal regulation of behavior in children*]. Moscow: Pedagogika (in Russian).

Luria, A. R. (1961). *The role of speech in regulation of normal and abnormal behavior*. Oxford: Pergamon.

Luria, A. R. (1979). [*Language and cognition*]. Moscow: Moscow University Press (in Russian).

Luria, A. R., & Homskaya, E. D. [*Frontal lobes and regulation of psychological processes*]. Moscow: Moscow University Press (in Russian).

Luria, A. R., & Yudovich, F. J. (1956). [*Speech and development of psychological processes in a child*]. Moscow: Academy Pedagog. Sciences Press (in Russian).

Malinowski, B. (1946). The problem of meaning in primitive languages. In C. K. Ogden & I. A. Richards (Eds.), *The meaning of meaning* (pp. 296–336). New York: Harcourt, Brace.

Maruszewski, M. (1970). [*Speech and brain*]. Warsaw: PWN (in Polish).

Mescheriakov, A. J. (1966). [Disturbances of simple motor reactions in massive lesions of the frontal lobes]. In A. R. Luria & E. D. Homskaya (Eds.), [*Frontal lobes and regulation of psychological processes*] (pp. 431–445). Moscow: Moscow University Press (in Russian).

Morice, R. (in press). Beyond language—speculations on the prefrontal cortex and schizophrenia. *Australian and New Zealand Journal of Psychiatry*.

Piaget, J. (1926). *The language and thought of a child* (M. Warden, Trans.). New York: Harcourt, Brace.

Pontius, A. A., & Yudowitz, B. S. (1980). Frontal lobe system dysfunction in some criminal actions as shown in the narrative test. *Journal of Nervous and Mental Disease, 168,* 111–117.

Pribram, K. H. (1973). The primate frontal cortex—executive of the brain. In K. H. Pribram & A. R. Luria (Eds.), *Psychophysiology of the frontal lobes* (pp. 293–314). New York: Academic Press.

Pribram, K. H., & Luria, A. R. (Eds.). (1973). *Psychophysiology of the frontal lobes*. New York: Academic Press.

Szuman, S. (1985). [*Selected writing*]. Warsaw: Wydawnictwa Szkolne i Pedagogiczne.

Teuber, H. L. (1972). Unity and diversity of frontal lobe function. *Acta Neurobiologiae Experimentalis, 32,* 615–656.

Vygotsky, L. S. (1962). *Thought and language* (E. Hanfmann & G. Vakar, Trans.). Cambridge, MA: MIT Press.

Warren, J. M., & Akert, K. (Eds.). (1964). *The frontal granular cortex and behavior*. New York: McGraw-Hill.

13

The Supplementary Motor Region and Speech

Saran Jonas

INTRODUCTION

According to Chusid, de Gutierrez-Mahoney, and Margules-Lavergne (1954), reports on the subject of frontal parasagittal lesions causing speech disorders can be found from as early as 1879. Brickner (1940) presented the first clinical neurophysiologic data on the subject; he demonstrated speech perseveration during electrical stimulation (at craniotomy under local anesthesia) of Area 6 on the mesial surface of the left cerebral hemisphere. His observations were confirmed and extended in a series of cases similarly studied by Penfield and his colleagues (see Penfield & Roberts, 1959), who called the described region the "supplementary motor area" because a variety of limb movements were also elicited by local electrical stimulation.

There is now a considerable clinical and experimental literature on speech disturbances from lesions in this frontal parasagittal supplementary motor region; in the sections that follow I will review this literature. I will then speculate on how this region participates in speech in the intact subject and on how its dysfunction leads to speech disturbances.

SPEECH DISTURBANCES SEEN WITH SUPPLEMENTARY MOTOR REGION LESIONS

From the clinical literature on supplementary motor region[1] (SMR) lesions (see the review of Jonas, 1981; for additional case reports and references see also

[1]I used the term *supplementary motor region* rather than *supplementary motor area* in my 1981 review so that I could use SMR as an abbreviation rather than SMA. The term *transcortical motor aphasia* has been applied to speech disturbances from lesions in this part of the brain; the latter term has been abbreviated by some as TMA (see Racy, Janotta, & Lehner, 1979). I found SMA and TMA unduly confusing.

ISBN 0-936925-00-0

Brust, Plank, Burke, Guobadia, & Healton, 1982; Freedman, Alexander, & Naeser, 1984; Gelmers, 1983; Peled, Harnes, Borovich, & Sharp, 1984; Tijssen, Tavy, Hekster, Bots, & Endtz, 1984) one perceives that a variety of speech disturbances can occur. These disturbances can be categorized in terms of the clinical setting: those disturbances seen in paroxysmal situations and those occurring in nonparoxysmal situations. The latter can be further classified in terms of the underlying disease process: acute; occurring during recovery after an acute lesion; and occurring in association with a slowly worsening process.

The great majority of unilateral SMR lesions disturbing speech are left SMR lesions. Disturbances do occur with right SMR lesions, however (see Brust et al., 1982; Gelmers, 1983; Jonas, 1981). It may be that these merely reflect the occurrence of occasional right cerebral dominance for speech (see Jonas, 1981, and Brust et al., 1982, for discussion).

Paroxysmal Situations

Partial seizures in some patients with SMR lesions can be manifested by speech arrest (with muteness or with the ability to emit inarticulate sounds only). In other patients the seizure is manifested by forced involuntary vocalizations. This can be a repetitive vowel sound ("ah, ah, ah . . .") or consonant-vowel syllable ("da, da, da . . ."). There are reports of patients who uncontrollably repeated a brief phrase many times; the word or phrase may be what the patient was about to say [as in Brickner's (1940) patient, who perseverated under cortical stimulation]. In the post-ictal state temporary speech suppression, stuttering, word-finding difficulties, etc., may be seen.

Nonparoxysmal Situations

Speech Disturbances with Acute SMR Lesions Strokes, surgery, and accidental trauma involving the SMR all cause suppression or arrest of speech.

Speech Disturbances in Patients Recovering from Acute SMR Lesions In the days or weeks following the acquisition of an acute SMR lesion, one may see a gradual recovery of speech. During this recovery phase a striking pattern can also be seen: that of *transcortical motor aphasia* in which there is a disparity between propositional speech (speech transmitting the subject's ideas) and nonpropositional speech (or automatic speech: echoing what others say, counting, completing nursery rhymes, etc.). A patient recovering from an SMR lesion may thus go through a period during which the emission of propositional speech remains severely impaired, yet during which nonpropositional or automatic speech may be produced readily at request or may be produced in an involuntary stimulus-bound manner.

Patient L. L. of von Stockert (1974), tested several weeks after a presumed infarct, had almost no spontaneous speech. She responded to questions with brief answers, such as "yes" or "two weeks." She did not speak when asked to describe complex scenery in a picture, but when questioned about the elements of the scenery, she named them correctly. She could complete sentences if given suitable cuing, could repeat long and complex sentences very well, and could count without difficulty, in a low voice.

Patient 4 of Környey (1975) was mute for a week after transfrontal surgery for an intraventricular tumor (no preoperative aphasia). During the second week she said her name but nothing else. At 2 weeks she could accurately repeat what she heard, even in foreign languages, but she could not initiate spontaneous speech. At 4 weeks she could repeat questions, transposing the verb into the first person form. This repetition was involuntary and could not be suppressed; she would put her left hand over her mouth in an unsuccessful attempt at suppression.

Case 1 of Rubens (1975) showed, during a 5-week period after a stroke, a striking absence of spontaneous conversational speech. If addressed, the patient would make one- or two-word replies, usually correct, with great effort. When asked to repeat long sentences, she consistently did so correctly, although slowly and with a "lack of melody." She was also able to repeat aloud short sentences mouthed inaudibly to her. As was true for the patient of Környey, Rubens's patient also had involuntary, stimulus-bound emissions; when the examiner said, "Roses are red," the patient would say, "White and blue," and could not prevent the response. Similarly, she would be unable *not* to say "D, E, F, G" when the examiner said "A, B, C," and she could not prevent herself from giving the last three words of a song title when the examiner gave the first three.

Speech Disturbances with Slowly Worsening SMR Lesions With neoplasms in the SMR, the most frequently reported speech disturbances seem to be reduced and labored output with initiation difficulty, word-finding problems, and dysarthria. Some patients with tumors can also show relative preservation of nonpropositional speech (see Ardila & Lopez, 1984).

Speech Disturbances Summarized

As has been seen above, there can occur general *speech suppression* in association with acute SMR injury, during tumor enlargement in the SMR, or during or after seizures occurring in patients with SMR lesions.

SMR lesions can also be associated with *involuntary vocalizations:* these can occur during seizures or can be seen as insuppressible echolalic responses or completion responses while patients are recovering from acute SMR lesions.

Also, and strikingly, in nonacute situations patients may *be able to produce nonpropositional speech* (repetition, counting, etc., either at request or involuntarily, as described above), *even though propositional speech remains suppressed.*

In addition to the above, it will be noted that SMR lesions also produce *disturbances of the mechanics of speech:* dysphonia, monotony of tone, stuttering, variability of speech rate, etc.

ARM-HAND-FINGER CONTROL FUNCTIONS OF THE SMR

Before one considers the role of the SMR in normal speech, and the mechanism whereby SMR dysfunction results in speech disturbances, it is profitable to review its role in nonspeech motor activities. This section reviews and interprets results of experiments concerning the SMR and arm-hand-finger control: an electrophysiologic study capable of identifying a single neuronal event; isotope studies in which regional cerebral blood flow, averaged over many seconds, was studied in the resting state and during activity (this technique, unlike the electrophysiologic technique, cannot identify single or brief events); and lesion studies in animals. All percentage changes given represent differences, over the resting state, that are statistically significant.

Tanji, Taniguchi, and Saga (1980) did single-unit extracellular recording from neurons in the monkey SMR via implanted electrodes. They found neurons that showed a firing rate higher than baseline while the monkey planned a simple arm response to what he anticipated would be one set of conditions; when he planned his arm response to an anticipated second set of conditions, the firing rate in these neurons dropped below baseline and indeed became silent. That the increase or inhibition of firing was concerned only with planning was documented by complete EMG silence in the limb during these times.

Roland, Skinhøj, Lassen, and Larsen (1980) studied the SMR in humans with respect to arm, hand, and finger movements. They demonstrated by isotopic technique that both SMRs showed 24–40% bilateral simultaneous blood flow increases while one hand of the subject (whose eyes were closed) felt its way in order to place the index finger in a stipulated cell of a grid defined by a rectangular framework of rods.

Similarly, when the thumb of one hand was touched to the fingertips in a complex previously practiced 16-movement sequence, 27–29% blood flow increases were seen in both SMRs simultaneously (Roland, Larsen, Lassen, & Skinhøj, 1980).

In contrast to these bilateral SMR flow increases, only the contralateral pre-Rolandic primary motor area (MI) for the hand showed flow increases (30–40%) during the arm, hand, and finger maneuvers described above. When subjects were asked to mentally simulate (but not physically execute) the thumb-finger touching sequence described above, 17–21% SMR flow increases, but no MI flow increases, were observed.

During a simple rhythmically repetitive movement (compressing a spring between thumb and index finger once per second), Roland, Larsen et al. (1980) saw a 30% increase in blood flow in the contralateral hand MI area, but no increase in the contralateral SMR.

Brinkman (1984) performed unilateral SMR ablation in monkeys. The only lasting deficit was an inability of the fingers of the two hands to execute different movements at the same time while the monkey attempted to retrieve small food morsels from a narrow slot; both hands tended to perform the same movement simultaneously. Sectioning the corpus callosum abolished the deficit.

From the above, taking into consideration the technique limitations of the isotope studies, one can make the following inferences.

1. The *planning* of motor activity involves the SMR.
2. The voluntary initiation of a motor act involves the transmission of an instruction from the SMR to the MI; the MI then emits the signal for the execution of the act.
3. When each element of a sequence of voluntary acts is different, the SMR must emit as steadily as the MI; therefore, averaging of activity over the duration of the sequence shows sustained activity in both areas.
4. When each element of a series of voluntarily undertaken simple motor acts is identical with the previous element, the MI can act without the need for a sustained flow of instructions from the SMR. (An initial triggering by a burst of SMR activity too brief to influence the averaged results over the duration of observation can be postulated.)
5. One can also see that the SMR, in addition to promoting desired motor activity, must also play an inhibitory or gating role with respect to the MI: It prevents entry into the MI of influences that would disrupt an ongoing MI program.

One can summarize the above as follows:

I. The SMR plans for motor acts and instructs the MI to put the plans into effect.
II. The SMR has an important inhibitory role as well: It prevents entry into the MI of influences that would disrupt an ongoing MI program.

SPEECH CONTROL FUNCTIONS OF THE SMR

With the above discussion in mind, one can review experiments aimed directly at elucidating speech mechanisms. I will discuss regional cerebral blood flow studies analogous to those done for finger-hand function, and some results of lesioning (for the data and references reflecting the work of Friberg, Ingvar, Larsen, Lassen, Roland, Schwartz, and Skinhøj, see the review of Roland [1985]).

In regional cerebral blood flow studies in intact people, the left SMR showed a 19% mean flow increase by the isotopic technique during non propositional speech (counting, reciting the months of the year, etc.); the mean increase in the right SMR was 12%. The left SMR showed a 26% mean flow increase during propositional speech (describing the furniture in one's living room, for example); the mean right SMR increase was 11%. For both nonpropositional and propositional speech the pre-Rolandic primary motor area (MI) for oral-lingual movements showed mean flow increases in the 20–30% range on both sides. Broca's area in the left cerebral hemisphere showed a 21% mean flow increase during propositional speech and no increase during nonpropositional speech. During propositional speech the right cerebral homolog of Broca's area showed a 9% mean flow increase; there was no increase during nonpropositional speech. The upper figure on page 80 of Lassen, Ingvar, and Skinhøj (1978) shows that there was increased flow in the SMR but not in Broca's area or in the MI while the subject counted in his head without speaking.

It is also of interest to review the work of Jürgens (1985), who placed lesions in the rostral portion of the SMR bilaterally in monkeys. The lasting consequence was a decrease in "isolation peep calls." These are calls the monkey makes in an attempt to regain contact with other monkeys who are out of sight. Thus the impetus to make the call comes from an internal mechanism. By contrast, "alarm calls," triggered by perceived external events or objects, were not reduced in lesioned animals.

ROLE OF THE INTACT SMR IN SPEECH

Based on the experimental data on hand activity and on speech, the following hypotheses about speech are promulgated (left cerebral dominance for speech is herein assumed; MI shall hereafter refer to the pre-Rolandic primary motor area for control of the labial-lingual-pharyngeal-laryngeal muscles).

Activation of the Final Common Pathway for Speech Emission

For speech, the final common pathway out of either cerebral hemisphere involves the MI, which can be activated in a specific manner or in a nonspecific manner. Specific speech activation of the MI is from the left SMR via the left Broca's area. The MI can also be activated nonspecifically for speech from various sites in both cerebral hemispheres by routes that do not involve the SMR or Broca's area. Broca's area, unlike the MI, can only be activated in the specific sequence, that is, by the SMR.

Control of Propositional Speech in the Intact Brain

Propositional speech depends on the specific pathway discussed above: The decision to make a statement is directed first into the left SMR, where it is processed and then relayed to the left Broca's area and thence to the MI of both cerebral hemispheres.

In addition to its role in processing the signals for propositional speech, the left SMR also gates other signals that might influence the MI. As a result, under normal speech circumstances, only one nonambiguous set of signals, that for the planned propositional output, ends up influencing the MI. Unwanted interjections are blocked, as are factors that might disrupt articulation, phonation, etc.

Emission of Nonpropositional Speech in the Intact Brain

In the intact subject, nonpropositional speech (e.g., counting) can be undertaken voluntarily through a brief burst of SMR-Broca activity. Nonpropositional speech can also occur *involuntarily,* without preceding SMR activity (e.g., an expletive can be involuntarily emitted on hitting one's thumb with a hammer). In both instances the output is via the MI.

Even when the SMR is not the activator for the MI during nonpropositional speech in the intact subject it nevertheless plays a role in such speech by providing suitable protective gating. Thus, when the intact subject makes the decision to count, the SMR is so informed, and subsequently acts to prevent extraneous influences from entering the MI and distorting the articulation, prosody, etc., of the output. Note that the "automatic act" of saying a sequence of different numbers, which is here postulated to maintain increased SMR activity for inhibitory purposes, is quite different from the "automatic act" of repeatedly compressing a spring between thumb and index finger (which does not cause sustained SMR activation). It would be of interest to see whether repeating the word "one" over and over out loud would result in the same degree of sustained SMR activity.

DISRUPTIONS IN SPEECH WITH SMR DYSFUNCTION

Based on the foregoing discussion and on the clinical data, the following hypotheses are proposed to explain the types of speech disturbances seen with SMR lesions.

The Consequences of Left SMR Dysfunction: The Nonparoxysmal Case

If the left SMR is not working properly, the normal sequence of events crucial to propositional speech emission is impaired upstream of Broca's area and the MI, and propositional output is impaired or impossible. In the presence of left SMR damage, nonpropositional speech is still possible since the external stimuli triggering such speech can still reach the MI. Indeed, if the left SMR is not working, it may be impossible *not* to emit nonpropositional speech in response to certain stimuli, since the mechanism that denies these stimuli access to the MI resides in the left SMR.

The nonpropositional output that occurs in the presence of left SMR dysfunction can differ from that seen with a normally functioning SMR in that difficulties with phonation, articulation, etc., may be present. These difficulties arise because gating of competing influences is an SMR function. In the absence of effective SMR gating, several such competing influences may have simultaneous access to the MI, resulting in distortion of the output.

The Consequences of SMR Dysfunction: The Paroxysmal Case

The two seemingly disparate manifestations of *paroxysmal* SMR dysfunction—forced vocalization versus mutism—result either from an abrupt stimulation of the Broca-MI areas or from sudden temporary loss of SMR activity.

The Mute Period Preceding the Emergence of Transcortical Motor Aphasia

In the period following acute SMR injury, there is muteness for nonpropositional as well as for propositional speech. This reflects not only loss of SMR function, but temporary suppression of all elements of the speech output mechanism, as a result of diaschisis, the widespread temporary cerebral blood flow reduction that occurs after an acute localized cerebral injury (see Ingvar & Lassen, 1978). If the SMR is still dysfunctional when diaschisis abates, then the nonpropositional versus propositional speech output disparity, as described above (which defines transcortical motor aphasia), can make its appearance.

SUMMARY

Clinical data and experimental evidence allow the following hypotheses, which one hopes will be submitted to appropriate testing:

1. The left supplementary motor region (SMR) programs Broca's area so that the latter can activate the pre-Rolandic primary motor area (MI) for propositional speech output.
2. When nonpropositional speech is undertaken voluntarily (e.g., counting), the initiation is via a brief burst of SMR-Broca activity, after which MI operates independently.

3. It is possible for the MI to be activated for automatic nonpropositional speech in the absence of SMR-Broca activity. In a person with a sufficiently damaged SMR, such activation can permit nonpropositional speech, even though propositional speech is impossible. This situation (nonpropositional speech present, propositional speech not possible) is called transcortical motor aphasia.
4. In addition to its activating role, the SMR also gates stimuli flowing into the MI. If the left SMR is sufficiently damaged, emitted speech may suffer from articulation and phonation disturbances because several conflicting stimuli may act on the MI simultaneously, and it may be impossible to *prevent* nonpropositional speech output in the presence of certain external MI-triggering stimuli.

REFERENCES

Ardila, A., & Lopez, M. V. (1984). Transcortical motor aphasia: One or two aphasias? *Brain and Language, 22,* 350–353.

Brickner, R. M. (1940). A human cortical area producing repetitive phenomena when stimulated. *Journal of Neurophysiology, 3,* 128–130.

Brinkman, C. (1984). Supplementary motor area of the monkey's cerebral cortex: Short- and long-term deficits after unilateral ablation and the effects of subsequent callosal section. *Journal of Neuroscience, 4,* 918–929.

Brust, J. C. M., Plank, C., Burke, A., Guobadia, M. M. I., & Healton, E.B. (1982). Language disorder in a right hander after occlusion of the right cerebral artery. *Neurology, 32,* 492–497.

Chusid, J. G., de Gutierrez-Mahoney, C. G., & Margules-Lavergne, M. P. (1954). Speech disturbances in association with parasagittal frontal lesions. *Journal of Neurosurgery, 11,* 193–204.

Freedman, M., Alexander, M. P., & Naeser, M. A. (1984). Anatomic basis of transcortical motor aphasia. *Neurology, 34,* 409–417.

Gelmers, H. J. (1983). Non-paralytic motor disturbances and speech disorders: The role of the supplementary motor area. *Journal of Neurology, Neurosurgery, and Psychiatry, 46,* 1052–1054.

Ingvar, D. H., & Lassen, N. A. (1978). Cerebral function metabolism, and blood flow. *Acta Neurologica Scandinavica, 57,* 262–269.

Jonas, S. (1981). The supplementary motor region and speech emission. *Journal of Communication Disorders, 14,* 349–373.

Jürgens, U. (1985). Implication of the SMA in phonation. *Experimental Brain Research, 58,* A12–A14.

Környey, E. (1975). Aphasie transcorticale et écholalie: Le problème de l'initiative de la parole. *Revue Neurologique 131,* 347–363.

Lassen, N. A., Ingvar, D. H., & Skinhøj, E. (1978). Brain function and blood flow. *Scientific American, 239,* 62–71.

Peled, R., Harnes, B., Borovich, B., & Sharf, B. (1984). Speech arrest and supplementary motor area seizures. *Neurology, 34,* 110–111.

Penfield, W., & Roberts, L. (1959). *Speech and brain mechanisms.* Princeton, NJ: Princeton University Press.

Penfield, W., & Welch, K. (1951). The supplementary motor area of the cerebral cortex: A clinical and experimental study. *Archives of Neurology and Psychiatry, 66,* 289–317.

Racy, A., Janotta, F. S., & Lehner, L. H. (1979). Aphasia resulting from occlusion of the left anterior cerebral artery. *Archives of Neurology (Chicago), 36,* 221–224.

Roland, P. E. (1985). Cortical organization of voluntary behavior in man. *Human Neurobiology, 4,* 155–167.

Roland, P. E., Larsen, B., Lassen, N. A., & Skinhøj, E. (1980). Supplementary motor area and other cortical areas in organization of voluntary movements in man. *Journal of Neurophysiology, 43,* 118–136.

Roland, P. E., Skinhøj, E., Lassen, N. A., & Larsen, B. (1980). Different cortical areas in man in organization of voluntary movements in extrapersonal space. *Journal of Neurophysiology, 43,* 137–150.

Rubens, A. B. (1975). Aphasia with infarction in the territory of the anterior cerebral artery. *Cortex, 11,* 239–250.

Tanji, J., Taniguchi, K., & Saga, T. (1980). Supplementary motor area: Neuronal response to motor instructions. *Journal of Neurophysiology, 43,* 60–68.

Tijssen, C. C., Tavy, D. L. J., Hekster, R. E. M., Bots, G. T. A. M., & Endtz, L. J. (1984). Aphasia with a left frontal interhemispheric hematoma. *Neurology, 34,* 1261–1264.

Von Stockert, T. R. (1974). Aphasia sine aphasia. *Brain and Language, 1,* 277–282.

14

The Microstructure of Action

Jason W. Brown

INTRODUCTION

This chapter describes a model of frontal lobe organization based on the idea that the symptoms of a frontal lobe lesion can be understood as disruptions in the microgenetic unfolding of an action. According to the microgenetic account, every behavior or mental state has a submerged infrastructure distributed over evolutionary planes in the forebrain. Cognitive processing retraces the direction of phyletic growth, so that evolutionary levels, and correlated processing stages, are entrained in behavior in the order of their evolutionary appearance. In a very real sense, microgeny recapitulates phylogeny as cognition rapidly unfolds over evolutionary structure.

We can begin by defining an action as a cognitive structure consisting of multiple representational planes, each of which is reconstituted moment to moment in the flow of behavior. In the course of the unfolding of an action, movements are deposited at successive points. However, there is a difference between an action and a movement. Movements are what actually happen in the behavior; they are physical events or chains of events that are extrinsic to cognition (mind). In contrast, an action is a mental event that participates in private experience. Actions are representations that are read off into movements. An action is a cognitive precursor that lays down or instantiates a movement in physical space, in the same way that a perception is a mental event that is configured by, or modeled through, external (physical) sensory experience.

MICROGENESIS OF ACTION

An action unfolds over a stratified system of levels that retraces the pattern of evolutionary growth. These levels instantiate the action through discharge into

ISBN 0-936925-00-0

keyboards at successive moments in the microgenetic sequence. The progression is from an archaic motility centered in the axial and proximal musculature and a body-centered space (Yakovlev, 1948), a stage in the action that is sensitive to or dependent on "internal context," toward discrete, asymmetric movements with the distal musculature that are "goal oriented," context-free, and directed to external objects. Early phases distribute into postural systems within body space, then into a space of body-on-body movement to a manipulation space of the arm's reach, and finally to action on outer objects.

In the course of this unfolding, the action proceeds "bottom up" as a type of propagated wave from a core system in upper brainstem and basal ganglia through structures on the mesial aspect of the frontal lobe, to systems on the frontal convexity, and finally to the contralateral motor cortex. Early stages constitute an "envelope" of the action, in a bodily space incorporating all of the to-be-realized constituents of the action. The forming postural, limb, respiratory, and vocal movements are prefigured in this preparatory phase. Early stages in the action structure have a unitary or global character with all of the incipient elements of the final act embedded in the same matrix of primitive motility and discharging at the same time. At these early stages, the act is bilaterally represented in the brain. Later stages are asymmetric in relation to neural structure. The action undergoes a progressive articulation into discrete motor elements that eventually appear to gain some independence. Yet speech, digital movement, and locomotion, which on the surface have little in common, are linked as the twigs of a tree to a single root.

In the microgenetic view there is no action plan that has been worked out or script guiding the movement sequence in the sense of a conscious representation of what the action is going to be. We plan actions for the future, but the plan is not the framework on the basis of which the action develops. Rather, the action unfolds according to intrinsic constraints—one could say microgenetic imperatives—in the action structure. The conscious awareness of the plan of an action does not generate the action that it appears to forecast but is secondarily elaborated by actions that are automatically laid down.

Neural processes underlying the action microgeny have the nature of rhythmic or oscillatory programs that may be derived as a series of harmonics from fundamental rhythms at the core of the action structure, possibly linked to other patterns of rhythmic motility such as respiration, and even circadian rhythms (Bernstein, 1967; Brown, 1982; Schepelmanns, 1979; Turvey, 1977). For example, a deep nodal rhythm might support a system for postural tone, while successive derivations of this rhythm might transform postural tone into actions such as rocking or walking and ultimately to selective limb action and digital movements, and the individuated vocal movements of speech. Speech, of course, can also be viewed as a type of rhythmic activity (Lashley, 1951; Martin, 1972). Rhythmic factors, tonality, and the engagement of respiratory mechanisms are important at the earliest stages of speech production.

The fundamental unit of an action, therefore, is a rhythmic, hierarchic module distributed over evolutionary stages in forebrain development, unfolding in a direction that retraces the pattern of evolutionary growth "bottom up" from archaic to recent motor systems. Successive moments or processing stages in the module discharge into keyboards at each evolutionary stage, and in this way sequentially lay down the movement, in milliseconds, as the structure of the action is serially traversed. Complex behaviors are bundles of individual action structures; they are reiterated packets of unfolding representations and the secondary perceptual representations that they leave behind.

THE ACTION PROGRAM

An action begins in a two-dimensional spatial map elaborated through mechanisms in the upper brainstem. Postural, vestibular, orienting, and locomotor mechanisms establish the core of the action structure. Ballistic movements emerge out of this core as the orientation precipitates into global action patterns. A target—for example, a prey—is seized by a sudden shift of the eyes or a rapid thrust of the body or jaw. The perception of a stimulus coincides with an action pattern targeted to that stimulus. The action discharges into symmetrical, axial, or midline motor systems. Some motor patterns that might result from the discharge of a configuration at this level (i.e., when it is not transformed to the next stage) are crying and sucking movements in the newborn, swimming, crawling, or other locomotor synergies.

This stage in the action development is as close as any to an action plan. Vestibular orienting and tonic postural and locomotor mechanisms are activated preparatory to a shift in orientation, that is, a commitment to a direction, signaling the ensuing motor sequence. This phase constitutes an embryonic core, a framework or "envelope" of the action embracing *in status nascendi* all of the elements of the action-to-be, none of which as yet have differentiated. The isolation of segmental movements and the increasing resolution and exteriorization of action and space are accomplished at later stages. Subsequently, the action will unfold through limbic mechanisms to a configuration representing segmental movement patterns. As this occurs, the object accompanying that action development also unfolds from a two-dimensional map at a tectal phase of object formation to an egocentric, volumetric space of limbic cognition.

We can examine this stage in the action development when it is displayed as a symptom in pathological cases. Damage to rostral brainstem gives rise to coma or akinetic mutism, a type of coma but with eyes open. This disorder has been interpreted as a loss of will or a loss of the impulse to act, without true paralysis. In fact, disruption of the core of the action exposes the action program at its inception, with inability to initiate any body movement (akinetic mutism) at an instinctual or motivational level in drive organization (the loss of drive or impulse to act) and a regression to an archaic pre-object level in perceptual space (coma). Unilateral lesions of rostral midbrain may lead to impaired ballistic movements in hemispace. We learn from this that the action program anticipates a stage of labile and precipitate motility discharging through the proximal muscles into a space beyond the body confines.

ACTION ON THE BODY

The action unfolds into the volumetric space of limbic cognition, a space of dream and hallucination (Brown, 1985b). The action moves outward beyond the body itself to an extrapersonal field of body movement that is still part of and continuous with subjective mental space. This is not a grasping or manipulation space, for objects have not yet exteriorized. The emerging action is read off into keyboards innervating the proximal musculature. Actions leave the body axis and are distributed through the proximal muscles into the space around the body or onto the body itself. At this stage, the first separation appears between perceiver and object, actor and object acted upon, agent and action. The motor envelope differentiates into partial actions, objects begin to clarify, and space begins to expand, fractionate, and draw away from the perceiver.

This phase of action development is mediated by extrapyramidal or basal ganglia mechanisms in relation to other limbic components. Disorders of these structures in man (e.g., Parkinson's disease) are characterized by difficulty in body and limb motility not directed outward to objects (Yakovlev, 1948). Changes in mood, hallucination, and impaired spatial perception in these disorders are predictable consequences of the disruption. Pathological objects and affects accompany action disorders in a level-specific manner. Lesions of basal ganglia have their maximal impact on the action microgeny, but other behaviors are affected in a manner referable to the same cognitive level.

The role of limbic mechanisms in action is brought home even more clearly by conditions in which there is damage to limbic-derived neocortex on the mesial aspect of the frontal lobe. Bilateral damage to the anterior cingulate gyrus gives rise to a state of akinetic mutism resembling that which can occur with damage to the upper brainstem. The patient appears to be in a catatonic stupor and, as in catatonia, there are periodic bouts of excitement that give way to a persistent vegetative state (Buge, Escourolle, Rancurel, & Poisson, 1975; Nielsen & Jacobs, 1951). Stimulation of this region in man produces motor and affective responses suggestive of "a primitive or archaic level in behavior" (Bancaud et al., 1976).

Stimulation adjacent to the anterior cingulate gyrus in the supplementary motor area (SMA) causes iteration or arrest of vocalization and proximal movement, especially of the upper limbs. With damage there may be a "release" of automatisms and primitive synergies of the arm and hand (alien hand) or difficulty initiating action with the arm though strength and coordination are intact (Brown, 1977, 1985a; Goldberg, 1985). There may also be difficulty initiating speech. This can lead to selective mutism or selective akinesia, that is, ambulatory mutism or good speech with imparied initiation of limb movement. Selective difficulty initiating movements with the lower extremities occurs in the so-called gait apraxia, or magnetic gait, often associated with hydrocephalus. Gerstmann and Schilder (1926) related this disorder to lesions of the medial and basal parts of the frontal lobe, and this was also found by Denny-Brown (1958; see Knutsson & Lying-Tunnell, 1985).

In the microgenetic theory set out in Brown (1977), the SMA mediates preparatory stages in action generation prior to conscious awareness. Lesions of this area disrupt speech, limb, and body action in a common manner early in the processing of the action, prior to the specification of constituent movement patterns. The disturbance of speech was viewed as motoric, not linguistic or propositional.

This account was based on an interpretation of clinical disorders with mesial and lateral frontal lesions. Subsequent physiological research has confirmed these speculations. Kornhuber's (1974, 1985) description of the readiness potential led to its correlation in 1980 with a paralimbic midline source. These findings have been confirmed and extended by Goldberg (1985). P. Chauvel and J. Bancaud (personal commmunication, 1984) have reported slow wave activity from the SMA preceding limb movement and motor cortex discharge in human subjects. Recent studies (Chauvel, Bancaud, & Buser, 1985) confirm the view that SMA speech disorders are motoric. Indeed, Jürgens (1985) notes that SMA lesions in the monkey decrease only spontaneous (isolation call) vocalizations, and not those elicited by perceptual stimuli.

Arguing from the neurophysiological literature primarily, Eccles (1987) claimed that the SMA was a locus for the initiation of voluntary movement. This idea recalls the old concept of *Willenlosigkeit,* a loss of the volitional impulse, described in early neuropsychology. In the microgenetic view, however, the sense of volition is a product of action development; it is realized with the action and is not something that gives rise to it. Volition is not a faculty that can be independently impaired. Disturbance of volitional or skilled action as in apraxia (see below) is associated with damage to subsequent levels of the action microgeny.

In sum, the motor envelope, a base level or early processing stage, elaborates an archaic stage in speech and motility, combining the incipient vocal and somatic elements of the action in a space centered on the body axis. The action is organized about the axial and proximal musculature, linked to respiratory, locomotor, and other rhythmic automatisms, and close to motivational and drivelike states. As it develops, the action undergoes specification of its motor components with an isolation of limb, body, and vocal motility. Pathology can give rise to selective impairments of vocalization (mutism) and of initiation of action involving both the upper limbs (inertia, alien hand) and lower limbs (gait apraxia). This phase is mediated by frontal paralimbic formations, including the anterior cingulate gyrus and the supplementary motor area. The action system is bilaterally represented at early stages with a gradual bias to a left-hemisphere representation, first apparent at the level of the supplementary motor cortex.

ACTION IN THE WORLD

The emerging representation is transformed to a phase of real actions on real objects in a space apprehended as real and independent of the action. This transition carries the representation from a rhythmic configuration that is bilaterally organized and centered in the proximal musculature to one that is asymmetrically organized—reflecting the degree of hemispheric dominance[1]—and distributed into the distal musculature. The generalized background configuration arising through paralimbic regions undergoes a progressive specification into its constituent elements, a transition mediated by left premotor and motor cortices.

The premotor phase in action development is characterized by a transition through a space of object manipulation, the perimeter of the arm's reach. The action proceeds from an incomplete exteriorization where the object is still part of an extended action space toward an eventual exteriorization of discrete, partial actions on fully independent external objects. Lesions of the convexity of the dominant hemisphere give rise to limb apraxia, with substitution and derailment of partial acts, chiefly on tasks in which object use is pantomimed. The disruption displays a stage in the unfolding of the act linked to the manipulation space of proximate objects. From this point the action configuration develops into the precentral motor keyboard as the distal structure of the act instantiates. Disruptions at the end point of the action development give rise to impairments of the highly individuated speech and limb musculature. In speech, there are phonetic, articulatory deficits leading to the so-called syndrome of phonetic disintegration (Alajouanine, Ombredane, & Durand, 1939; Lecours & Lher-

---

[1]The transition from *bilateral* representation in paralimbic cortex to crossed or *contralateral* representation in motor cortex may occur by way of an intermediate stage of unilateral *asymmetric* representation in the dominant hemisphere (Brown, 1978). That is, the action pattern develops first in both hemispheres, then through the left hemisphere, and finally through the contralateral hemisphere. Put differently, early stages in action development are bilaterally represented in both hemispheres, late stages are unilaterally represented in the opposite or contralateral hemisphere, with a stage of (dominant) left hemisphere representation of bilateral action interposed in the microgenetic sequence. This interpretation entails that evolutionary advances in brain organization, such as dominance, do not spring from highly adapted systems of evolutionary recency but from earlier, more plastic stages.

mitte, 1976), with "peripheral" disorders of the vocal apparatus, including paresis and hypotonicity. In limb movement, there is the so-called limb kinetic apraxia, with disruption of separate distal movement patterns, leading to paresis and altered motor tone. The transition from a central to a more peripheral manifestation of an action disorder captures stages in the "physicalization" of the act as it passes from an origin in mind to an effectuation in external space.

The more intense affective content of early stages, which is expressed in the form of instinctual drive or motivational state, for example, will or the impulse to act, undergoes a simultaneous analysis into partial affects. These partial affects—depression, apathy, euphoria—are revealed by frontal lobe lesions (Borod, Koff, Perlman, & Nicholas, 1983) and reflect a transitional stage in affect development, a stage that is midway between deeper instinctual drive and subsequent affect-free behaviors. One can say that the affective tonality of the act discharges into a world of independent acts and objects. In other words, affect and action distribute together into extrapersonal space, the affective content discharging along with the action as it exteriorizes. The discrepancy between the intense affect at the depths of the action development and the affect-free nature of surface motility contributes to the sense of an active movement going out toward the world and the experience of agency and volition.

The analysis of an action into constituent elements or features is accompanied by an elaboration of its underlying rhythmic structure into oscillators that mediate the rapid and discrete digital and articulatory sequences. For example, an oscillator(s) linked to respiratory and other rhythms that elaborates the speech melody or the prosodic contour of an utterance would be derived to one that mediates the programmation of phonetic units in speech. An oscillator that organizes axial and proximal motility would be derived to one that mediates the serial unfolding of separate motor units in limb, orofacial, and other finely individuated movements. One can envision a stratified system of oscillators, each discharging or peeling off into motor templates at successive evolutionary planes, creating an action structure that is a dynamic pyramid of rhythmic or vibratory levels.

THE FRONTAL SYNDROME

There are many other symptoms of action disorder in animals and man that can be related to this structural model. For example, damage—usually bilateral—to the orbital and mesial area and the convexity of the frontal lobes gives rise to a number of changes—the "frontal syndrome"—that can be interpreted on a motoric basis. These changes include an increase or decrease in activity level (hyper- or hypoactivity), apathy and impaired initiation of movement, impulsiveness and distractibility, persistence or recurrence of limb or vocal actions (perseveration), difficulty in shifting set or changing response patterns from one task to another (response bias), and substitutions in speech and recall (paraphasia and confabulation) as well as in limb movement (apraxia).

These disorders appear to be quite distinct from each other and this fact alone has made attempts at a unitary explanation somewhat unconvincing. The elements of the frontal syndrome are not easily reduced to a single underlying deficit, particularly a deficit that is so general as to account for almost any pathological change. Interpretations of the syndrome as a disturbance of a synthetic, regulatory, or integrative function, as a disorder of abstraction, prediction, anticipation, or temporal processing, as an uncoupling between inner states and outer experience, or as a loss of will or self-consciousness achieve a unitary character by extracting one variable from the richness of (abnormal) behavior and then resolving all of this richness in terms of this variable. The element that is *ad hoced* from the diversity of symptoms becomes an explanatory principle under which all of the symptoms are grouped. This problem is avoided in the microgenetic approach by positing a single process in continuous transformation, where symptoms are deposited as signposts of pathology at successive points. Here, symptoms are processing stages that differ with respect to their positions in the transformational sequence. The unity in this account is thematic in that different symptoms reflect a single coherent process unfolding from one state to another. In the microgenetic view, each response represents a bundle of action structures, consisting of the series of stages through which the action develops. Pathology disrupts the action at different points in this process. The site of the lesion determines the point in the sequence that is disrupted, and this point or processing stage constitutes the symptom or abnormal behavior.

Microgeny maps onto patterns of phyletic growth. The structure of an action and the symptoms that correspond to levels in this structure are distributed over stages in forebrain evolution. Damage to older orbital and mesial frontal limbic formations leads to impaired activation (response bias or perseveration and lack of initiation), damage along the convexity leads to derailment of the action after adequate initiation (distractibility, apraxia, and confabulation), and damage to premotor and motor cortices leads to a defect in implementation of distal targets (misarticulation, clumsiness, and weakness).

Specifically, the evolutionary progression from limbic to motor cortices retraces the sequence of processing stages in the microtemporal elaboration of an action. Disruption at successive points—at deep bilateral levels, at unilateral surface levels—gives rise to symptoms that reflect this progression:

1. Damage at the base of the system produces an impairment in the initiation of an action (inertia, apathy, hypomotility, or mutism). This difficulty can appear as a failure to begin an act (impaired initiation) or an inability to switch from one action to the next (perseveration, response bias). There can also be a heightened transition to successive behaviors, a lability of initiation, with distractibility and impulsiveness or "dyscontrol." The activation of an action module, the switching from one module to the next, persistence or lability of the

transition across modules, and the maintenance or interruption of set are all phenomena of the early stages of action microgeny.

2. Damage at intermediate stages derails the flow of an action after it has been initiated. This can appear in a more general way (impulsiveness and distractibility) or it can affect specific performances, for example, substitution in limb action (apraxia) or in retrieval (confabulation). In limb action the disruption will involve the more distal musculature according to that point in the sequence that is interrupted. In confabulation, the general meaning of the utterance is preserved in the presence of an extravagance of detail. For example, on story recall the subject may free-associate but eventually retrieves all of the salient elements. Such performances show that the base organization is preserved but that there is a disturbance in the serial elaboration of the action out of this base level.

3. Damage at the surface or end point of the action development produces a defect at the final implementation. The disturbance involves the digital and/or articulatory musculature with misarticulation (Broca's aphasia) and clumsiness (dyspraxia) proceeding to slurring of speech (dysarthria) and limb weakness (paresis).

The elements of the frontal syndrome reflect subtle disorders of action, not complex or high-level cognitive impairments. The action disorder is subtle in that it is a step removed from pure motility and simulates an impairment in planning or self-monitoring. In part, the impression of a cognitive deficit arises from the dissociation between action and awareness. The subject seems unable to inhibit or regulate his own actions. This occurs because the action disorder is a manifestation of a subsurface content to which the surface perceptual representation lacks access. That is, the fully unfolded perceptual development, which maintains awareness, is unable to penetrate submerged processing stages in the action, and these early encapsulated stages represent the nucleus of the action disorder. There is also the more general problem of awareness of an action—how this awareness arises and what action contributes to cognition. Before taking up these questions, however, it is useful to consider the problem of subsurface action in greater detail, in relation to a recently described motor analogue of "blindsight" (see below).

SUBSURFACE ACTION AND MENTAL REPRESENTATIONS

A dramatic illustration of the role of evolutionary levels in action comes from studies of patients with damage to the left hemisphere, paralysis of the right side, and severe aphasia. Such patients may be unable to communicate in speech or in writing with the left hand, and they cannot type or use block letters to construct words. The right arm is paralyzed, though usually some shoulder movement is possible.

A prosthesis has been designed that enables the paralyzed right arm to write by means of steering movements from the residual shoulder musculature (Brown, Leader, & Blum, 1983). With this device, patients with total aphasia are able to produce words to dictation and even write complete and fully grammatical sentences when asked to describe a picture. This is all the more astonishing in view of the loss of articulate speech and the complete inability to write with the normal left hand. Moreover, the performance of global aphasics with the prosthesis is often superior to that of milder aphasics without hemiparesis, suggesting that severe aphasia and hemiplegia are required to "release" or access preliminary language levels. It is also our observation that patients do not appear to have full awareness of their correct performances, which often come as something of a surprise to them.

Although the basis for this phenomenon is not clear, one interpretation might be that the destruction of the distal phase of the action development permits the more archaic proximal motor system to tap into coordinate levels in language representation. Specifically, the older proximal motor system actualizes as an end point in the action microgeny when the distal limb is centrally paralyzed. This system is instantiated through the residual shoulder movement, which is able to penetrate (i.e., is coextensive with) submerged or "buried" levels of language processing. In other words, deep levels in the representation of an action express deep levels in the representation of language. The phenomenon is akin to preserved vision ("blindsight"), audition, and tactile perception with destruction of the primary perceptual zones in the cortex. Hemiplegic writing, like blindsight and related conditions, provides strong evidence that action as well as perception are ordered from bottom to top in the brain, and that actions, like perceptions, do not begin with arousal in the primary cortical areas but are emergent phenomena issuing out of deeper evolutionary strata.

ACTION AND PERCEPTION

In the microgenesis of a perception a neural configuration unfolds so as to represent an object in a progressively more articulated and externalized form (Brown, 1983). Perception is an active process that builds up, partitions, and arborizes external space. Objects in the world are like tributaries that draw out and at the same time punctuate an external space that is like a body for the perceptual process. This is also the case for action.

The microgenesis of action proceeds in a parallel manner and fractionates movement into discrete elements. Unlike perception, where early processing stages are bypassed on the way to the final object, early stages in action appear as postural, orienting, or locomotor (axial and proximal) components of the action structure, discharging early in the movement sequence. This is one way that acts and objects differ. We are aware of an object and not the object development, the object being realized at the expense of its formative structure. In action the development is displayed in the unfolding of the movement.

According to the microgenetic concept, objects are not "out there" in the world waiting for acts to engage them but have to be constructed in parallel with developing actions. Although there are differences between action and perception, there are deep inner similarities. Early stages in object formation provide the contextual background from which objects develop and persist abstractly as levels of conceptual or symbolic content within the object itself. Similarly, early stages in action elaborate the instinctual and affective bases that drive the action forward to its goal. Act and object also undergo a similar development. The "zeroing in" on target movements in the specification of an action has its correlate in the featural modeling of object form. Both act and object are analyzed into finer units. The exteriorization of a target movement and its effectuation on extrapersonal objects correspond with the realization of an external object field. Act and object exteriorize together. A world of real objects and the effects of actions in that world are part of the same microgenetic end point. The deception that a movement is voluntary or willed by the self as an agent corresponds to the deception that we are independent of our own objects. The increasing passivity and then final detachment of an object representation mirror the activity of an action and the realization of an intentional attitude to movements directed toward those object representations.

The tightly locked character of act and object is more prominent at early stages. As action and object undergo increasing differentiation they diverge into widely distributed neural systems. Movements can be interrupted with minimal impact on perceptions, and the reverse, giving the mistaken impression that act and object are independent constructions. But every action has a perceptual residue and every object has an action to which it corresponds. This is true for the most highly differentiated functions. Damage to a phonetic device mediating articulation can lead to an equivalent disturbance of speech perception, and disturbed speech production can occur when there is impaired "phonemic hearing." Acts and percepts both lead outward to the world, they carve up and elaborate space, and, though implemented by different neural mechanisms, they entail a fundamentally unitary psychological process.

Action is required for the development of spatial perception. Animals that are passively moved through environments do not acquire normal depth judgments and other spatial cues. Infants show a preference for objects that can be manipulated. Infants who wear a cast or brace show altered acquisition of spatial perception. Similarly, the space of action is disturbed when perception does not develop normally. The congenitally blind have a distortion of space built up on the action perimeter.

Damage to areas in the temporal and parietal lobes produces a perceptual deficit that is displayed in the context of an action disorder. Parietal lesions give rise to impairments in drawing and other constructional tasks. Posterior aphasic and apraxic errors reflect an underlying perceptual disruption. The idea of a disturbance in speech and limb action secondary to a sensory impairment has a lengthy history. Bastian (1898/1984; Brown, 1984a) and Luria (1962/1966) have both interpreted motor aphasias on a kinaesthetic basis. The work of Mountcastle (1976; Lynch, 1980), demonstrating responsiveness of parietal cells to reaching in relation to an object, provides experimental support for the concept that action and perception share a common perceptuomotor space.

This common space of act and object provides a basis for the tacit knowledge of which movements to make in relation to an object, that is, the more or less automatic sequence of movements that corresponds to levels in object formation. These levels represent different perceptual spaces with a different movement sequence linked to each level in the object representation. In other words, the hierarchy of motor responses is built up in relation to the layered space of perception. One could perhaps go even further and say that the movements in a movement sequence are an expression of successive levels in the transition leading to the final object; they are the residues of an object construction. In a very real sense an action pursues an object, for phases laid down in the action appear before the final object individuates.

AWARENESS OF AN ACTION

These observations demonstrate an inner bond between act and object that is fundamental to the problem of volition and awareness for action. The phenomenon of hemiplegic writing and the occurrence of impaired regulation of behavior in frontal cases are relevant to this problem and to our understanding of the way in which the action development builds up or enters mental representation.

A consideration of the problem of awareness for an action begins with the recognition that the action microgeny does not contribute a content directly to awareness. The awareness of an act and the act itself are contents *in perception* that the action lays down. There is no act that is experienced. The experience of an action is a feeling of its forward development, not an awareness of a particular content. The action generates a feeling of effort or tension, an awareness that an action has or has not taken place, in other words, a self-initiated or "intentional" quality. This is the only *direct* contribution to mind of the dynamic of the action structure.

This is an old problem in neuropsychology. William James (1890) argued that "in perfectly simple voluntary acts there is nothing else in the mind but the kinaesthetic idea . . . of what the act is to be." On the other hand, Wundt believed there was only a feeling of the current of outgoing energy, the *Innervationsgefuhl*. Experimental studies of this problem (see Roland, 1979) tend to emphasize techniques of peripheral paralysis or anesthesia rather than the nature of central processes. Thus, passive and active motions have a different effect on perception. Since passive motion can stimulate the peripheral receptors, the perception of this difference (the distinction between passive and active motion) indicates a contribution from the central structure of the action. This contribution could be a motor effect, or it could arise through recurrent collaterals activated in the motor discharge.

For example, object stability depends on whether an action is volitional or passive. Objects are displaced when the eyes are passively moved. If an eye movement is weak or prevented an effort to divert the gaze in the direction of the deficit may result in object displacement. With total paralysis the illusion of movement disappears (Brindley, Goodwin, Kulikoski, & Leighton, 1976; Siebeck & Frey, 1953). During total paralysis from curare an attempt to move the eyes is accompanied by a feeling of spatial displacement even though the object does not move. An effort to move a paralyzed limb may result in illusory displacement, or the action may occur several moments after the attempt with uncertainty as to whether it occurred or to what point the limb has been displaced (Stevens, 1978). Myasthenics have been described who continue to have the feeling they are speaking even after the articulators are paralyzed. These observations indicate that the central action structure deposits a perceptual representation of the act and that the effects of this representation are not erased by an abolition of peripheral motility.

Conversely, a change in perception can give a change in action. In a sense, a perception is a movement, a disposition to act (Bergson, 1896/1959). Patients may have a limb paralysis secondary to a sensory, not a motor deficit. Sensory impairments of the hand lead to pseudo-athetoid or writhing movements of the fingers of which the subject is often unaware. Phantom limb phenomena in amputees offer a rich source of material relevant to this question. There can be an experience of willed or passive action without movement, with a different feeling for volitional as opposed to spontaneous displacement. An effort to move the absent limb gives rise to stronger impressions. In such cases, imagined movements of the phantom may be accompanied by movements of the stump. These are not the cause of the phantom. Such movements are comparable to subvocal articulatory movements during inner speech. The image calls up the movement. There is a similarity between the imagined movements of the phantom and the feeling of motility in a dream. These observations demonstrate the close bond, indeed the common basis, of action, space, and perception. They also show that awareness for an act is built up on perception.

In sum, the action contributes to awareness a feeling of activity, an intuition that the subject is the agent of his or her actions, while the content or description of the act, the awareness that a particular act has taken place, is built up on perceptual residues laid down by the action as it unfolds. Patients with frontal lesions have an alteration in the feeling of agency, which appears in various forms of inertia and dyscontrol. It is not clear whether there is also a deficit in the perception of the act generated by collaterals of the action discharge.

VOLUNTARY ACTION

Volition is the feeling that one is an agent who reflects upon, chooses, and implements an action. It implies more than a direction toward a goal. Action of that type we call purposeful, and purposeful action is not necessarily volitional. An individual can be in a trance or hypnotic state and engage in purposeful action, but we would not say that the act is voluntary. There is a decisional element in volition and a sense in which an action can be withheld. One can choose not to act, and that would also qualify as volitional behavior. A central part of the feeling of volition seems to be the idea of choice, and the implication of an opposition between the self and its actions. The self initiates and guides actions *at will*.

The term *will* is often used interchangeably with volition, but it seems to presume or take on the status of a separate faculty or agency in the mind. Will applies to the engagement of self in a volitional act. Will and volition imply essentially the same mode of action, though will is more thing-like and volition more like a process. Free will entails a belief in the autonomy of the self in the initiation and propagation of acts. The free will problem can be linked to the issue of social and biological constraints on action; the fewer there are, the more the freedom (Dennett, 1985).

The concept of control over action and degrees of constraint, however, shifts the problem outside the intrapsychic context, where it belongs, and in so doing sidesteps many fundamental issues, for example, the nature of the self that is deciding which actions to take, the question of what is involved in the neuropsychology of choice, and the nature of the interaction, if any, between the self (construed as a mental or biological entity) and a motor apparatus. These are the more crucial issues, for which it matters little to what extent an act is obligated by environmental conditions. The first question that needs to be asked is: What is an action?

THE PHYSIOLOGY OF WILL

The old idea that voluntary movement begins with discharge in motor cortex is inconsistent with the clinical material. A consideration of the variety of motor and speech disorders occurring with frontal lesions obligates an interpretation of volitional action as a series of states unfolding in a direction *toward* motor cortex, not away from it. Each state is accompanied by a different awareness experience, so that one can reconstruct from this material the emergence not only of action but of consciousness of action and the volitional attitude. The conclusion of a microgenetic analysis of this material is that consciousness, volition, and action all develop together as a reiterated series of hierarchic modules, and that this development unfolds over evolutionary brain structure (Brown, 1977).

Physiological research has demonstrated that the initiation of an act begins well before cell discharge in motor cortex. There is a bilateral surface negative potential (*Bereitschaftspotential;* Kornhuber, 1974), the end of which begins about 90 msec before simple finger movement. Mesial frontal slow activity has been described .2–.3 sec (P. Chauvel & J. Bancaud, personal communication, 1984; Goldberg, 1985) prior to motor cortex activation, prior even to the conscious decision to act. Libet, Gleason, Wright, and Pearl (1983) found that neural activity associated with voluntary action occurs prior to the conscious decision to act. Discharge in basal ganglia prior to motor cortex during "purposeful" limb movement in the monkey (Evarts, 1979) and the work at Haskins Laboratories demonstrating that purposeful movements arise at the peaks of physiological tremor are also consistent with early programming of the action at subsurface levels.

One interpretation of these observations is that areas associated with activation preceding an action are the same areas that mediate volition. It is claimed that brain correlates of early slow wave activity constitute the substrate of volition, and that these areas are also responsible for the motor plan and the initiation of movement. Some have found in this work physiological evidence for a mind–brain interaction, that is, the effects of mental states on physical brain states (Eccles, 1982). Alternatively, these findings show that an action commences prior to awareness, that it is a result or outcome of early preparatory stages whether or not the action is volitional, and that the decision to act occurs prior to introspective access to decisional content. In other words, the decision to act rises into consciousness on the heels of the action development. Put differently, the consciousness of an act, or the choice involved in the decision to act, appears in awareness subsequent to the onset of the act that is being decided upon. The will, it seems, rises to the occasion a split second too late.

THE PATHOLOGY OF VOLITION

An action is not a concatenation of movements but has a momentary prehistory of some complexity. Weakness and paralysis are only a fraction of the ways in which actions can degrade. Some action disorders are characterized by automatic behaviors, others are purposeful, and still others involve volitional behaviors. The degree to which the action is willed is related to the type of action that appears and the brain region that is involved. Pathological actions expose part of the structure of volition.

A disruption at the core of the action produces inertia and an inability to initiate any action at all. This is not due to a loss of the will because there is no evidence of a self that is deciding, or even trying, to act. One cannot infer a loss of volition from the simple absence of movement. Moreover, preservation of this system associated with initiation disorder with destruction of the distal segment of the action hierarchy may "release" automatic behaviors—brief latency laughing or crying, even rage attacks that are explosive and not directed at objects. The individual has little control over these behaviors and is unable to acknowledge their conceptual or affective content. The appearance of automatic behaviors and "sham" displays reflects discharge of submerged levels in action structure for which subsequent levels associated with content awareness lack access.

From such cases one can surmise that there is an inner relationship between a stage of onset of an action and the features of lability and automatism. The action discharges early in its development prior to the full microgenetic derivation of its content. The action is not truly released or disinhibited from higher control, but expresses directly the characteristics of early cognition. The strong affective tonality of the behavior, its brief latency, and its lack of object orientation point to archaic cognition. The fact that lesions of deep action systems give rise to either automatisms or impaired initiation indicates that actions are not instigated by the will or the self but rather the initiation process is automatic because it is subsurface, and automaticity is the expression of early or subsurface cognition. Moreover, it confirms that the initiation of an action is prior to consciousness of the action and that, by inference, the feeling of willed or voluntary action is elaborated by the action development, not the other way around.

Subsequent to the initiation of the envelope of the action, damage can produce selective impairments of initiation—the initiation of partial (limb, vocal) actions—while stimulation of the pertinent brain areas (the SMA) leads to automatisms that are quasi-purposeful, such as grasping, lip smacking, or similar behaviors. Seizures involving mesial frontal limbic cortex can lead to stereotypical actions of a purposeful type, such as scratching one's head, manipulating imaginary objects, or pacing. The alien hand syndrome also represents a type of released automatism (see G. Goldberg, this volume, Chapter 15). Here a more complex integrated behavior of a purposeful but not volitional type is associated with damage or stimulation to zones intermediate in the action microgeny. The inner relationship between (impaired) initiation and ("released") automatism recurs but now in the context of a more differentiated action pattern, involving segmental or vocal movements. The more intense affective, instinctual, or motivational states associated with the preceding stage fractionate to partial affects that still have a heightened intensity. The developing action is accompanied by a developing object, and the greater degree of object resolution draws the action outward to a space of object manipulation. This gives direction and goal orientation to the emerging action, and elaborates a feeling of purposefulness. The developing action hones in on a developing object.

With dominant convexity lesions there is apraxia, a condition affecting skilled movements requested in pantomime, such as hammering a nail or snapping one's fingers. These actions are disturbed instead of actions done spontaneously or with objects. The disruption involves an action in its most volitional context, when the subject deliberately performs a given behavior. Pantomime lacks the context of an object development to constrain and facilitate its development. In limb apraxia, the action is initiated properly and is usually correctly targeted to a goal, but there is a disturbance in the seriation of partial movements. Apraxia is the primary disorder of voluntary action. The affective state of a patient with apraxia approaches the norm because the affect development has largely completed its course. The volitional character of the disorder reflects involvement of late processing stages in action microgeny. The disorder is for an action in response to verbal request; a conscious decision and a representation—in propositional form—of the action are required. Apraxia satisfies the description of a disorder of voluntary action but it is elaborated late in the action development near the surface of the action structure. One can say that the action penetrates a level in mind coextensive with introspection and awareness of perceptual content.

The erroneous idea that impaired initiation reflects a disturbance of volition derives from the concept of volition as a faculty that initiates action, whereas the phase of initiation actually precedes that of awareness and the feeling of agency. Disorders of this stage do not involve volition in the sense of a separate faculty but rather action in a volitional framework, again demonstrating that volition is an effect or an accompaniment of the action development, not something that instigates the action from the beginning.

There are many other observations that provide insight into the relationship between action and volition. Stimulation of motor cortex, for example, gives rise to limb movements, but the individual may be uncertain as to whether the movement was deliberate. Many of us experience a similar feeling with jerks of the legs just before falling asleep. Patients with choreic movements may round out the choreic twitch to a completed action sequence, such as transforming a sudden jerk of the arm to rubbing the chin, not to mask the movement disorder but because they are unsure whether or not they have activated the behavior.

Such observations show that the automatic nature of an action, its purposefulness, and its volitional quality are not descriptions of a relation between a self and its behavior, but are features of the action generated by the action development and determined by the degree to which the action is completed. Similarly, we learn that the feeling that an action is willed and the distinction of active and passive movement are fragile sensitivities that can be challenged by a variety of pathological disturbances. The individual may (falsely) believe that a spontaneous and fragmentary twitch is willed and so complete it (i.e., the action completes itself) to produce a meaningful sequence, or there may be uncertainty as to whether it is automatic, passive, or active and self-generated.

The pathological material is instructive in showing that automaticity, purposefulness, and volition characterize actions at successive points in their development. A corollary to this is that an action that is automatic is not identical to one that is volitional. One can walk automatically or in a deliberate manner, but these two types of walking are not quite the same. Of course, automaticity is to be desired in the acquisition of skills where deliberation can be disadvantageous (Brown, 1984b).

THE MEANING OF VOLUNTARY ACTION

The implication of these observations is that the volitional feeling that accompanies an action has to be achieved along with and as part of the action itself. It is not the specific action that establishes the volitional attitude but the microgenetic stage that is realized in the action development. Volition is not applied to an action from outside but is intrinsic to the unfolding sequence, and in pathological conditions follows the same fate as the action development. The persistence of a prior act, the maintenance of a present state or a resistance to change, and further action are all nonetheless actions. It is the developmental level, not the specific behavior, that determines its volitional quality.

Volition inheres in an action but what, more precisely, is the volitional state? Clearly more than the action is required—a self has to be constructed and there have to be objects for actions to impinge upon. The action contributes an active attitude to behavior, a sense of agency, a feeling that the act is self-generated. This feeling follows the formative direction of the action. The surge and flow of the action outward—its forward growth in this one direction—are part of the feeling of (inter)action with external objects and events. Actions carve out the space of perception; they help to define objects. They flow into a space they have helped to articulate. This too is part of volition, the deception that an action that begins in the mind ends in the world when, after all, the action is only distributed into the mind's extrapersonal component.

The feeling that actions externalize and are active events that influence real objects parallels the passive or receptive quality that we experience in relation to our own objects. Both acts and objects are products of an emergent cognition, but objects "detach" and become independent. In contrast, the self exteriorizes in action, that is, action carries the self outward into the world. We are convinced that objects act on us and that we act on objects, when in truth the object development is laying down the action while the action deposits in advance of the object and seems always in pursuit.

ACTION AND CAUSATION

If cognitions and actions emerge from below and the programming of the action is preset before reaching awareness, then conscious deliberations—which are in any event also products of subsurface mentation—do not propel behavior but inform us of actions that have already been initiated. A decision state preceding an action is itself an action (an inaction or a covert action) and is not a preparation for an ensuing behavior. There is simply a train of actions of different types, some leading to decision states and others to overt behaviors. The precedence of one state over another is not a sign of causality. The configuration that gives rise to a conscious state provides the context that configures an ensuing state, but the causation is across subsurface configurations, not contents in awareness. In other words, causation, if it applies at all in an emergent system, pertains to the sequence from depth to surface, not from one surface phenomenon to another.

This does not mean that we are propelled by hidden forces and secret motives. Nor does it mean that we have no control or responsibility for our own actions. Indeed, precisely the opposite conclusion can be drawn. Since in its development an action traverses, and in a sense lays down, levels in affect and experience (levels that are part of the concept of a personality), the action can be said to develop out of the very core of one's being. The action is driven by the self—not the self that is exposed in awareness, but a subsurface phase in the development of the self out of which awareness also develops.

ACTION AND PERSONALITY

The observation that damage to the frontal lobes seems to alter complex aspects of behavior and the interpretation of the frontal syndrome as a disturbance in the microgeny of action imply that action plays a critical role in elaborating and maintaining the personality. Certainly, there is some evidence that personality development reflects early patterns of motor activity. The direction of postural preferences in infancy may predict subsequent handedness (Coryell & Michel, 1978), suggesting that manual dominance may derive out of a primitive vestibular or orientation bias. Infants with forceful grasping and active Moro reflexes (sudden tensing and opening of the arms with startle) may show greater assertiveness and a more forceful personality as they grow older. Conversely, children with cerebellar disease or Down's syndrome with hypotonicity tend to be more passive and docile (Goldstein, 1938; Schilder, 1964). There is a well-known case of early frontal damage with abnormal personality development (Ackerly & Benton, 1948).

Such observations show that a personality is not just a set of traits for which an action is a means of expression; instead, the process that lays down the action flows through and elaborates aspects of the personality. We say, "You know a man by his deeds, not his words." Action is less prone to dissimulation than speech. Gestures, facial expressions, and body language are markers of the authenticity of statements. These movements are deposited on the path to conscious ideas and serve as guides to underlying motives. Actions emerge out of memory and layers in the infrastructure of the self. Actions express these early layers in cognition but do not themselves generate mental contents; rather, actions generate an attitude, an orientation or approach to the environment, confidence, participation and withdrawal, going out into the world, and a sense of control over objects. Stages in the exteriorization of an action are also stages in the realization of other mental contents. The self and its actions are reconstituted each moment to the degree to which the action unfolds.

REFERENCES

Ackerly, S., & Benton, A. (1948). Report of a case of bilateral frontal lobe defect. *Research Publications—Association for Research in Nervous and Mental Disease 27,* 479–504.

Alajouanine, T., Ombredane, A., & Durand, M. (1939). *Le syndrome de désintégration phonétique dans l'aphasie.* Paris: Masson.

Bancaud, J., Talairach, J., Geier, S., Bonis, A., Trottier, S., & Manrique, M. (1976). Manifestations comportementales induites par la stimulation ëlectrique du gyrus cingulaire chez l'homme. *Revue Neurologique, 132,* 705–724.

Bastian, H. C. (1898). *Aphasia and other speech defects.* London. (Reprint, AMS Press, New York, 1984)

Bergson, H. (1896). *Matter and memory,* (Engl. Trans. Doubleday, New York, 1959)

Bernstein, N. (1967). *The coordination and regulation of movements.* Oxford: Pergamon.

Borod, J., Koff, E., Perlman, M., & Nicholas, M. (1983). *The expression and perception of facial emotion in patients with focal brain damage.* Presentation at the International Neuropsychology Society, Mexico City.

Brindley, G., Goodwin, G., Kulikoski, J., & Leighton, D. (1976). Stability of vision with a paralyzed eye. *Journal of Physiology, 258,* 65–66.

Brown, J. W. (1977). *Mind, brain, and consciousness.* New York: Academic Press.

Brown, J. W. (1978). Lateralization: A brain model. *Brain and Language, 5,* 258–261.

Brown, J. W. (1982). Hierarchy and evolution in neurolinguistics. In M. Arbib, D. Caplan, & J. Marshall (Eds.), *Neural models of language processes.* New York: Academic Press.

Brown, J. W. (1983). Microstructure of perception: Physiology and patterns of breakdown. *Cognition and Brain Theory, 6,* 145–184.

Brown, J. W. (1984a). Introduction to Bastian (1898).

Brown, J. W. (1984b). Review of *The expression of knowledge,* R. Isaacson and N. Spear (Eds.). *Journal of Nervous and Mental Disease, 172,* 232–234.

Brown, J. W. (1985a). Frontal lobe syndromes. In J. A. M. Fredericks (Ed.), *Handbook of clinical neurology* (Vol. 1), Amsterdam: North-Holland. (Reprinted with additions in *Journal of Neurolinguistics, 1,* 31–77, 1985)

Brown, J. W. (1985b). Imagery and the microstructure of perception. *Journal of Neurolinguistics, 1,* 89–141.

Brown, J. W., & Grober, E. (1983). Age, sex and aphasia type. *Journal of Nervous and Mental Disease, 170,* 431–434.

Brown, J. W., Leader, B., & Blum, C. (1983). Hemiplegic writing in severe aphasia. *Brain and Language, 19,* 204–215.

Buge, A., Escourolle, R., Rancurel, G., & Poisson, M. (1975). Mutisme akinetique et ramollisement bi-cingulaire. *Revue Neurologique, 131,* 121–137.

Chauvel, P., Bancaud, J., & Buser, P. (1985). Participation of the supplementary motor area in speech. *Experimental Brain Research, 58,* A14

Coryell, J., & Michel, G. (1978). How supine postural preferences of infants can contribute toward the development of handedness. *Infant Behavior and Development, 1,* 245–257.

Dennett, D. (1985). *Elbow room.* Cambridge, MA: MIT Press.

Denny-Brown, D. (1958). The nature of apraxia. *Journal of Nervous and Mental Disease, 216,* 9–32.

Eccles, J. (1982). The initiation of voluntary movements by the supplementary motor area. *Archiv für Psychiatrie und Nervenkrankheiten, 231,* 423–441.

Evarts, E. (1979). Brain mechanisms of movement. *Scientific American,* September.

Gerstmann, J., & Schilder, P. (1926). Uber eine besondere Gangstörung bei Stirnhirnerkrankung. *Wiener Medizinische Wochenschrift, 3,* 97–102.

Goldberg, G. (1985). The supplementary motor area. *Behavioral Brain Sciences, 8,* 567–616.

Goldstein, K. (1938). Moro reflex and startle pattern. *Archives of Neurology and Psychiatry, 40,* 322–327.

James, W. (1890). *The principles of psychology.* New York: Holt.

Jürgens, U. (1985). Implications of the SMA in phonation. *Experimental Brain Research, 58,* A12–A14.

Knutsson, E., & Lying-Tunnell, U. (1985). Gait apraxia in normal-pressure hydrocephalus. *Neurology, 35,* 155–160.

Kornhuber, H. (1974). Cerebral cortex, cerebellum and basal ganglia. In F. Schmitt & F. Worden (Eds.), *The neurosciences: Third study program.* Cambridge, MA: MIT Press.

Kornhuber, H. (1985). Bereitschaftspotential and the activity of the supplementary motor area preceding voluntary movement. *Experimental Brain Research, 58,* A10–A11.

Lashley, K. (1951). The problem of serial order in behavior. In L. Jeffress (Ed.), *Cerebral mechanisms in behavior.* New York: Wiley.

Lecours, A. R., & Lhermitte, F. (1976). The "pure form" of the phonetic disintegration syndrome (pure anarthria): Anatomo-clinical report of a historical case. *Brain and Language, 3,* 88.

Libet, B., Gleason, C., Wright, E., & Pearl, D. (1983). Time of conscious intention to act in relation to onset of cerebral activity (readiness-potential). *Brain, 106,* 623–642.

Luria, A. R. (1962). *Higher cortical functions.* (Engl. Trans. Basic Books, New York, 1966)

Lynch, J. (1980). The functional organization of posterior parietal association cortex. *Behavioral Brain Sciences, 3,* 485–534.

Martin, J. (1972). Rhythmic (hierarchical) versus serial structure in speech and other behaviors. *Psychological Review, 79,* 487–509.

Mountcastle, V. (1976). The world around us: Neural command functions for selective attention (The F. O. Schmitt Lecture in Neuroscience, 1975). *Neurosciences Research Program Bulletin, 14,* Suppl, 1–47.

Nielsen, J., & Jacobs, L. (1951). Bilateral lesions of the anterior cingulate gyri. *Bulletin of the Los Angeles Neurological Society, 16,* 231–234.

Roland, P. (1978). Sensory feedback to the cerebral cortex during voluntary movement in man. *Behavioral Brain Sciences, 1,* 129–171.

Schepelmanns, F. (1979).. Rhythmic patterns of motor activity after lesions of the central nervous system in man. *Acta Neurochirurgica, 49,* 153–189.

Schilder, P. (1964). In L. Bender (Ed.), *Contributions to developmental neuropsychiatry.* New York: International Universities Press.

Siebeck, R., & Frey, R. (1953). Die Wirkungen muskelerschlaffender Mittel auf die Augenmuskeln. *Anaesthesist, 2,* 138–141.

Stevens, J. (1978). Commentary. *Behavioral Brain Sciences, 1,* 163–165.

Turvey, M. (1977). Preliminaries to a theory of action with reference to vision. In R. Shaw & J. Bransford (Eds.), *Perceiving, acting and knowing*. Englewood Cliffs, NJ: Erlbaum.

Yakovlev, P. (1948). Motility, behavior and the brain. *Journal of Nervous and Mental Disease, 107,* 313–335.

15

From Intent to Action

Evolution and Function of the Premotor Systems of the Frontal Lobe

Gary Goldberg

INTRODUCTION

intent:

1. That which is intended; aim; purpose.
2. The state of mind operative at the time of an action.

—*The American Heritage Dictionary of the English Language*

Fundamental to human experience is the feeling that we maintain agency in the physical actions of our bodies, that we have conscious control over the movements of our limbs so that we can use them to perform specific tasks directed to solving everyday problems. Intentionality in action implies directedness toward a goal: that action is directed toward the achievement of a particular outcome. Frequently this involves directedness toward external objects. Philosophers have for many years struggled with the problem of understanding intentionality in human action, but usually in the context of attempting to deal with somewhat broader issues. Only recently have direct attempts been made to fuse philosophical approaches with the scientific study of action (Brand, 1984). It would appear that the time is ripe for such interaction, as issues such as "volition," "intentionality," "will," and "agency" in relation to human action come to be addressed in a scientific context (Libet, 1985; see Brown, this volume, Chapter 14). In this chapter, I wish to address the question of the relationship between intention and expressed action vis-à-vis the participation of frontal lobe regions in the organization of voluntary movements.

I will first consider adaptive change occurring in neural systems across different time scales. I will argue that parallels may be drawn between changes

ISBN 0-936925-00-0

occurring on phylogenetic, ontogenetic, and microgenetic time scales in a reconsideration of the biogenetic law. It will be argued that, rather than being related by *forward causation* as originally put forward by Haekel, the defining processes of phylogenesis, ontogenesis, and microgenesis are related by *mutual constraint* (Katz, 1983). Thus, the biogenetic law may be revised, and the concepts of parallelism and recapitulation reinstated, although in a modified form (Alberch, 1984). The concept of progressive differentiation of a neural system archetype from uniform simplicity to parcellated complexity and compartmentalization occurring in evolution as well as ontogeny can be supported using modern neuroanatomic tracing techniques in comparative studies (Ebbesson, 1984). This may then permit one to use information regarding change developing over one scale (e.g., through comparative neuroanatomy applied across the phylogenetic scale) to provide valuable insights with regard to change developing over another (e.g., the activation of neural structures in action microgenesis—see Chapter 14 by Brown, this volume). It is this possibility which lies at the heart of this chapter, and which will enable *evolutionary cortical architectonics* (Goldberg, 1985b; Pandya & Barbas, 1985; Pandya & Yeterian, in press) to be used to examine the functional participation of the frontal lobes in the organization of action on the microgenetic time scale.

The *dual premotor systems hypothesis* (Goldberg, 1985a, 1985c) will be developed in the context of supportive clinical evidence and a brief review of physiologic investigations consistent with the hypothesis. The hypothesis states that there are at least two frontal premotor systems, a lateral and a medial, which correspond to two evolutionary trends in frontal lobe differentiation over phylogeny. The lateral system controls action that is environmentally based (i.e., data driven). It is normally used when action must be generated in a "responsive" mode rather than in a predictive one. In this operational mode, action follows directly in response to external information *indicating* (Reed, 1981), or "triggering," the action. This control mode would normally be used when (1) there is no inherent temporal structure in the sensory information that would allow predictive control to be utilized or (2) the situation in which action is occurring takes place in a novel context and/or there is no prior knowledge available that would permit predictive control. The second situation would apply particularly during development as well as during the learning of a new skill.

A much more developed medial system (probably significantly more developed in human than in primate brain) is used to control action when temporal structure is present and memory (i.e., some form of internal model) can be used in conjunction with selective perception of such temporally ordered information to allow *prospective control of behavior*. Since intentionality implies the capacity to follow a plan and thus control action prospectively (Brand, 1984), it is primarily though the participation of the medial system that a feeling of volitional control over behavior emerges and the capacity for acting autonomously—with selective rather than obligatory dependence on external information for behavioral cuing (see Lhermitte, 1983, 1986; Lhermitte, Pillon, & Serdaru, 1986)—develops. The organism is engaged in a continual process of actively extracting consistent temporal structure from its interactions with the environment. This information, which attains its greatest reliability and consistency through the operation of physical law (Turvey, 1986), is, in turn, used to synthesize a "model of the future," which, through the operation of the putative medial frontal premotor system, supports the capacity to prospectively control behavior and successfully achieve desired outcomes (Bernstein, 1961/1984a).

One of a series of patients presenting with the "alien hand sign" (Bogen, 1979; Brion & Jedynak, 1972) in the limb opposite to a medial hemispheric infarct (Goldberg, Mayer, & Toglia, 1981) will be described and the clinical presentation will be related to the model. It will be argued that a wide range of clinical and basic physiological observations may be understood in the context of the dual premotor systems hypothesis, which itself may be inferred from a consideration of the evolution of the circuitry and function of the frontal lobes and interrelated subcortical structures (Goldberg, 1985a).

TIME FRAMES OF NEUROBIOLOGIC ADAPTATION: REFLECTIONS ON THE BIOGENETIC LAW AND MICROGENETIC THEORY

adaptation:
An alteration or adjustment . . . by which a species or individual improves its condition in relationship to its environment.

recapitulation:
Biol. The apparent repetition of some of the evolutionary stages of the species during embryonic development of the individual organism.
—*The American Heritage Dictionary of the English Language*

Adaptations are a defining property of life. . . .Adaptations must constitute some kind of partial match with the external world. . . .The formation of an adaptation is partly the result of gaining and storing information about the world. The nub of the problem, therefore, is whether all adaptations can be accounted for by a single adaption-forming process, or whether more than one process is required.
—H. C. Plotkin and F. J. Odling-Smee (1981, p. 227)

Creation is a process of evolution of which man is not merely a witness but a participant and partner as well.
—Theodosius Dobzhansky (1956)

Living systems are continuously in a state of massively dynamic change in the adaptive struggle to surmount environmental conditions that may threaten survival. The most powerful result of the evolutionary elaboration of the mammalian central nervous system is the unequaled capacity for adaptive change and learning which its operation makes possible for the individual organism on the behavioral (microgenetic) time scale. This capacity confers a degree of autonomy and independence from changing environmental circumstances. Adaptive change leading to improved capacity to compete for survival, to actively surmount limiting environmental circumstances, and to anticipate environmental contingencies can occur in an analogous manner on different time scales (see Figure 1) with different degrees of permanence and dynamic response.

On the phylogenetic time scale, neurobiologic adaptation involves structural change in the nervous system guided by changes in the genome. The information is stored in the genome, change may occur through differential fitness of random variants in an intergenerational frame (speciation), and adaptation occurs slowly and *does not occur over the course of the life span of the organism*. Thus, this primary evolutionary adaptive process "may not be able to supply successions of individual organisms with all the adaptations they need at a fast enough rate for them to track the conditions of the changing world" (Plotkin & Odling-Smee, 1981, p. 230). This limitation leads to the adaptive selection of organisms with "subsidiary units" (Plotkin & Odling-Smee, 1981, p. 230) which enable the organism to adapt to changes in environmental circumstances occurring in an ongoing fashion over its lifetime. On the ontogenetic scale, adaptation involves the active structuring of the individual organism (epigenesis) with some plasticity in the specification of structure of the individual nervous system (variable

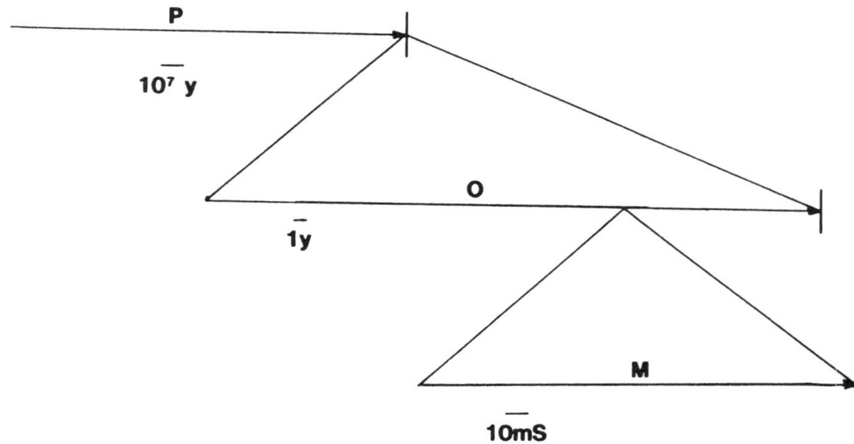

FIGURE 1 Time frames of neurobiologic adaptation. P, phylogenetic time scale; O, ontogenetic time scale; M, microgenetic time scale.

epigenesis) occurring through environmental interaction (construction of a "secondary repertoire"—see Edelman [1978]). Adaptive function is at its most dynamic level on the microgenetic time scale, conferring on the individual organism, through the operation of its nervous system, a capacity for autonomous information gathering, information storage, and adaptive action ("learning"). These "levels of neurobiological adaptation" can be viewed as interrelated by mutually constraining conditions.

What is interesting in this general consideration is that it is the apparent outcome of an adaptive process which appears to drive its activity. In action, for example, it appears that the organism uses activity to solve particular action problems by increasing the probability of a particular desired outcome toward unity (Bernstein, 1961/1984a). The process of the act appears to be directed by its goal. "Intentional contents" seem to be able to constrain the forces of natural law (Turvey, 1986). The idea that the goal of the action is the primary element driving its organization suggests backward causation (the goal "causing" the behavior; the end determining the means) and an apparently teleological point of view. This viewpoint, however, isolates the act from its formative history during the course of which iterative selection for adaptive capacity in living systems has occurred: All self-preserving, self-regulating living systems must display active purposive behavior within their environments as a fundamental characteristic that helps to ensure their survival. Evolution selects for such purposiveness and the capacity of the organism to extract order from its environment and to actively lower the entropy of the environment/organism system (hence to reduce unpredictability and enhance the likelihood of self-preserving outcomes). Since forward linear causation does not really fit in this situation, Pittendrigh (1958) introduced the term *teleonomy* to describe this process whereby, through a historical, cyclical interaction of necessity and chance, biological systems attain the capacity for goal-directed behaviors (Pickenhain, 1984). Thus, parallel processes characterized by adaptation may be operating on these different time scales across which neurobiologic differentiation (in its widest possible sense) is occurring.

Ontogeny and phylogeny are thus related in a rather interesting way:

> . . . the genome is not the organism. It is the organism and not the genome that directly interacts with the environment, and it is the organism and not the genome that directly produces viable germ cells that perpetuate the phylogeny. . . . Evolution is expressed through ontogeny . . . [and] phylogeny is a sequence of transformed ontogenies." (Katz, Lasek, & Kaiserman-Abramof, 1981, p. 397)

These authors suggested the term *ontophyletics* (see Katz, 1983) to refer to the study of the relationships between ontogeny and phylogeny. Katz (1983) argues that the characteristics of ontogenetic neural "buffer" mechanisms (such as compensatory innervation and the matching of interconnected neural populations) constrain and orient phylogenetic change. This interaction between ontogeny and phylogeny might be better viewed as one of mutually interactive constraint since controlling elements of the ontogenetic mechanisms are, themselves, encoded in the genome, and epigenesis may be viewed as a subroutine directed from within the genome through selective mechanisms (see Edelman 1978, 1984, 1986; Jerne, 1970).

One can take this argument one step further and assert that the actual mechanisms associated with the ongoing behavior of the individual organism in its moment-to-moment adaptive interactions with the environment are similarly influential in determining evolutionary potential. It is at this ecological interface that the active struggle for survival of the organism, governed by natural physical laws, is occurring (see Turvey, 1986). This is the critical existential interface at which the individual organism acts in the present in order to survive into the future through selecting a strategy based on an active recombination of mechanisms and internalized information about natural order and physical law accumulated over the past experience of the individual and its evolutionary history (Bernstein, 1962/1984b; Ingvar, 1985). It is where the actual test of survival of the individual organism—the selective process of evolution—takes place. Yakovlev (1948) phrased the idea as follows:

> At any given moment, the behavior of a living organism represents the culmination of the evolution not only of its own behavior, but of the behavior of the species and of all living matter as a common stock of all species. (p. 315)

These considerations suggest a mutually constraining relationship between phylogenetic change and the dynamic changes occurring on the time scale of evolving behaviors: the "microgenetic scale" (Brown, this volume, Chapter 14; Brown, 1986). The term *microphyletics* could be proposed to identify the study of the relationship between microgeny and phylogeny. It is this relationship to which we will turn later in this chapter.

Microgenetic theory of adaptive cognitive function is described by Brown (this volume, Chapter 14) as follows:

> . . . every behavior or mental state has a submerged infrastructure distributed over evolutionary planes in the forebrain. Cognitive processing retraces the direction of phyletic growth, so that evolutionary levels, and correlated processing stages, are entrained in behavior in the order of their evolutionary appearance. In a very real sense, *microgeny recapitulates phylogeny* as cognition rapidly unfolds over evolutionary structure. (p. 251, emphasis added)

This phrasing of the relationship between microgeny and phylogeny immediately brings the biogenetic law ("ontogeny recapitulates phylogeny") to the fore and suggests an interesting corollary ("microgeny recapitulates phylogeny"). Although beyond the scope of this consideration, it is instructive to reflect momentarily on the controversies surrounding the biogenetic law, its history, and the stormy path this idea has followed through this century (for more ıorough treatments, the reader is urged to examine Russell [1916], Gould 1977], and Churchill [1980]).

In 1828, von Baer, an embryologist, showed that organism development roceeded from the homogeneous to the heterogeneous as a simple form changes ıto a more complex one. This concept was embraced by the European rational ıorphologists of the early nineteenth century, the French transcendentalists, and ıe German *Naturphilosophie* school, who, encouraged by successes in the hysical sciences, were attempting to formulate a unified morphogenetic theory. 'hey were engaged in a "search for order" (Ghiselin, 1980, p. 183), seeking out egularities in spatial arrangements of parts, symmetries in structure, and omologies between structures. This theory maintained that form was elaborated ırough a fundamental structural plan operating on an archetype—a "common ncestor"—and that parallels could be drawn between the operation of such a plan" in the series of transformations occurring during ontogeny and the changıg design of the adult ancestors of the organism. The advent of evolutionary ıeory transformed this effort to assemble a theory of organismic form. The xplanatory element became one which involved historical content and continency, rather than one of universal law (Goodwin, 1982). As a result, the effort n the part of the rational morphologists to derive a morphogenetic theory ıdependent of historical contingencies, analogous, for example, to the atomic ıeory of matter, has been pursued, with many attempts to salvage the "old ntology" (Ghiselin, 1980). This effort to dispense with contingencies in evoluonary and morphogenetic law continues (Goodwin, 1982; Webster & Goodwin, 981).

Darwin's emphasis on hereditary issues led Haekel to reformulate the arallel between ontogeny and phylogeny in the historical terms of evolutionary ıeory: Ontogeny recapitulates the adult form of preceding organisms in the hyletic sequence with the insistence that phylogeny *causes* ontogeny. Darwin, imself, commented that the basic facts of embryology "can be explained on the iew of descent with modification" (Darwin, 1859, p. 443). A more precise onnection between embryology and evolution was not possible because the rocesses whereby the genetic material is expressed during development were, nd continue to remain, poorly understood (Webster & Goodwin, 1981). Recent ısights gained in examining the capacity of the immune system to produce, nder direct genetic control, all macromolecules necessary for antigenic recognion may begin to provide clues about how *selective* processes, possibly also ıvolving controlled synthesis of macromolecules embedded in neural memrane, may also underlie the genetic control of epigenesis (Edelman, 1978, 984, 1986; Jerne, 1970) and the formation of structured neural networks.

Interestingly, the biogenetic law has been repeatedly attacked by mbryologists and anatomists. Gould (1977, p. 2) notes: "Haekel's biogenetic ıw was so extreme, and its collapse so spectacular, that the entire subject ecame taboo." It has, however, recently been recognized that a fresh appraisal of the relationship between evolution and development is now due (Alberch, 1982) and that important insights about evolution may be obtained from ontogenetic (and microgenetic) studies and, more to the point for this consideration, vice versa. It is also possible that the rational extension of these considerations to the behaving organism (and thus to cognition and microgeny) may occur through the development of population genetics and the sociobiological extensions of evolutionary theory, which recognize relationships between multiple levels of adaptation (Plotkin & Odling-Smee, 1981) associated with interactive adaptive processes (evolution, variable epigenesis, and learning) operating on the different time scales on which organismic adaptation can occur.

The detailed relationships between these processes have yet to be worked out and the basis for recapitulation continues to be elusive and controversial, though useful empirically. The full acceptance of these ideas and the detailed expression of the "biogenetic law" with respect to the nervous system must await the further elucidation of mechanisms that interrelate the processes of evolution, development, and adaptive behavior. Until such time that an analytic elucidation of these interrelationships is possible, two separate and somewhat antagonistic biological perspectives will be maintained:

1. The historical and somewhat descriptive approach in which only a posteriori principles can be drawn to try to explain observations of existing and past conditions (e.g., evolutionary theory; clinicopathologic correlation).

2. The causal-analytic approach in which biological mechanisms are governed by physical laws (of physics and chemistry), which are independent of historical contingencies and define future possibility through current conditions acting within the constraint of natural law (Churchill, 1980; see also Turvey, 1986; de Beer, 1938; Goodwin, 1982).

FUNCTIONAL EVOLUTIONARY ARCHITECTONICS OF THE FRONTAL LOBE: LINKING ETHOLOGY AND COMPARATIVE NEUROANATOMY OF THE FRONTAL LOBE

Functional evolutionary architectonics may be defined as the comparative study of variation of architectonic structure (most often of the cerebral cortex), the identification of evolutionary trends of structural differentiation and their spatial directions and patterns, and the relationship between these changes in structure and changes in behavior (Goldberg, 1985a, 1985b, 1985c; Pandya & Barbas, 1985; Pandya and Barnes, this volume, Chapter 3; Pandya & Yeterian, in press; Sanides, 1964, 1969, 1970, 1972). Sanides recognized sets of cortical growth rings in frontal cortex with regions of more recent evolutionary appearance encompassing the older zones. The model developed by Sanides states that these progressively changing architectonic fields represent waves of circumferential differentiation in evolution originating from separate neural sources—one archicortical and one paleocortical (see Pandya, and Barnes, this volume, Chapter 3). An attempt is made to associate an evolutionary trend in structural differentiation with an evolutionary trend in behavioral differentiation and environmental adaptation. Architectonic analysis may be supplemented by examinations of connectivity. Furthermore, patterns of intracortical laminar distribution of projections, particularly in corticocortical projections, may provide additional information in attempting to analyze and identify directionality in evolutionary trends (Deacon, 1985, 1986; Pandya & Yeterian, in press). Comparative anatomy is also critically important in helping to identify homologies between brain structures and thus defining directions of structural elaboration over phylogeny. Such information can then be correlated with changes in behavior to gain insight into the functional significance of particular evolutionary trends in brain structure.

Sanides (1964), in performing an architectonic analysis of the human frontal lobe, recognized three different evolutionary trends in the differentiation of the frontal cerebral cortex:

1. A medial archicortical trend originating in the periarchicortical proisocortex of the medial wall of the frontal lobe, the anterior cingulate cortex, and proceeding superiorly, anteriorly, and inferiorly away from this origination. This trend gives rise to the supplementary motor area (SMA) in paralimbic cortex, characterized by an accentuated Layer II, on the medial surface of the frontal lobe. The architectonic trend extends out onto the lateral convexity down to the level of the principal sulcus in the primate brain and the inferior frontal sulcus in the human frontal lobe. The two trends interact on the lateral convexity in the region of greatest differentiation, the dorsolateral prefrontal cortex. The trends also interact on the ventral surface in the region of the orbitofrontal cortex. The medial trend is thought to have differentiated progressively away from hippocampal cortex (see also Abbie, 1940; Dart, 1934; Pandya & Yeterian, in press) and gives rise to the somatosensory and motor isocortex.

2. A lateral paleocortical trend begins in the peripaleocortical proisocortex of the insula and proceeds superiorly up the lateral convexity (as well as, presumably, over the superior aspect of the temporal lobe and the inferior aspect of the parietal lobe—see Eidelberg and Galaburda [1984] for an examination of the application of these concepts to the human parietal lobe). This trend gives rise to the second somatosensory representation (SII) and related sensory regions in the vicinity of the insula, frontoparietal operculum, and superior temporal lobe. The trend originated in the piriform cortex—primitive olfactory sensory cortex (the prototypical sensory processing area)—and gives rise to sensory isocortex.

3. The third trend in cortical differentiation of the frontal lobe involves the primary motor representation of the precentral gyrus (MI). This is a recent trend

in phylogeny and is associated with the formation of a hypergranular core in the lateral convexity of the human frontal lobe. Sanides (1964) postulated that this was a trend which appeared much later in evolution than the previous two trends and evolved for the purpose of controlling discrete fractionated distal hand movements, a function developing relatively late in terrestrial mammalian evolution and best developed in humans.

It is of particular interest, in this regard, that the dolphin cerebral cortex appears to have maintained an archetypal mammalian architectonic structure which, despite massive increases in cortical area, has not progressed beyond the paralimbic-parainsular phase of evolutionary development (Morgane, Jacobs, & Galaburda, 1985) in terms of its architectonic differentiation. This would suggest that the processes acting to elaborate the amount of area of the cerebral cortex are separable from those leading to further differentiation. It is likely that the evolutionary push toward further differentiation and specialization within human brain arose through continuing adaptation to terrestrial life, including a trend toward dextrous functional use of the upper limbs. The very different marine environment in which the Cetacean mammals evolved has apparently produced a cortical mantle which is highly elaborated but relatively undifferentiated (Morgane, Jacobs, & Galaburda, 1985). This is a most intriguing experiment of nature demonstrating the influence of radically different environments on brain evolution. One can only speculate about the implications such differences in brain structure may have for the ways in which the mental life of Cetaceans may differ from that of humans.

As noted earlier, such evolutionary trends may also influence patterns of connection between cortical regions. Nauta (1964) noted a tendency for projections from the prefrontal regions to follow two separate routes: a medial course through the cingulum and a lateral course through frontooccipital and uncinate fasciculi. A recent examination of the dorsolateral prefrontal cortex, where the two coronal evolutionary trends interact, indicates that the connections between this area and hippocampal structures are transmitted through two separate routes: a larger medial route that terminates in the presubiculum and adjacent transitional cortex (regions that send output back to cortex and also receive input from parietal cortex), and a smaller lateral route that terminates in the entorhinal cortex, a region that also receives direct input from the orbital prefrontal cortex and the superior temporal gyrus (Goldman-Rakic, Selemon, & Schwartz, 1984). It is possible to interpret this hodology in light of the hypothesis put forward above in which the lateral projection route is related to the development of the lateral evolutionary trend, while the medial projection indicates a relationship with the medial evolutionary trend.

Consideration of what this may imply in terms of the functional interpretation of these distinct pathways between the dorsolateral prefrontal cortex and the hippocampal region would extend beyond the scope of this chapter. In the context of evolutionary architectonics, however, it would suggest a certain duality of function of these component structures within the hippocampal formation which can be placed in the general framework of the dual premotor systems hypothesis. In this regard, it is most interesting that the medial system appears to be related to a major *output* region of the hippocampal formation—the presubiculum (e.g., Rosene & Van Hoesen, 1977)—while the lateral system is related to a major *input* region that receives convergent cortical information being directed to the hippocampus—the entorhinal cortex (Van Hoesen, 1982; see also discussion in Goldman-Rakic et al., 1984). This pattern of connectivity between frontal cortex and the hippocampal formation may have extremely important implications for understanding the general function of the regions of the frontal lobe that give rise to these projections and may also provide important clues about the ways in which the general function of the lateral parainsular and medial paralimbic evolutionary trends may be distinguished (see also Gray [1982] for a functional model of the septohippocampal system and the role of presubicular and entorhinal cortex within this context).

It is also important to note that the output from the basal ganglia appears to be directed toward the medial component of the frontal cortex (Schell & Strick, 1984; Wiesendanger & Wiesendanger, 1985) and thus connects preferentially with regions in the medial paralimbic trend, including the supplementary motor area. This direction of outflow from the basal ganglia—now thought to be a highly conserved set of structures—to a neocortical target appears to be an innovation of mammalian evolution since the major target of basal ganglia output in avian and reptilian brain is directed to the tectum (superior colliculus) via the pretectum (Reiner, Brauth, & Karten, 1984). This transformation in basal ganglia connectivity (see Figure 2) is crucial to understanding the significance of the medial paralimbic evolutionary trend in mammalian neocortex to the organization of motor behavior as well as the role of basal ganglia in this process.

While in more primitive species the basal ganglia serve to control stereotyped species-specific behavior (MacLean, 1978; MacLean, this volume, Chapter 7), the reentrant basal ganglia (i.e., pallidal) outflow to premotor frontal cortex (i.e., the SMA and adjacent medial frontal regions in primates [Schell & Strick, 1984; Wiesendanger & Wiesendanger, 1985], and presumably also in humans) elaborated in mammalian evolution via a thalamotelencephalic route suggests a particularly important role for frontal premotor cortex in the organization of intentional action (Goldberg, 1985a). This trend toward increasing cortical participation in the control of such action in mammals correlates with a greater range and complexity of learning and adaptation in motor behavior and a progressive development of behavioral autonomy in mammalian evolution.

Many corticocortical projection patterns are bidirectional but asymmetric in terms of the pattern of laminar termination of projections (e.g., Rockland & Pandya, 1979; Pandya & Yeterian, in press). These patterns of projection have

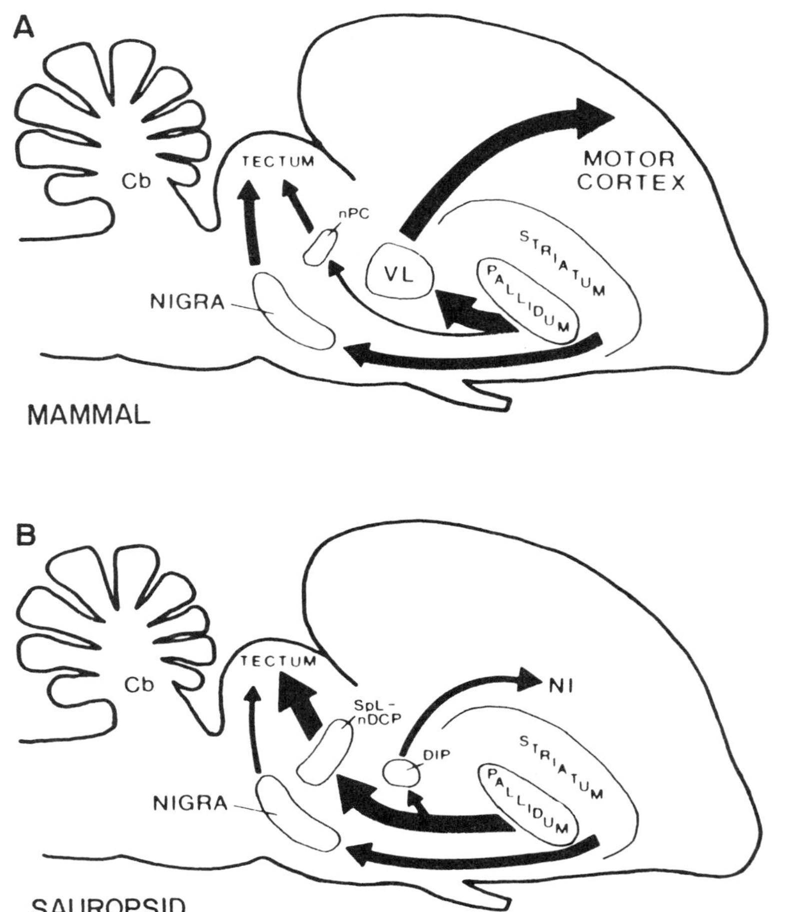

FIGURE 2 Evolutionary transformation of basal ganglia (pallidal) outflow projection pattern from sauropsid to mammalian brain. Note the redirection of pallidal outflow from midbrain targets in sauropsid brain to thalamocortical targets in mammalian brain. See text. (Reprinted with permission from Reiner, Brauth, & Karten, 1984.)

been used to infer directions of informational flow within cortical hierarchies in visual cortex (Rockland & Pandya, 1979; Van Essen & Maunsell, 1983), and similar questions have been raised with regard to the directionality of interconnected regions of premotor and motor cortex (Primrose & Strick, 1985). It is possible, however, that these asymmetries in interconnections between cortical regions may be related to evolutionary trends in cortical differentiation. Projections that arise primarily from superficial layers and terminate primarily in Layer IV, labeled "forward" or "ascending" by Van Essen and Maunsell (1983), may correspond to projections from more recently differentiated regions that connect to older regions along a gradient of evolutionary elaboration. This direction of projection may be called *retrograde* since it is oriented opposite to the direction of phylogenetic differentiation. Projections that arise from superficial and deep layers and project to cells outside of Layer IV, labeled "feedback" or "descending" (Van Essen & Maunsell, 1983), may correspond to projections from older regions in an evolutionary trend toward those regions that are more recent in phylogeny. This direction of projection may be referred to as *orthograde* since it follows the direction of phylogenetic differentiation. Regions that are at parallel stages in the parainsular and paralimbic trend may give rise to "lateral" types of interconnection patterns (Van Essen & Maunsell, 1983), which have combined features (see Figure 3).

With regard to the frontal lobe, this suggests, for example, that the SMA should connect with the primary motor cortex (MI) in such a way that the projections from the SMA to MI are orthograde, while those from MI back to the SMA are retrograde. This appears to be the case (Primrose & Strick, 1985; see also Deacon, 1986, for a detailed discussion), as it is also for connections from the arcuate premotor area (APA) to MI.

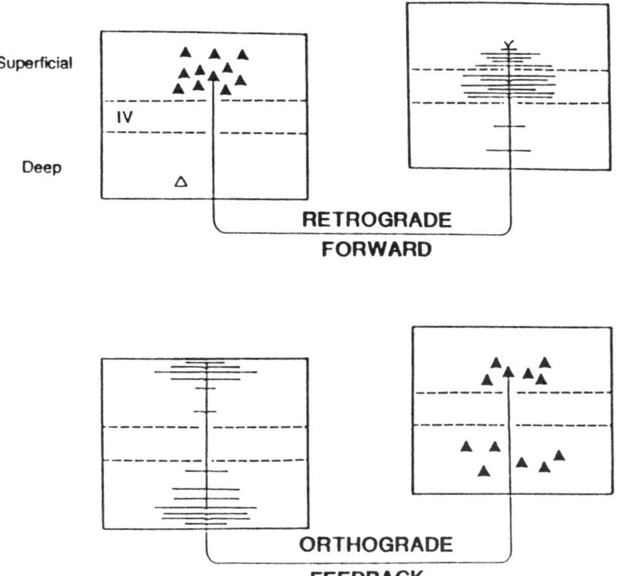

FIGURE 3 Patterns of laminar termination of corticocortical projections. (Adapted from Maunsell & Van Essen, 1983.)

THE DUAL PREMOTOR SYSTEMS HYPOTHESIS: APPLYING FUNCTIONAL EVOLUTIONARY ARCHITECTONICS TO THE FRONTAL LOBES

The shifting balance between dependence and independence with relation to the environment is one of the basic components of personal autonomy.
—F. Lhermitte (1986, p. 335)

Having introduced the notion of evolutionary architectonics and the concept of relating ethology to phylogenetic trends of brain differentiation, we will now turn to examine the functional aspects of the paralimbic and parainsular trends of the frontal lobes. An attempt will be made to link the medial and lateral evolutionary trends in frontal cortex to the premotor function in the frontal agranular cortex rostral to MI—the primary motor cortex (see Wise [1985] for a recent extensive review of the history and current status of the premotor concept).

Clues about behavioral modes in which these trends participate may be gained by considering the putative neural sources for each of these trends: the hippocampus for the medial paralimbic trend, and the piriform cortex for the lateral parainsular trend. Such considerations suggest that, while the lateral trend may be linked to registration and decoding of external sensory information, the medial trend may be more directly linked to interoceptive and internal mnemonic sources of information as well as to ordered temporal structure. Thus, while the lateral trend may be associated with a data-driven or "responsive" mode of operation, the medial trend would be related to a memory-driven or "projectional" mode (Goldberg, 1985c; Norman & Bobrow, 1975). This distinction may also be applied to understanding different forms of behavioral conditioning that depend differentially upon stimulus characteristics and timing of stimuli (see Perruchet [1984] for an expanded treatment of this idea; see also Petrides, this volume, Chapter 5).

The lateral trend is much more developed in the parietal lobe (Eidelberg & Galaburda, 1984), while the medial trend predominates in the frontal lobe of the human brain. Furthermore, there may well be important hemispheric asymmetries in the development of these two trends in the parietal and frontal lobes (Eidelberg & Galaburda, 1984). Though this point and its functional significance cannot be elaborated here, note that it allows one to place the dual premotor systems hypothesis into the context of the cortical "tropisms" recognized by Denny-Brown (1966; see also Denny-Brown & Chambers, 1958; Lhermitte, 1986), in which parietal cortex is viewed as a center for approach behavior while frontal cortex facilitates withdrawal behavior, and together these tendencies are mutually inhibitory in the maintenance of an "approach-avoidance equilibrium" with respect to the environment (Mesulam, 1986). This concept has been recently restated by Mesulam (1986) as follows:

> Prefrontal lesions could promote not only an excessive approach to the environment . . . but perhaps also an *excessive distance from the intrapsychic processes necessary for insight, foresight and abstraction*. In contrast, lesions of the parietal network could promote an avoidance of the extrapersonal world and perhaps an excessive reliance on intrapsychic data, even when these are in conflict with external reality. This state could lead to the anosognosia and psychotic hallucinations that emerge in conjunction with parietal lesions. This janusian view of frontoparietal interactions with one face, under frontal control, directed inward and the other, under parietal influence, directed outward may have considerable value for investigating the physiological foundation of complex psychological states, especially those related to self-awareness. (p. 322, emphasis added)

The dual premotor systems hypothesis argues that this interactive functional dichotomy within the hemisphere follows from evolutionary considerations and that the structural dichotomy is not so much "frontal-parietal" but is much better understood in terms of an interaction between functionally complementary evolutionary trends of cortical differentiation—that is, archicortical-paleocortical or paralimbic-parainsular—and their respective neural sources. I very much agree with Mesulam's statement that the recognition of this dichotomy has far-reaching implications.

This concept suggests the following:

1. The medial paralimbic trend is primarily involved in "projectional" action (Goldberg, 1985c) or "forward-directed" (Perruchet, 1984) conditioning processes associated with the development of a preparatory state of the organism that anticipates receipt of the unconditioned stimulus. In a more general sense, it is involved in the prospective control of behavior associated with the development of intentional states and the active utilization of a memory-based "model of the future" for predictive anticipatory control (Bernstein, 1962/1984b) that capitalizes on ordered temporal structure. The activity of this system is associated with the development of volitional states with respect to the generation of future action. The major frontal "premotor" structure in this system is the SMA.

2. The lateral parainsular trend is activated in "responsive" action (Goldberg, 1985c) or "backward-directed" (Perruchet, 1984) conditioning processes in which the response is related to the value or affective significance of the unconditioned stimulus. In a general sense, this trend is related to the organization of "responsive action" and is utilized in the retrospective control of behavior which is environmentally based such that behaviors are "triggered" by environmental stimuli that *indicate* a particular response (see Lhermitte [1986] for a discussion of the "environmental dependency syndrome" in which this action mode is inappropriately predominant to the detriment of personal autonomy). The major frontal "premotor" region in this trend is the arcuate premotor area (Schell & Strick, 1984), which is closely linked to the inferior parietal cortex

(Petrides & Pandya, 1984). This lateral system must then be involved in the registration, recognition, and assignment of affective value to an external stimulus which then triggers a responsive, environmentally driven action (see also Petrides, this volume; Petrides, 1986; Dabrowska, 1971). Such behaviors are not particularly sensitive to temporal structure (i.e., are relatively rate independent) and involve fairly rapid *retroactive* or "backward-directed" responses with immediate survival value (Perruchet, 1984).

On the other hand, the "projectional" aspect of function of the medial system utilizes predictable temporal structure to anticipate future contingencies by functioning in a *proactive* mode and allowing the organism to develop preparatory states. These states use selected *specificational* information (Gibson, 1979; Turvey, 1986) from the environment, which has predictive value due to the constraints of physical law and allows anticipation to occur. Here, the process of using this information in action may well be critically rate dependent. Such information makes possible the prospective control of behavior and has intentional content (Turvey, 1986). It is hypothesized that this information gains access to the medial system through its relationship with the basal ganglia (Schell & Strick, 1984), which effectively act as a selective filter that allows specific aspects of cortical activity (functioning to extract critical sensory features) to reach medial frontal cortex and the SMA (Goldberg, 1985a). The medial paralimbic trend, possibly through its relation to the hippocampus (Goldman-Rakic et al., 1984), would also have access to mnemonic functions, which would allow anticipation to develop based on reproducible temporal organization (Ingvar, 1985). It is further hypothesized that it is the action of the medial system (including the basal ganglia) that primarily conveys intentionality to action. We will now turn to a peculiar disturbance of intentionality in patients who sustain damage to the medial aspects of the frontal lobe that would tend to support this contention.

THE ALIEN HAND SIGN: CLINICAL EVIDENCE FOR ORGANIZATION OF PREMOTOR SYSTEMS IN THE FRONTAL LOBE

wayward:
1. disposed to go counter to the wishes or advice of others or to what is reasonable; wrong-headed, intractable, self-willed . . .
2. capriciously wilful . . .
—*The Shorter Oxford English Dictionary*

Denny-Brown (1966) recognized the presence of "cortical tropisms" or tendencies for certain cortical regions to control general forms of behavior. The SMA was felt to be a center for avoidance or withdrawal patterns while the insula and parietal operculum (SII) were thought to facilitate movements of exploration and grasping. With damage to one system, the other predominates, since these two systems normally are maintained in a state of balance through mutually interactive inhibition. Thus, damage to medial frontal cortex would lead to an increased tendency for visual- and tactile-directed exploration, with the observation of a grasp reflex and the instinctive grasp reaction (Seyffarth & Denny-Brown, 1948) driven by either tactile or visual stimulation.

Lhermitte (1986) has recently extended this concept to the general issue of the role of environmental cues in the facilitation of certain behavioral programs. Patients with large, bilateral frontal lobe lesions were noted either to compulsively use presented objects ("utilization behavior") or to imitate the actions of the examiner ("imitation behavior") in spite of the fact that they were not instructed to do so. Patients would continue to perform the behaviors even after being asked to stop. This was in distinct contrast to the behavior of normal subjects under similar conditions. Lhermitte (1986) attributes this disturbance to a disinhibition of parietal-based sensorimotor control mechanisms secondary to the frontal lobe lesion. The dual premotor systems hypothesis would predict that these disturbances are infrequently found in patients with lesions of the ventrolateral segments (i.e., below the inferior frontal sulcus on the lateral convexity) of the frontal lobes and would be more likely to be seen with lesions of dorsolateromedial elements (see Fuster, 1980). This prediction is not readily confirmed by the data of Lhermitte et al. (1986, Figure 2, p. 331) since the frontal lesions observed in their patients appear to be quite extensive.

We have observed a series of eight patients with relatively limited, well-documented lesions of the medial frontal cortex secondary to infarction in the territory of the anterior cerebral artery. These patients display a somewhat related problem in the hand opposite to the infarcted hemisphere. We have previously reported a description of the first two patients we observed (Goldberg et al., 1981), both of whom had lesions of the dominant left hemisphere and displayed difficulties with their right hand, including a grasp reflex, tactile and visual instinctive grasp reaction, and the alien hand sign (Bogen, 1979; Brion & Jedynak, 1972). What is most remarkable about these patients is the manner in which they themselves perceive these behaviors. When the affected hand begins to perform apparently purposeful actions, the patients do not feel that they have initiated or are controlling the behavior themselves—the behaviors appear to be occurring extravolitionally even though they display an apparent intentional content. The patients react with dismay to this situation and will usually attempt to restrain the movement of the impaired hand by holding it with the other (self-restriction). While they clearly recognize the hand as their own, thus distinguishing this condition from anosognosia, they do not recognize the intentionality associated with the behavior of the hand as their own. One patient objected to the term "alien hand" and preferred to describe it as her "wayward" hand. In view of the nature of the problem, this may actually be a better term. This condition has been attributed to damage of the corpus callosum (Bogen, 1979; Brion & Jedynak, 1972; Watson & Heilman, 1984), but the observation in our series that a left hemispheric infarct leads to a right alien hand and a right hemispheric infarct leads to a left alien hand (all in right-handed subjects who were neurologically intact prior to their strokes) makes this conclusion somewhat suspect. I would suggest, instead, that it is the combination of damage to medial frontal cortex together with damage to the body of the corpus callosum that gives rise to this condition (see Goldberg, 1985a). This situation essentially *isolates* the lateral premotor system in the damaged hemisphere, thus leading to a free-running "responsive" system controlling the contralateral hand. We can illustrate this situation with a case report:

B. D. is a right-handed 53-year-old woman who was medically and neurologically well except for mild hypertension prior to her illness. While at work, she was suddenly overcome by a feeling of nausea and began to notice that her left leg felt "as if it did not belong to me." This feeling of being dissociated from her body spread to the rest of the left side, and, though she could walk and talk, she felt very ill and anxious about this disturbance and went to an emergency room where she was evaluated. At that time, she apparently had no weakness in the left limbs or localizing neurological signs and was sent home with a diagnosis of "hyperventilation." At home, her symptoms continued to worsen over the next 24 hours and she returned to the hospital, now with weakness primarily in the left leg and an "inconsistent" ability to move the left arm. A CT scan performed showed an extensive infarction of the medial surface of the left frontal lobe (see Figure 4A). A subsequent MRI scan showed the infarct as well as damage to the body of the corpus callosum (see Figure 4B). There was no noticeable speech deficit. While sleeping one night a few days after admission to the hospital, she woke up suddenly with the feeling of something pressing against her neck and right shoulder. When she looked down she noticed it was her own left hand scratching her right shoulder. This act had apparently been initiated without her being aware of it. Several other similar events occurred subsequently while she was awake in which the left hand would reach out and grasp onto objects or perform actions with objects without a feeling that she was voluntarily controlling the action. She would frequently look down to find the hand doing something that she had no idea it had been doing. She found this circumstance very disturbing and was convinced that she was "going crazy." This became very distressing for her and she found that she could control these unwanted actions by grasping the left hand with the right hand. She noted that the left hand had a strong tendency to grasp onto objects around her and, once grasped, it was extremely difficult for her to voluntarily release her grip. If an object was placed in the grasp of the left hand or if the hand had something to "play with," the alien activity could be controlled. Initially, she had to resort to peeling her fingers off an object using the right hand in order to release her grasp. After several weeks, she was able to voluntarily release a grasp but only with a concentrated effort applied over several seconds. She had a great deal of difficulty performing bimanual tasks that required simultaneous activation of nonhomologous muscle groups (e.g., rapidly opening and closing the hands with one side opening while the other is closing) and would tend to quickly shift to performing such tasks such that homologous muscles contracted in phase (e.g., opening and closing both hands together). She also demonstrated some signs of an incomplete callosal apraxia (Bogen, 1979; Watson & Heilman, 1984) consistent with her MRI scan (see Figure 4).

When asked to perform rapid unilateral movements, it was possible to discern two different modes of action operating in the impaired limb. When asked to voluntarily rapidly tap her left hand on her thigh, her movements quickly became hypometric (see also Meador, Watson, Bowers, & Heilman, 1986) and she spontaneously commented that it felt to her as if she controlled the whole limb from the shoulder, moving the limb as a whole, rather than perceiving a distal locus of control in the wrist and hand, as she did performing the same movements on the intact side. To this extent, she was able to voluntarily control the impaired limb. However, this ability to control the limb in a volitional mode deteriorated significantly when the right visual hemifield was obstructed, and the alien behaviors became more frequent. Voluntary control of the limb improved somewhat when the limb was brought across the midline into the right hemispace, suggesting "hemispatial motor neglect" (see also Meador et al., 1986). When tactile stimulation was applied to the palm of the impaired hand, rapid grasping movements of the hand were readily produced although the patient had no associated feeling of volition with these movements. We have observed similar findings in all patients in our series. These findings suggest that there are at least two different action modes that may be able to produce activity in the impaired hand (see Table 1):

1. *Alien mode:* Activity of the distal aspect of the limb can be generated and controlled by the intact lateral premotor system of the impaired hemisphere. This activity is usually characterized by a bias toward responses linked to presentation of objects or to the provision of tactile inputs to the hand. Under this mode of control, the activity appears to be based in the distal aspects of the limb and the hand has a tendency to stay within its own hemispace and not cross the midline. This form of control over action is not associated with a feeling of volitional control and is thus the "alien mode."

2. *Volitional mode:* The patient may retain a degree of volitional control over the limb that is usually limited to movements based in the more proximal aspects of the limb. The fact that this mode is impaired by "blinding" the intact left hemisphere and is assisted by bringing the hand across into the right hemispace suggests that *the volitional mode of control over the involved left hand is being driven by the intact medial system of the left hemisphere* (see Figure 5). This mode of control is characterized by a perceived locus of control in the proximal muscles of the limb and by hypometria when the patient tries to move the distal aspect. It is also clearly associated with a feeling of voluntary control of the limb.

TABLE 1
Dual Action Modes Recognized in the Impaired Limb Contralateral to Medial Frontal Lobe Damage

Volitional Mode

1. Action involves activation of proximal musculature (primarily shoulder)—proximal locus of control
2. Attempts to move hand are clumsy and hypometric, but improve by bringing hand across the midline
3. Hand readily crosses the midline
4. Perceived locus of control is at the shoulder
5. Action perceived as intentionally controlled
6. Postulated neural basis: Medial premotor system of undamaged ipsilateral hemisphere

Alien Mode

1. Forced groping and instinctive grasp
2. Object-driven action or action directed toward the body
3. Hand tends to stay within its own hemispace and rarely crosses the midline
4. Action involves activation of distal musculature—distal locus of control (hand and forearm primarily)
5. Opposite hand used to restrain these actions
6. No perception of intentional control
7. Postulated neural basis of this action mode is through the isolated lateral premotor system of the damaged contralateral hemisphere ("free-running operation")

This evidence suggests that the alien movements of the affected hand occur secondary to the creation of an unbalanced, "free-running" lateral premotor system in the damaged hemisphere.

It is interesting that, over a period of 2 or 3 months after the stroke, the alien activity slowly becomes less frequent and the patient seems to be able to develop strategies for controlling it through mental effort. This could possibly take place through subcortical compensation mechanisms (MacKay & MacKay, 1982; Sergent, 1986) that somehow reintegrate volitional control of the impaired limb. The patients will initially often use their verbal system to help enhance volitional control over the impaired hand by "talking to the hand" in order to try to get it to obey. Patients also notice that an increased level of anxiety is usually associated

FIGURE 4 (A) Computerized tomography X-ray scan of the brain of Patient B.D. described in the text. This scan demonstrates a hypodense region in right medial frontal cortex involving the SMA and anterior cingulate cortex. (B) Magnetic resonance image (T2-weighted image) of midsagittal plane in Patient B.D. demonstrating damage in the body of the corpus callosum. (Scans provided courtesy of the Department of Radiology, Albert Einstein Medical Center, Philadelphia, PA.)

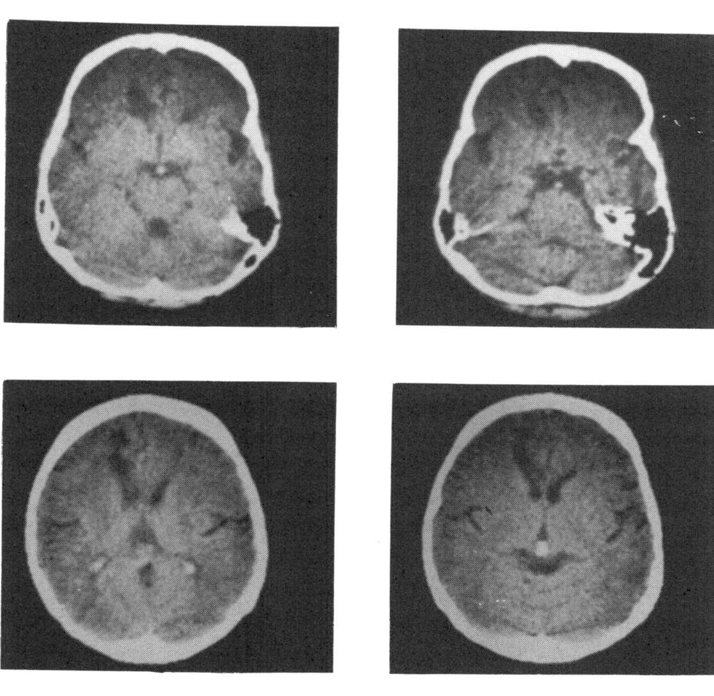

A

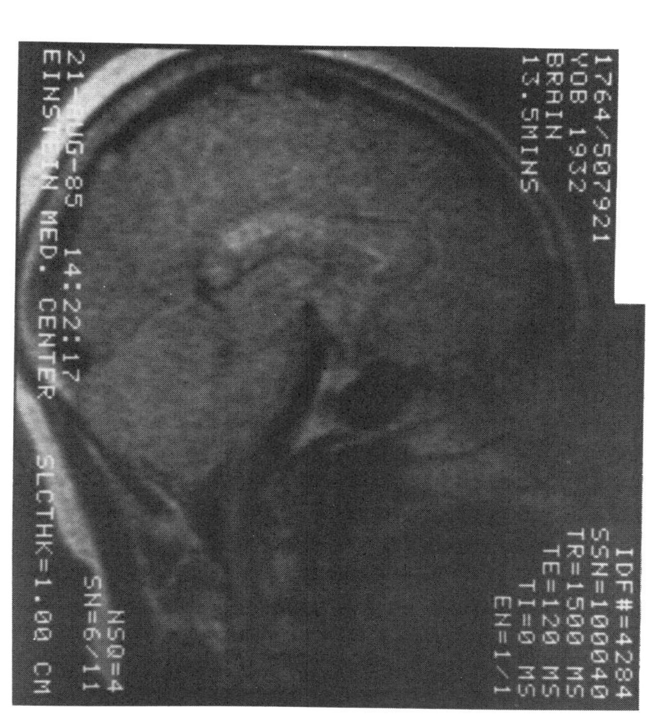
1764/507921
YOB 1932
BRAIN
13.5MINS
14:22:17
MED. CENTER
IDF#=4284
SSN=100040
TR=1500 MS
TE=120 MS
TI=0 MS
EN=1/1
NSO=4
SN=6/11
SLCTHK=1.00 CM

B

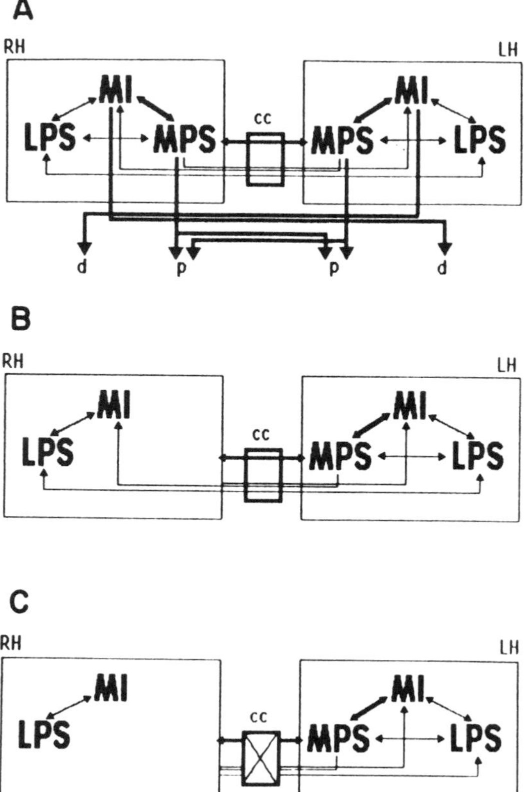

FIGURE 5 Bihemispheric interaction between premotor systems. (A) Normal pattern of connection between medial (MPS) and lateral (LPS) premotor systems and primary motor areas (MI) of the two hemispheres. Note that while MI tends to influence contralateral distal musculature via corticospinal projections, MPS has bilateral influence over proximal limb and axial musculature as well as influence on distal musculature through ipsilateral and callosally mediated contralateral projection to MI. The MPSs of the two hemispheres are also tightly linked by reciprocal callosal connections. cc, Corpus callosum; RH, right hemisphere; LH, left hemisphere; p, proximal postural musculature; d, distal limb musculature. (B) With unilateral damage involving the MPS, the contralateral MPS predominates in volitional control of both the ipsilateral and contralateral limb through its bilateral projection pattern. This increases the tendency for mirror-symmetric bimanual movements (Brinkman, 1984) and the persisting impairment of simultaneous nonhomologous bimanual action seen with SMA lesions. This lesion also produces an impaired ability to voluntarily control independent distal movement in the hand contralateral to the lesion, leading to the appearance of hypometria and apraxia involving this hand (Watson, Fleet, Gonzalez-Rothi, & Heilman 1986). Voluntary control over the proximal muscles of the impaired limb can be exerted by the ipsilateral SMA. (C) With additional damage to the corpus callosum, the fibers from the intact MPS to the contralateral MI are disrupted, thus releasing the MI on the left side of the diagram from any medial system control from either hemisphere. This leaves a "free-running" LPS on the left side of the diagram which may produce alien movement in the contralateral hand. Some volitional control over the limb may be maintained by ipsilateral projections from the MPS on the right side of the diagram. This leads to two different control modes apparent in the activity of the impaired extremity. See Table 1.

with a greater amount of alien behavior of the limb. They will frequently attempt to rationalize the intentional content of the alien action of the impaired limb:

One patient described an incident in which she was lying in bed with the window open when suddenly the impaired limb reached down and pulled up the covers, functioning entirely in the alien mode. She concluded that "it" must have felt cold and needed to cover her up. She felt that frequently the "alien" did things that were generally "good for her."

Another patient had a problem whenever she held a telephone receiver in her affected limb. Often, the arm would hang up the receiver without warning in the middle of a conversation. The patient would then have to call the person back and attempt to explain what had happened.

Additional questions arise regarding lateralization of functions within the frontal premotor systems. With damage to the medial aspect of the left frontal lobe, there is a greater likelihood for the development of a disturbance of vocal output in addition to the disturbance of limb control. This disturbance is characterized by a decrease in the ability to express propositional speech in a spontaneous fashion but a preserved ability to repeat phrases when instructed to do so. This has been labeled a "partial mutism" (J. W. Brown, 1977) and may thus be viewed as a disorder of the "drive" to generate self-initiated speech rather than as an actual aphasic condition (Damasio & Van Hoesen, 1980). Recent studies in primates confirm the important role that the medial system, including anterior cingulate and the SMA, plays in activating vocal mechanisms (Jürgens, 1985; Sutton, Trachy, & Lindeman, 1985) and in the development of different types of species-specific vocalizations (Jürgens, 1985). In their series of patients with SMA lesions, Watson, Fleet, Gonzalez-Rothi, and Heilman (1986) also found a greater tendency for disruption of vocal output with left SMA lesions when compared to right-sided lesions. On the other hand, right SMA lesions appeared to be more effective in disrupting activation control in the contralateral limb. Patients with left SMA lesions also appear to be significantly more apractic and their apraxia is bilateral, while patients with right SMA lesions maintain good functional control over the right hand. It is possible that the left SMA is more critical in the linkage between intentional and language systems and in control of sequential action, whereas the right SMA has a more focal effect on the left hand, tending to be involved in volitional control of activation of that hand, a function that may be partially a compensation by the intact ipsilateral left SMA, producing a hemispatial modulation effect.

It is interesting that the effects of a unilateral medial lesion of frontal cortex gradually disappear except for the problems experienced with bimanual coordination. This would tend to suggest that, under normal conditions, the medial systems of the two hemispheres function together as a unit maintaining contact through callosal and subcortical connections. With unilateral damage, problems may be transient as the medial system of the intact hemisphere may be able to substitute for some of the lost function. Activation studies tend to support the idea that there is bilateral participation of the SMA and basal ganglia in motor behavior, even when action is performed unilaterally (e.g., Roland, Meyer, Shibasaki, Yamamoto, & Thompson, 1982).

To summarize, patients with medial frontal infarcts can be observed to have behaviors of the hand opposite to the lesion that suggest purposeful action occurring independent of conscious volition. The patients clearly identify one hand as "alien" or "wayward," and the other hand—the "normal" hand—is frequently used to control it (the "Dr. Strangelove effect"—self-restriction). This striking finding can be interpreted in the context of the framework developed earlier in this chapter, in that these wayward behaviors may result from the unconstrained action of the lateral premotor system of the damaged hemisphere. A certain amount of volitional control over the impaired limb remains but is limited primarily to proximal limb musculature with voluntary attempts to produce distal movement in the limb leading to a hypometric performance. It is proposed that this remaining volitional control occurs through activation of the medial system of the intact ipsilateral hemisphere. There is a great deal yet to be learned from a detailed examination of these patients and there remains a need to confirm the ideas presented here through careful examinations as well as activational studies of patients who have developed a wayward hand.

THE DUAL PREMOTOR SYSTEMS HYPOTHESIS: ADDITIONAL CONSIDERATIONS

Evidence has been marshaled elsewhere to support the suggestion that there are separate medial and lateral premotor systems resident in the frontal lobe (Goldberg, 1985a). Additional data will be examined here.

Kurata and Tanji (1986) have recently reported a study of neuronal units in the premotor cortex on the lateral convexity near the arcuate sulcus that demonstrates that these units have properties similar to those recorded in the same paradigm from the SMA, suggesting that both the SMA and the APA may be involved in sensorially guided movement (Tanji & Kurata, 1982). In monkeys trained to respond to visual, tactile, and auditory cues, unit activity was time-locked to the sensory cue with relatively short delays which were significantly shorter for visual and auditory modalities than the responses in MI neurons. This would suggest that, for this paradigm, in a highly trained animal, it may be difficult to distinguish the properties of the SMA neurons from those of the APA neurons. This may be related to the fact that the task is overlearned and that the differences in activity between these two regions may not be well demonstrated in this type of task.

Mauritz and Wise (1986) examined the "set-related" activity of premotor neurons in the monkey when the timing of the stimulus presentations or the probability of temporal linkage between warning and imperative stimuli was manipulated in the trained animal. They found that neuronal activity was "strongly influenced by event predictability," indicating that these neurons are sensitive to the change in temporal structure of the task and normally anticipate events that can be predicted on the basis of previous experience. No such studies appear to have been reported in examining the discharge of neurons in the SMA. It should be mentioned that any translation of observations made in the primate brain to humans must be made with extreme care, particularly with reference to operations of different regions of the prefrontal cortex, in which there has clearly been a major structural elaboration between monkey and man.

Fox, Fox, Raichle, and Burde (1985) have reported a study in which regional cerebral blood flow (rCBF) changes were examined using positron emission tomography (PET) in normal human subjects who were moving their eyes or opening and closing a hand at a regular pace. These studies clearly documented a focus of activity (associated with a relative increase in rCBF) seen symmetrically in the midline in the region of the SMA when subjects performed either hand or eye movements with the midline focus with eye movements being rostral to that with hand movements. This finding suggests that the SMA participates even in the organization of relatively simple voluntary movements, which tends to contradict the alternative suggestion that the SMA becomes active only with increasingly complex tasks in which a greater degree of planning and "programming" is necessary (Roland, Larsen, Lassen, & Skinhoj, 1980). Fox et al. suggest that the SMA is involved in the process of initiating action, by participating in the establishment of "motor set" or the "readiness to move." This position would be in agreement with conclusions drawn from recording movement-associated potentials at the scalp (i.e., "readiness" potential—e.g., see Barrett, Shibasaki & Neshige, 1986; Goldberg, Kwan, Borrett, & Murphy, 1984; Kornhuber & Deecke, 1985). The question of whether the extent of SMA activation is related to the complexity of a task and the level of intentional engagement of the subject (Orgogozo, Larsen, Roland, & Lassen; Orgogozo & Larsen, 1979) remains to be settled. The question of whether the preparation-to-act associated with SMA activity should be interpreted as merely providing a route through which to activate postural muscles in anticipation of a focal movement, or whether this medial frontal activity contributes critically to the microgenetic process whereby the establishment of a goal, the development of a plan, and the emergence of intentionality (i.e., the "feeling of volition"—see Brown, this volume, Chapter 14; see also Libet, 1985) associated with the impending act emerge, is also an important and intriguing one. From observations of the difficulties experienced by patients who have sustained damage to this structure, it would appear that the apparent participation of the SMA in the process whereby a purposeful act is organized has very much to do with the development of a feeling of volition associated with its performance.

SUMMARY

An understanding of the evolutionary history of brain structures and functions should be no less important to the neurobiologist than the evolutionary history of galaxies is to the astronomer.

—S. O. E. Ebbesson (1984, p. 321)

This chapter presents an attempt to integrate a model of evolution of brain structure into a general model of brain operation, focusing on the issue of how different regions of the frontal lobe participate in the organization of action. The implications of the model, however, may be much more far-reaching and I have hinted at this somewhat in this account. Space limitations preclude a more careful examination of the concepts presented in the context of other issues and experimental paradigms. A table has been composed to raise some of these additional issues as well as to summarize some of the material presented here (Table 2). The following are additional questions for which this model may be of some value:

1. With respect to developmental psychology, how do the two different evolutionary trends and their functional interpretations interact in changing behavioral patterns during maturation and senescence?
2. Can new concepts relating the adaptive processes associated with phylogeny, ontogeny, and microgeny help us to understand how the damaged organism is able to reconstruct itself, with some capability for dynamic reorganization, into an adaptive whole? An important step in this direction appears to be the recent recognition that damaged systems may reorganize and reassemble themselves through a reversion to and reenactment of ontogenetic processes that originally constructed the systems (M. C. Brown, 1984; Finger & Almli, 1985; Jenkins & Merzenich, in press). An improved understanding of this issue will have profound implications for the question of how to rehabilitate brain-damaged patients (Goldberg, in press).
3. How can this conceptual model be used to understand memory processes and different forms of memory in relation to action and perception (Gloor, 1986; Squire, 1982)?
4. How can this model of brain function be used to shed light on processes involved in learning and skill acquisition? How might this model be used to better understand normal as well as pathological disruption of intentional processes, as, for example, when "unintended" acts occur "by accident" in normal subjects (see Norman, 1981)?
5. How can this model be integrated into an understanding of different mechanisms in the active control of directed attention? Can we, for example, use these concepts developed for action to help develop a directly analogous

understanding of the different brain systems involved in the "voluntary" and "automatic" shifting of attentional focus (Jonides, 1981; Posner, 1980)?

6. Can a general theory of adaptive processes drawing on insights from cognitive science and machine learning through rule-based iterative change (e.g., Hinton, Sejnowski, & Ackley, 1984) be developed within the structure of the conceptual framework presented here?
7. How can this model be utilized in the interpretation of different components of event-related potentials such as the contingent negative variation (CNV) and the readiness potential (RP)? One element of this issue is entered into the table as Item 13.
8. How can this model be utilized to understand in greater detail the lateralization of structure and function in the cerebral hemispheres (e.g., Eidelberg & Galaburda, 1984)?
9. How can this model be utilized to understand functional relationships between subcortical (e.g., cerebellum, basal ganglia, hippocampal formation, amygdala) and cortical structures? How, for example, might we be able to understand better how different parts of the limbic system function in relationship to cortical function (e.g., Gloor, 1986; see Table 2, Item 21)? Can further insights into subcortical component function be obtained through careful comparative studies examining the evolution of the hodologic relationships between various subcortical structures and regions of cerebral cortex?
10. How can this model be incorporated into an understanding of the dynamic brain correlates of cognition within the context of microgenetic theory (see Brown, this volume, Chapter 14; see also a speculative model presented in Goldberg, 1985a)?
11. How can this model be used to deepen our understanding of the relationship between brain function and the defining features of human consciousness (e.g., cognitive agency) (see Lhermitte, 1986)?
12. What philosophical and epistemological implications might this model have for understanding the nature of biological intelligence and formative processes relating structure and function in biological systems?
13. What additional insights can the basic recognition of an ongoing mutual interaction between form and function within biological systems ("the indissoluble unity of structure and function [behavior] of living matter" [Yakovlev, 1948, p. 314]) provide about understanding brain function and structure, the separable, formative processes of growth and maturation (i.e., differentiation), and the *dynamic interaction between form and function occurring on various time scales?*

These questions are but a few that may emerge from the considerations reviewed in this chapter, and which must await further elaboration.

TABLE 2
Distinguishing Features of Medial and Lateral Premotor Systems and Functional Interpretations of Evolutionary Trends in Brain Structure

	Medial	Lateral
1. Evolutionary origin	Archicortex (hippocampus)	Paleocortex (piriform cortex)
2. Proisocortical root	Cingulate cortex	Insular cortex
3. Architectonic emphasis	Pyramidal cells	Granular cells
4. Transitional premotor region	Paralimbic (SMA and SSA)	Parainsular (APA and SII)
5. Subcortical dependence	Basal ganglia and cerebellum (Wiesendanger & Wiesendanger, 1985)	Cerebellum
6. Control mode	Projectional	Responsive
7. Temporal relationship	Rate dependent	Rate independent
8. Informational type	Specificational (see Reed, 1981)	Indicational
9. Context sensitivity	Internal	External
10. Primary input control source	Interoceptive	Exteroceptive
11. Bimanual coordination	Simultaneous	Parallel
12. Type of conditioning process (Perruchet, 1984)	Forward directed	Backward directed
13. Contingent negative variation component	E(expectancy)-wave	O(orientation)-wave
14. Speech mode	Propositional	Nonpropositional
15. Output mode	Spontaneous (endogenous)	Repetitious (imitative)
16. Associated with volitional quality	Yes	No
17. Dependence on environmental input	Endogenously based selection	Exogenously based instruction
18. Lesion effects	a. Enhanced environmental dependency of behavior (Lhermitte, 1986)	a. Detachment from environmental stimuli (neglect)

(continued)

TABLE 2 (*continued*)

	b. Diminished self-awareness (e.g., alien hand sign)	b. Enhanced intrapsychic dependency (e.g., anosognosia)
19. Projectional relationship to structures of the hippocampal formation (see text; Goldman-Rakic, Seleman, & Schwartz, 1984)	Presubiculum (output)	Enthorhinal cortex (input)
20. Lateralization asymmetry:[a]		
Nondominant frontal	Relatively diminished	Relatively enhanced
Nondominant parietal	Relatively enhanced	Relatively diminished
Dominant frontal	Relatively enhanced	Relatively diminished
Dominant parietal	Relatively diminished	Relatively enhanced
21. Forms of memory and perception (Gloor, 1986)	Instrumental "becoming an instrument in the execution of behavior" (Gloor, 1986, p. 167)	Ethotropic "identification of a specific behavioral context" (Gloor, 1986, p. 166)

[a]Speculations regarding hemispheric asymmetries in the development of the putative premotor systems.

ACKNOWLEDGMENTS

These ideas were initially developed while the author was supported by a fellowship from the Medical Research Council of Canada during an association with the Department of Physiology at the University of Toronto. The author is grateful to have had this opportunity.

The author acknowledges the interaction and comments of Dr. B. Coslett of the Department of Neurology, Temple University Hospital, in the identification and examination of the patients reported, as well as the assistance of Drs. S. Tabby, D. Schilling, J. Davila, and J. Cahack, who helped to bring the reported patients on the Stroke Rehabilitation Service at Moss Rehabilitation Hospital to my attention.

The author would also like to thank Drs. W. Garfinkel and M. Scanlon of the Department of Radiology at Albert Einstein Medical Center for their help and cooperation in obtaining and interpreting neuroradiologic studies.

Discussions with Dr. P. T. Fox and Dr. M. E. Raichle of the Mallinckrodt Institute of Radiology at Washington University regarding brain activation patterns observed in their PET laboratory were particularly helpful and the author very much appreciates their willingness to openly share with him some of these data prior to their complete publication.

The author wishes to acknowledge the support of J. T. Demopoulos, MD, and the board and administration of Moss Rehabilitation Hospital who have provided seed funding and a supportive environment for the continuation of this work.

Dr. T. W. Deacon kindly made his manuscript available to me prior to publication and provided important insights into the possible relationship between evolutionary architectonics and laminar termination patterns of corticocortical projections.

Dr. J. W. Brown also kindly provided access to a copy of the manuscript for his chapter in this volume, which served as an important reference point throughout the development of my own chapter.

Several discussions with Dr. E. S. Reed regarding some of these ideas helped the author to develop them further in particular directions.

Ms. Marian Schmier and Mr. Ron Kalstein provided excellent technical assistance and Ms. Barbara Jermyn assisted in the preparation of the manuscript.

The author would finally wish to thank Dr. N. H. Mayer for ongoing guidance, support, encouragement, and stimulating discussions during the process of assembling this chapter.

REFERENCES

Abbie, A. (1940). Cortical lamination in the monotremata. *Journal of Comparative Neurology, 72,* 428–467.

Alberch, P. (1982). Developmental constraints in evolutionary processes. In J. T. Bonner (Ed.), *Evolution and development.* Berlin: Springer-Verlag.

Alberch, P. (1984). Commentary: A return to the *Bauplan. Behavioral and Brain Sciences, 7,* 332.

Barrett, G., Shibasaki, H., & Neshige, R. (1986). Cortical potentials preceding voluntary movement: Evidence for three periods of preparation in man. *Electroencephalography and Clinical Neurophysiology, 63,* 327–339.

Baer, K. E. von (1828). Über Entwickelungsgeschichte der Thiere. *Beobachtung und Reflexion,* Vol. 1. Königsberg: Bornträger.

Bernstein, N. (1984a). Trends and problems in the study of investigation of physiology of activity. In H. T. A. Whiting (Ed.), *Human motor actions: Bernstein reassessed* (pp. 441–466). Amsterdam: North-Holland. (Original work published 1961)

Bernstein, N. (1984b). Trends in physiology and their relation to cybernetics. In H. T. A. Whiting (Ed.), *Human motor actions: Bernstein reassessed* (pp. 531–544). Amsterdam: North-Holland. (Original work published 1962)

Bogen, J. E. (1979). The callosal syndrome. In K. M. Heilman & E. Valenstein (Eds.), *Clinical neuropsychology.* London & New York: Oxford University Press.

Brand, M. (1984). *Intending and acting. Toward a naturalized action theory.* Cambridge, MA: MIT Press.

Brinkman, C. (1984). Supplementary motor area of the monkey's cerebral cortex: Short- and long-term deficits after unilateral ablation and effects of subsequent callosal section. *Journal of Neuroscience, 4,* 918–929.

Brion, S., & Jedynak, C. P. (1972). Trouble du transfert interhémisphérique à propos de trois observations de tumeurs du corps calleux: Le signe de la main étrangère. *Revue Neurologique, 126,* 257–266.

Brown, J. W. (1977). *Mind, brain and consciousness.* New York: Academic Press.

Brown, J. W. (1986). Cognitive microgenesis: Review and current status. *Progress in Clinical Neurosciences, 2.*

Brown, M. C. (1984). Sprouting of motor nerves in adult muscles: A recapitulation of ontogeny. *Trends in Neurosciences, 7,* 10–14.

Churchill, F. B. (1980). The modern evolutionary synthesis and the biogenetic law. In E. Mayr & W.

B. Provine (Eds.), *The evolutionary synthesis: Perspectives on the unification of biology*. Cambridge, MA: Harvard University Press.

Dąbrowska, J. (1971). Dissociation of impairment after lateral and medial prefrontal lesions in dogs. *Science, 171,* 1037–1038.

Damasio, A. R., & Van Hoesen, G. W. (1980). Structure and function of the supplementary motor area. *Neurology, 30,* 359.

Dart, R. A. (1934). The dual structure of the neopallium: Its history and significance. *Journal of Anatomy, 69,* 3–19.

Darwin, C. (1859). *On the origin of species*. London: Murray.

Deacon, T. W. (1985). "Counter-current flow" of information processing through laminar segregation of cortico-cortical connections. *Society for Neurosciences Abstracts, 11*.

Deacon, T. W. (1986). *Laminar organization of connections in monkey cortex suggests a revision of theories of cortico-cortical information processing* (unpublished manuscript).

de Beer, G. R. (1938). Embryology and evolution. In G. R. de Beer (Ed.), *Evolution: Essays presented to E. S. Goodrich*. London & New York: Oxford University Press.

Denny-Brown, D. (1966). *The cerebral control of movement*. Liverpool: Liverpool University Press.

Denny-Brown, D., & Chambers, R. A. (1958). The parietal lobe and behavior. *Research Publications—Association for Research in Nervous and Mental Disease, 36,* 35–117.

Dobzhansky, T. (1956). *The biological basis of human freedom*. New York: Columbia University Press.

Ebbesson, S. O. E. (1984). Evolution and ontogeny of neural circuits. *Behavioral and Brain Sciences, 7,* 321–331.

Edelman, G. M. (1978). Group selection and phasic reentrant signaling: A theory of higher brain function. In *The mindful brain: Cortical organization and the group-selective theory of higher brain function*. Cambridge, MA: MIT Press.

Edelman, G. M. (1984). Cell adhesion and morphogenesis: The regulator hypothesis. *Proceedings of the National Academy of Sciences of the U.S.A., 81,* 1460–1464.

Edelman, G. M. (1986). Cell adhesion molecules in neural histogenesis. *Annual Reviews of Physiology, 48,* 417–430.

Eidelberg, D., & Galaburda, A. M. (1984). Inferior parietal lobule: Divergent architectonic asymmetries of the human brain. *Archives of Neurology (Chicago), 41,* 843–852.

Finger, S., & Almli C. R. (1985). Brain damage and neuroplasticity: Mechanisms of recovery or development? *Brain Research Reviews, 10,* 177–186.

Fox, P. T., Fox, J. M., Raichle, M. E., & Burde, R. M. (1985). The role of cerebral cortex in generating voluntary saccades: A positron emission tomography study. *Journal of Neurophysiology, 54,* 348–369.

Fuster, J. M. (1980). *The prefrontal cortex: Anatomy, physiology and neuropsychology of the frontal lobe*. New York: Raven Press.

Ghiselin, M. T. (1980). The failure of morphology to assimilate Darwinism. In E. Mayr & W. B. Provine (Eds.): *The evolutionary synthesis: Perspectives on the unification of biology*. Cambridge, MA: Harvard University Press.

Gibson, J. J. (1979). *The ecological approach to visual perception*. Boston, MA: Houghton-Mifflin.

Gloor, P. (1986). Role of the human limbic system in perception, memory and affect: Lessons from temporal lobe epilepsy. In B. K. Doane & K. E. Livingstone (Eds.): *The limbic system: Functional organization and clinical disorders* (pp. 159–169). New York: Raven Press.

Goldberg, G. (1985a). Supplementary motor area: Review and hypotheses. *Behavioral and Brain Sciences, 8,* 567–588.

Goldberg, G. (1985b). Author's response: Where there is a will there is a way (to understand it). *Behavioral and Brain Sciences, 8,* 601–615.

Goldberg, G. (1985c). Response and projection: A re-interpretation of the premotor concept. In E.

A. Roy (Ed.): *Neuropsychological studies of apraxia and related disorders* (pp. 251–266). Amsterdam: North-Holland.

Goldberg, G. (in press). Principles of rehabilitation of the elderly stroke patient. In R. E. Dunkle & J. W. Schmidley (Eds.), *New issues in stroke: Prevention, diagnosis and rehabilitation*. Berlin & New York: Springer-Verlag.

Goldberg, G., Kwan, H. C., Borrett, D., & Murphy, J. T. (1984). Topography of the movement-associated scalp potential suggests initiation of the movement-associated scalp potential by the supplementary motor area. *Archives of Physical Medicine and Rehabilitation, 65,* 662. (Abstract)

Goldberg, G., Mayer, N. H., & Toglia, J. U. (1981). Medial frontal cortex infarction and the alien hand sign. *Archives of Neurology, (Chicago), 38,* 683–686.

Goldman-Rakic, P. S., Selemon, L. D. & Schwartz, M. L. (1984). Dual pathways connecting the dorsolateral prefrontal cortex with the hippocampal formation and parahippocampal cortex in the rhesus monkey. *Neuroscience, 12,* 719–743.

Goodwin, B. C. (1982). Development and evolution. *Journal of Theoretical Biology, 97,* 43–55.

Gould, S. J. (1977). *Ontogeny and phylogeny*. Cambridge, MA: Harvard University Press.

Gray, J. A. (1982). *The neuropsychology of anxiety: An inquiry into the functions of the septo-hippocampal system*. London & New York: Oxford University Press.

Hinton, G. E., Sejnowski, T. J., & Ackley, D. H. (1984). *Boltzmann machines: Constraint satisfaction networks that learn* (Technical Report CMU-CS-84-119). Pittsburgh, PA: Department of Computer Science, Carnegie-Mellon University.

Ingvar, D. H. (1985). "Memory of the future": An essay on the temporal organization of conscious awareness. *Human Neurobiology, 4,* 127–136.

Jenkins, W. M., & Merzenich, M. M. (in press). Reorganization of neocortical representations after brain injury: A neurophysiological model of the bases of recovery from stroke. *Progress in Brain Research*.

Jerne, N. K. (1970). Antibodies and learning. Selection versus induction. In G. C. Quarton, T. Melnechuk, & F. O. Schmitt (Eds.) *The neurosciences. A study program*. New York: Rockefeller University Press.

Jonides, J. (1981). Voluntary vs. Automatic control over the mind's eye's movement. In J. Long & A. Baddeley (Eds.), *Attention and performance IX*. Hillsdale, NJ: Erlbaum.

Jürgens, U. (1985). Implication of the SMA in phonation. *Experimental Brain Research, 58,* A12.

Katz, M. J. (1983). Ontophyletics: Studying evolution beyond the genome. *Perspectives in Biology and Medicine, 26,* 323–333.

Katz, M. J., Lasek, R. J., & Kaiserman-Abramof, I. R. (1981). Ontophyletics of the nervous system: Eyeless mutants illustrate how ontogenetic buffer mechanisms channel evolution. *Proceedings of the National Academy of Sciences of the U.S.A., 78,* 397–401.

Kornhuber, H. H., & Deecke, L. (1985). The starting function of the SMA. *Behavioral and Brain Sciences, 8,* 591–592.

Kurata, K., & Tanji, J. (1986). Premotor cortex neurons in macaques: Activity before distal and proximal forelimb movements. *Journal of Neuroscience, 6,* 403–411.

Lhermitte, F. (1983). Utilization behavior and its relation to lesions of the frontal lobes. *Brain, 106,* 237–255.

Lhermitte, F. (1986). Human autonomy and the frontal lobes. Part II. Patient behavior in complex and social situations: The "Environmental Dependency Syndrome." *Annals of Neurology, 19,* 335–343.

Lhermitte, F., Pillon, B., & Serdaru, M. (1986a). Human autonomy and the frontal lobes. Part I. Imitation and utilization behavior: A neuropsychological study of 75 patients. *Annals of Neurology, 19,* 326–334.

Libet, B. (1985). Unconscious cerebral initiative and the role of conscious will in voluntary action. *Behavioral and Brain Sciences, 8,* 529–539.

MacKay, D. M., & MacKay, V. (1982). Explicit dialogue between left and right half-systems of split brains. *Nature (London), 295,* 690–691.

MacLean, P. D. (1978). In N. Greenberg & P. D. MacLean (Eds.), *Behavior and neurology of lizards* (pp. 1–10). Washington, DC: U.S. Department of Health, Education & Welfare.

Maunsell, J. H. R., & Van Essen, D. C. (1983). The connections of the middle temporal visual area (MT) and their relationship to a cortical hierarchy in the macaque monkey. *Journal of Neuroscience, 3,* 2563–2586.

Mauritz, K.-H., & Wise, S. P. (1986). Premotor cortex of the rhesus monkey: Neuronal activity in anticipation of predictable environmental events. *Experimental Brain Research, 61,* 229–244.

Meador, K. J., Watson, R. T., Bowers, D., & Heilman, K. M. (1986). Hypometria with hemispatial and limb motor neglect. *Brain, 109,* 293–305.

Mesulam, M.-M. (1986). Editorial: Frontal cortex and behavior. *Annals of Neurology, 19,* 320–325.

Morgane, P. J., Jacobs, M. S., Galaburda, A. (1985). Conservative features of neocortical evolution in dolphin brain. *Brain, Behavior, and Evolution, 26,* 176–184.

Nauta, W. J. H. (1964). Some efferent connections of the prefrontal cortex in the monkey. In J. M. Warren & K. Akert (Eds.), *The frontal granular cortex and behavior* (pp. 397–409). New York: McGraw-Hill.

Norman, D. A. (1981). Categorization of action slips. *Psychological Review, 88,* 1–15.

Norman, D. A., & Bobrow, D. G. (1975). On data-limited and resource-limited processes. *Cognitive Psychology, 7,* 44–64.

Orgogozo, J. M., & Larsen, B. (1979). Activation of the supplementary motor area during voluntary movement suggests it works as a supramotor area. *Science, 206,* 847–850.

Orgogozo, J. M., Larsen, B., Roland, P. E., & Lassen, N. A. (1979). Activation de l'Paire motrice supplémentaire au cours des mouvements volontaire chez l'homme: Etudes par le débit sanguin cérébral focal. *Revue Neurologique, 135,* 705–717.

Pandya, D. N., & Barbas, H. (1985). Commentary: Architecture and connections of the premotor areas in the rhesus monkey. *Behavioral and Brain Sciences, 8,* 595–596.

Pandya, D. N., & Yeterian, E. H. (in press). Architecture and connections of cortical association areas. In *Cerebral cortex* (Vol. 4). New York: Plenum.

Perruchet, P. (1984). Dual nature of anticipatory classically conditioned reactions. In S. Kornblum & J. Requin (Eds.), *Preparatory states and processes* (pp. 179–198). Hillsdale, NJ: Erlbaum.

Petrides, M. (1986). The effect of periarcuate lesions in the monkey on the performance of symmetrically and asymmetrically reinforced visual and auditory go, no-go tasks. *Journal of Neuroscience, 6,* 2054–2063.

Petrides, M., & Pandya, D. N. (1984). Projection to the frontal cortex from the posterior parietal region in the rhesus monkey. *Journal of Comparative Neurology, 228,* 105–116.

Pickenhain, L. (1984). Towards a holistic conception of movement control. In H. T. A. Whiting (Ed.): *Human motor actions: Bernstein reassessed* (pp. 505–528). Amsterdam: North-Holland.

Pittendrigh, C. S. (1958). Adaptation, natural selection and behavior. In A. Roe & G. G. Simpson (Eds.), *Behavior and evolution.* New Haven: Yale University Press.

Plotkin, H. C., & Odling-Smee, F. J. (1981). A multiple-level model of evolution and its implications for sociobiology. *Behavioral and Brain Sciences, 4,* 225–268.

Posner, M. I. (1980). Orienting of attention. The VIIth Sir Frederic Bartlett Lecture. *Quarterly Journal of Experimental Psychology, 32,* 3–25.

Primrose, D. C., & Strick, P. L. (1985). The organization of interconnections between the premotor areas of the primate frontal lobe and the arm area of primary motor cortex. *Society for Neurosciences Abstracts, 11,* 1274.

Reed, E. S. (1981). *Indirect action.* Unpublished manuscript, Center for Research in Human Learning, University of Minnesota, Minneapolis.

Reiner, A., Brauth, S. E., & Karten, H. J. (1984). Evolution of the amniote basal ganglia. *Trends in Neurosciences, 7,* 320–325.

Rockland, K. S., & Pandya, D. N. (1979). Laminar origins and terminations of cortical connections of the occipital lobe in the rhesus monkey. *Brain Research, 179,* 3–20.

Roland, P. E., Larsen, B., Lassen, N. A., & Skinhoj, E. (1980). Supplementary motor area and other cortical areas in organization of voluntary movements in man. *Journal of Neurophysiology, 43,* 118–136.

Roland, P. E., Meyer, E., Shibasaki, T., Yamamoto, Y. L., & Thompson, C. H. (1982). Regional cerebral blood flow changes in cortex and basal ganglia during voluntary movements in normal human volunteers. *Journal of Neurophysiology, 48,* 467–480.

Rosene, D. L., & Van Hoesen, G. W. (1977). Hippocampal efferents reach widespread areas of cerebral cortex and amygdala in the rhesus monkey. *Science, 198,* 315–317.

Russell, E. S. (1916). *Form and function: A contribution to the history of animal morphology.* London: John Murray.

Sanides, F. (1964). The cyto-myeloarchitecture of the human frontal lobe and its relation to phylogenetic differentiation of the cerebral cortex. *Journal füer Hirnforschung, 6,* 269–282.

Sanides, F. (1969). Comparative architectonics of the neocortex of mammals and their evolutionary significance. *Annals of the New York Academy of Sciences, 167,* 404–423.

Sanides, F. (1970). Functional architecture of motor and sensory cortices in primates in the light of a new concept of neocortex evolution. In C. Noback & W. Montagna (Eds.): *The primate brain: Advances in primatology* (Vol. 2, pp. 137–208). New York: Appleton-Century-Crofts.

Sanides, F. (1972). Representation in the cerebral cortex and its areal lamination patterns. In G. H. Bourne (Ed.), *The structure and function of the nervous tissue* (Vol. 5, pp. 329–453). New York: Academic Press.

Schell, G. R., & Strick, P. L. (1984). The origin of thalamic input to the arcuate premotor and supplementary motor areas. *Journal of Neuroscience, 4,* 539–560.

Sergent, J. (1986). Subcortical coordination of hemisphere activity in commissurotomized patients. *Brain, 109,* 357–369.

Seyffarth, H., & Denny-Brown, D. (1948). The grasp reflex and the instinctive grasp reaction. *Brain, 71,* 109–181.

Squire, L. (1982). The neuropsychology of human memory. *Annual Review of Neuroscience, 5,* 241–273.

Sutton, D., Trachy, R. E., & Lindeman, R. C. (1985). Discriminative phonation in macaques: Effects of anterior mesial cortex damage. *Experimental Brain Research, 59,* 410–413.

Tanji, J., & Kurata, K. (1982). Comparison of movement-related activity in two cortical motor areas of primates. *Journal of Neurophysiology, 48,* 633–653.

Turvey, M. T. (1986). Intentionality: A problem of multiple reference frames, specificational information, and extraordinary boundary conditions on natural law. *Behavioral and Brain Sciences, 9,* 153–155.

Van Essen, D. C., & Maunsell, J. H. R. (1983). Hierarchical organization and functional streams in the visual cortex. *Trends in Neurosciences, 6,* 370–375.

Van Hoesen, G. W. (1982). The parahippocampal gyrus. New observations regarding its cortical connections in the monkey. *Trends in Neurosciences, 5,* 345–350.

Watson, R. T., Fleet, W. S., Gonzalez-Rothi, L., & Heilman, K. M. (1986). Apraxia and the supplementary motor area. *Archives of Neurology (Chicago), 43,* 787–792.

Watson, R. T., & Heilman, K. M. (1984). Callosal apraxia. *Brain 106,* 391–403.

Webster, G. C., & Goodwin, B. C. (1981). History and structure in biology. *Perspectives in Biology and Medicine, 25,* 39–62.

Wiesendanger, R., & Wiesendanger, M. (1985). The thalamic connections of medial area 6 (supplementary motor cortex) in the monkey (macaca fascicularis). *Experimental Brain Research, 59,* 91–104.

Wise, S. P. (1985). The primate premotor cortex: Past, present and preparatory. *Annual Review of Neuroscience, 8,* 1–19.

Yakovlev, P. I. (1948). Motility, behavior and the brain. *Journal of Nervous and Mental Disease, 107,* 313–335.

Index

Date Due

BJJH
